A REFERENCE
TO BAS.
ELECTRONICS ERMS

Other Titles of Interest

A REFERENCE GUIDE TO BASIC ELECTRONICS TERMS

by

F. A. WILSON
C.G.I.A., C.Eng., F.I.E.E., F.I.E.R.E., F.B.I.M.

**BERNARD BABANI (publishing) LTD
THE GRAMPIANS
SHEPHERDS BUSH ROAD
LONDON W6 7NF
ENGLAND**

Please Note

Although every care has been taken with the production of this book to ensure that any projects, designs, modifications and/or programs etc. contained herewith, operate in a correct and safe manner and also that any components specified are normally available in Great Britain, the Publishers do not accept responsibility in any way for the failure, including fault in design, of any project, design, modification or program to work correctly or to cause damage to any other equipment that it may be connected to or used in conjunction with, or in respect of any other damage or injury that may be so caused, nor do the Publishers accept responsibility in any way for the failure to obtain specified components.

Notice is also given that if equipment that is still under warranty is modified in any way or used or connected with home-built equipment then that warranty may be void.

First Published — February 1992

British Library Cataloguing in Publication Data
Wilson, F. A. (Frederick Arthur)
    A reference guide to basic electronics terms
    I. Title
    621.3810321

ISBN 0 85934 231 X

Printed and bound in Great Brtain by Cox & Wyman Ltd, Reading

PREFACE

Conception, my boy, fundamental brainwork is what makes the difference in all art. Hall Caine (Recollections of Rosetti)

How often do we encounter a technical term not fully understood, one which we have forgotten or which we never really got to grips with. Take heart, herein is help, especially with the basic or fundamental terms.

There is a companion book entitled "A Reference Guide to Practical Electronics Terms" which deals with affairs more worldly. Although it would be gratifying to be able to proclaim that the two books together constitute a guide to the whole of electronics, this cannot be but at least they should engender an awareness of the more important electronics principles and how they find their way into the practical world. However, each book stands on its own and relies on its companion no more than any technical publication relies on other work to fill in the gaps. Both books have their own system of references and those terms in the same book are preceded by an asterisk (*), those in the companion book by >> (see the example below).

The references are no more than enlightened suggestions, the reader can choose which, if any, should be explored further. Certainly by following them from term to term one can easily get down to the real roots of any concept.

There is an inherent danger in an approach which is too technical for the less experienced readers hence the explanations avoid overwhelming the reader with more than sufficient detail or mathematics. Also the level of explanation is tailored to the term itself. As an example, the experienced engineer will have little need for "Ohm's Law" or "Resistance" but the new recruit may be glad of them, hence in such cases the explanation is kept simple. Conversely the professional may be interested in the more esoteric terms and for such people simplification would be wrong. Apart from electronics engineers, students and enthusiasts, the books are also likely to have appeal for those in other disciplines of engineering, science or even medicine who are now realizing that with electronics now so much a part of our lives, some understanding of the subject must be enlisted.

Modern equipment is often little more than a cluster of unfathomable integrated circuits so we learn better from circuits of discrete components. Accordingly these are frequently used for illustration even though in the practical world integrated circuits have taken over.

A reminder about the references:

(* Resonance, Damping, Forced Oscillation >> Shock Excitation)

other terms in this book for extra
clarification as required

a term in "A
Reference
Guide to Practical
Electronics Terms"
— not essential but
may be of interest.

Please note that an Index appears on page 465.

F. A. Wilson

ABSOLUTE TEMPERATURE This is temperature measured from absolute zero – see Thermodynamic Temperature.
(* Absolute Zero, Kelvin)

ABSOLUTE UNIT is perhaps best explained by an example from the SI in which all the units are absolute. Take the quantity *resistance* as a simple example. Resistance is a function of two other quantities, current and voltage. The *unit* of resistance, the *ohm*, is an absolute unit if it is a function of the units of the other two quantities (amperes and volts), with no other factors included. In the case of resistance this is so for one ohm is equal to one volt divided by one ampere.
    The earlier centimetre-gram-second (cgs) system also employs absolute units.
(* SI)

ABSOLUTE ZERO is the lowest temperature which theoretically can be achieved. Normally, even though locked into the crystalline structure of a solid, the atoms continually vibrate. As temperature falls the vibration decreases until at absolute zero it is minimum. That some vibration may remain is demonstrated by liquid helium which it is thought remains liquid at absolute zero, indicating that atomic motion still exists.
    If however, we use the definition that absolute temperature is directly proportional to the average particle kinetic energy, then clearly when the temperature is zero, the particle kinetic energy and therefore its velocity are also zero. The indication therefore is that at absolute zero, molecular (or atomic) motion ceases altogether.
    The unit of temperature has been established by dividing the freezing and boiling temperatures of water into 100 degrees. On this basis absolute zero is 273.16 degrees below the freezing point of water.
    The thermodynamic temperature scale has its zero at absolute zero, i.e. absolute zero has a temperature of 0 degrees Kelvin (0 K).
(* Thermodynamic Temperature, Kelvin)

ABSORPTION is the reduction in magnitude of an electrical quantity by physical or chemical action:
  (i)   radio signals cause free electrons to oscillate in gas molecules in the atmosphere. The transfer of energy to the electrons reduces

the wave power, i.e. the signal undergoes absorption;

(ii) when light traverses a medium, some is scattered, some is absorbed. In the latter case those photons which have the required energy levels are absorbed from the incident light by electrons, hence energy is transferred and the light weakened;

(iii) capacitor dielectrics absorb some of the charge (*dielectric absorption*). This is shown by the fact that if a charged capacitor is discharged and then left on open circuit for some time, a small charge can be detected, this is the absorbed charge reappearing.
(* Atom, Energy, Photon, >> Residual Charge)

A.C. – see Alternating Current

ACCEPTOR CIRCUIT is another name for a series resonant circuit which at resonance presents a high impedance.
See Resonant Circuit.

ACCEPTOR IMPURITY is a term used in semiconductor manufacture. It is a trivalent element such as boron or gallium, so called because it accepts electrons from other atoms within a lattice to complete the bonds.
See Doping.

ACOUSTIC WAVE is a wave which is transmitted through the vibration of the particles of a medium, it is perhaps more generally known as a *sound wave.* The everyday example is the acoustic wave travelling through air. When a body vibrates in generating sound, it compresses and rarifies the air surrounding it. On compression for example, the pocket of compressed air subsequently expands and compresses the air in contact with it and in this way the compression moves away from the vibrating body. Similarly with rarefaction, hence overall there is a series of alternately compressed and rarified waves travelling outwards. Because the particles move to and fro in the direction in which the wave is travelling, this type of wave is said to be *longitudinal.* Note that the air particles do not travel with the wave, they merely vibrate about their rest (undisturbed) positions, passing the energy onwards.

The medium through which an acoustic wave propagates can be solid, liquid or gaseous and the velocity is affected by the characteristics of the medium. Acoustic wave velocity is considerably lower than that for radio waves. In air at normal temperature and pressure, the acoustic wave velocity is about 344 m/s whereas in sea water for example, the velocity is around 1500 m/s.

The frequency range for acoustic waves is that which can be heard by human beings and is from about 20 Hz to as high as 20 kHz although not many of us can reach the latter. Waves of higher frequency are classified as ultrasonic.

It is possible to produce a travelling acoustic wave in a solid material by applying stress to the crystal e.g. through the *piezoelectric effect* or by *magnetostriction.*

(* Frequency, Wave, Waveform, Piezoelectric Effect, Magnetostriction >> Magnetostrictive Transducer)

A.C. RESISTANCE – see Effective Resistance

ACTIVE is a term generally applied to a component or circuit which is capable of introducing gain, e.g. a transistor or electronic valve. A power supply is required so that a component can become active. See also the opposite, Passive.

ACTIVE COMPONENT . . . CURRENT . . . VOLTAGE – see In-Phase Component

ADMITTANCE   This in an alternating current circuit expresses the degree to which the circuit facilitates the passage of an electric current. It is denoted by the symbol Y with the unit, the siemens (S). Admittance is the reciprocal of impedance (Z) and when a circuit contains reactance, both admittance and impedance are complex, i.e. they have real and imaginary components. For admittance the real component is known as the conductance (G) and the imaginary as the susceptance (B) such that:

$$Y = G + jB \quad \text{(all quantities in siemens)}$$

The calculation of admittance is often most conveniently obtained from the components of impedance:

$$Y = \frac{1}{Z} = \frac{1}{R + jX} = \frac{R - jX}{R^2 + X^2} \quad \text{(see Rationalization)}$$

The concept of admittance is especially useful in the analysis of parallel circuits where the various branches are complex (i.e. contain reactance). In this case the conductances of the various paths are simply added (according to sign), similarly with the susceptances. These are finally combined to produce a single value for the admittance. This can be changed to impedance if required by taking the

3

reciprocal.
(* Complex Notation, Impedance, Conductance, Susceptance)

AERIAL – see Antenna

ALLOWED BAND is a band of energy levels on an energy level diagram which electrons are permitted to have. Figure E12 is such a diagram and at (ii) the allowed bands are indicated. The conduction and valence bands shown in (iii) to (v) are also allowed bands. See also Forbidden Band.
(* Electron, Energy, Energy Bands, Energy Levels, Valency)

ALLOY JUNCTION This is one of the earlier types of semiconductor junction, still in use for special devices but mainly superseded by the planar process. Considering for example, transistors which have two such junctions, a small pellet of an impurity material is placed on each side of a thin slice of semiconductor material containing the opposite impurity. This thin slice is the base and as an example, for an n-type base of germanium, the pellets could be of a trivalent

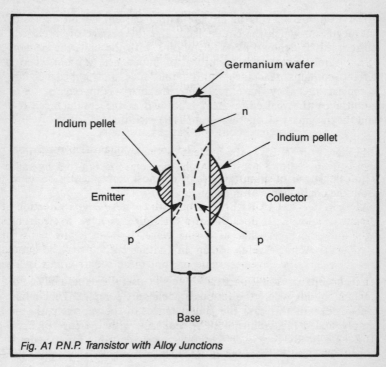

Fig. A1 P.N.P. Transistor with Alloy Junctions

material such as indium as illustrated in Figure A1. The combination is heated in an oxygen-free atmosphere to a temperature slightly above that at which an alloy forms between each pellet and the base wafer. On cooling the appropriate p-n junctions are formed.
(* P-N Junction, Impurity, Doping, Transistor >> Planar Process, Diffusion)

ALPHA CUT-OFF FREQUENCY   In a transistor as in any other device, the movement of charge carriers takes time. From this it is evident that there must be some high frequency at which the performance of the transistor as an amplifier begins to fall simply because the charge carriers are unable to complete their flow in one direction by the time that the incoming signal reverses. The performance can be expressed by the *common-base current amplification factor,* α (Greek, alpha), equally described as the *common-base forward current transfer ratio.* This is calculated as the rate of change of collector current with emitter current with the output terminals (collector to base) short-circuited to a.c.

It is possible to calculate the reduction in performance at high frequencies but this is a complicated process. From it however, as might be expected, two factors emerge as having a significant effect, (i) the electron *diffusion coefficient* which is closely related to the electron mobility and (ii) the width of the base.

In a more practical sense the alpha cut-off frequency is defined as the frequency at which the common-base forward current transfer ratio (or current amplification factor) falls to $1/\sqrt{2}$ (0.707, equivalent to 3 dB) of its low frequency value.
(* Charge Carrier, Mobility, Drift Velocity, Transistor, Decibel >> Hybrid Parameters, Common-Base Connection)

ALPHA PARTICLE is the nucleus of the helium atom consisting of 2 neutrons with 2 protons. Alpha particles are emitted by radioactive nuclei — see Radioactivity.

ALTERNATING CURRENT is one which reverses its direction at regular intervals. It does this at a certain *frequency.* In electronics the simplest form, that of a sine wave, is used as the basis for analysis. A single value for an alternating current may be quoted as its peak value, average value or root mean square (r.m.s.). The UK electricity mains is approximately sinusoidal (of sine wave shape) with a peak value of about 340 volts, an average value of 153 volts and r.m.s. value of 240 volts.

The term is frequently abbreviated to a.c. and used as an adjective, e.g. a.c. motor, a.c. bell, a.c. supply.
(* Frequency, Sinusoidal, Sine Wave, Root Mean Square, Form Factor)

AMMETER (short for ampere meter) is an instrument for the measurement of current. There are several different types, each of which has its own particular field of use.

(* Galvanometer >> Moving Coil Meter, Moving Iron Meter, Thermocouple Meter, Hot Wire Ammeter, Instrument Transformer)

AMPERE — the basic unit of electric current, denoted by the symbol A (after Andre Marie Ampère, a French mathematician and physicist). One ampere is the current when one coulomb of charge flows past a given point in one second. Since the charge of a single electron is 1.602×10^{-19} C, then for one ampere the number of electrons flowing past the point per second is $1/(1.602 \times 10^{-19}) = 6.24 \times 10^{18}$, a truly enormous number.

The S.I. definition is "that constant current which, if maintained in two straight parallel conductors of infinite length, of negligible circular cross-section, and placed one metre apart in vacuum, would produce between these conductors a force equal to 2×10^{-7} newton per metre of length."

(* Coulomb, Charge, Electron, Current, Newton)

AMPERE–LAPLACE LAW (BIOT-SAVART LAW) This is a law relating electrical with mechanical energy, more specifically, current with force. It applies to two parallel conductors with currents I_1 and I_2 flowing. If very short elements of length dl_1 and dl_2 are considered as shown in Figure A2, then the incremental force, dF acting between the two current elements in free space or almost equally in air is given by:

$$dF = \frac{\mu_0 I_1 \, dl_1 I_2 \, dl_2 \, \sin \theta}{4\pi r^2}$$

where μ_0 is the permeability of free space, r is the distance between the two elements and θ the angle between the direction of r and the direction of the conductors as shown in the figure. With current directions as shown, the force is one of attraction (see Fig. E7). Note that the equation is of similar form to that expressing the force between two charges (Coulomb's Law).

However, this (Ampere-Laplace) law tends to the theoretical rather than to the practical because to total the force between all the elementary lengths (i.e. between the two conductors) requires much mathematical manipulation and even then, it is almost impossible to check experimentally.

(* Force, Current, Permeability)

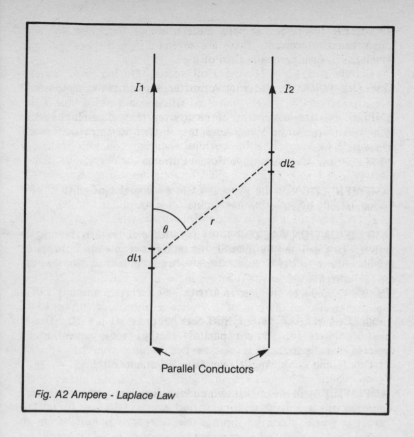

Fig. A2 Ampere - Laplace Law

AMPERE PER METRE is the S.I. unit of magnetic field strength. The symbol is A/m. It is defined in terms of the magnetic field strength within a uniformly wound solenoid carrying a current such that the current density is equivalent to one ampere per metre of axial distance.

(* SI, Magnetic Field Strength, Current Density >> Solenoid)

AMPERE'S LAW is a law relating magnetic field strength with current. It is derived from the Ampere-Laplace law relating force with current. It is also known as *Ampere's circuital law* or *theorem*, sometimes as *Ampere's work law*. The law states that the summation of the magnetic field strength, H round a closed path is proportional to the total current crossing the surface enclosed by the path.

The law provides the basis for certain of the more practical magnetism formulae.

(* Magnetic Field Strength, Current)

AMPERE-TURN — an alternative and perhaps more descriptive unit for magnetomotive force, symbol At (the recommended unit is the *ampere*, A). Magnetomotive force is given by the product of the number of turns on a coil and the current in amperes flowing through them.

(* Magnetism, Magnetomotive Force, Current)

AMPLIFICATION is the process of increasing the magnitude of a signal, usually by an electronic circuit — see Amplifier.

AMPLIFICATION FACTOR is a term used mainly with thermionic valves. It is denoted by μ and is the ratio between a small change in anode voltage to the change in grid voltage required to maintain the anode current constant. As an example, if a reduction of 20 V on the anode reduces the anode current by a certain amount and a positive change on the grid of 2 V restores the anode current to its original value, then the amplification factor is $20/2 = 10$. This is measured over the straight portion of the anode current/anode voltage characteristic.

(* Thermionic Valve, Anode, Amplifier, Characteristic)

AMPLIFIER — in a nutshell an amplifier is a circuit or device which increases the strength of an electrical signal. Because its output power is greater than the input power energy is required from an external source and this is provided by a *power supply*. Amplifiers are one of the corner stones on which modern electronics has been built, in fact radio, television, telephony and many other branches of electronics are unable to function without them. More specifically, a *linear amplifier* has an electrical output which is a faithful copy of the input except that it has a greater magnitude. This infers that no noise is added and no distortion products are generated. On the other hand a *non-linear amplifier* has an output which is not an exact copy of the input, the waveform is distorted on its journey through. The output therefore comprises a fundamental wave at the input frequency plus added harmonics.

Let us consider an amplifier as a 4 + 2 terminal network (2 input, 2 output and 2 power supply) as shown in Figure A3(i). If the input and output terminating resistances R_S and R_L are known then by measurement and calculation the performance of this network as an amplifier can be determined. What we need to know in any particular case is:

    (i)   the input resistance, R_{in}

   (ii)   the output resistance, R_{out}

  (iii)   the maximum voltage swing which can be applied to the input

  (iv)   the frequency range over which the amplifier is to operate

   (v)   the gain, G. This is expressed in decibels or as a ratio, either in terms of power, voltage or current

  (vi)   the harmonic distortion introduced

 (vii)   the amount of noise added

(viii)   the voltage range for the power supply and the current drawn from it.

Much of this information is obtained from manufacturers' data followed by analysis of the circuit using transistor hybrid or y-parameters. Distortion components and noise are usually measured when a model of the amplifier has been constructed. Note that for high frequency working, where internal capacitances have an effect, the R's in the figure must give way to Z's (impedances) to account for the fact that we are no longer able to class everything as resistive.

The simplest of the many different types of amplifier is the single transistor *stage* as shown typically in Figure A3(ii). The input to the n-p-n transistor is at its base and the output is taken from the collector (common-emitter connection). The output current flows via a capacitor C which prevents d.c. potentials from mingling with the next stage. The resistor, R provides bias to the base. A small current or voltage change at the base gives rise to a greater one at the collector — this is amplification. Such an elementary amplifier has input and output resistances in the medium range. For greater gain, two or more stages can be linked or *cascaded*, the output of one stage being connected to the input of the next. Some other features of amplifiers in general are as follows:

Direct Coupled Amplifiers — these can amplify a direct current or one which has a very slow rate of variation. For this, coupling capacitors such as C in (ii) of the figure cannot be used.

A.C. Amplifiers — are used with frequencies from a few Hz upwards and may have narrow bandwidths (tuned amplifiers) or large, running into MHz.

Voltage Amplifiers — are designed for a high a.c. output voltage, hence R_{out} must be high.

Power Amplifiers — are required when work, such as moving the coil of a loudspeaker has to be done. For this the output current is appreciable.

Negative Feedback Amplifiers — in these a fraction of the output energy is sent back to the input of a single stage or over several

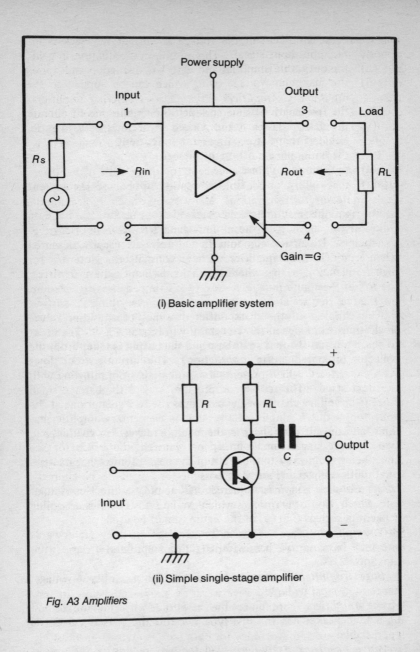

Power supply

Input
1

Output
3

Load

R_s

R_{in}

R_{out}

R_L

2

4

Gain = G

(i) Basic amplifier system

R

R_L

C

Output

Input

(ii) Simple single-stage amplifier

Fig. A3 Amplifiers

stages. In the input circuit the voltage or current fed back is in opposition to the input signal. This results in a reduction in gain but with a more stable amplifier and with less distortion and noise output.

Class A, AB, B and C Amplifiers — these classes describe amplifiers according to the length of time current flows in the output circuit during each cycle. Classes A and AB are linear amplifiers, Class B is linear provided that a twin transistor (push-pull) arrangement is used, Class C is non-linear.

Integrated Circuit Amplifiers — except for those with high power outputs, hence with considerable dissipation of heat, amplifiers are ideal candidates for integration. Many stages are easily accommodated within one small integrated circuit.

(* Transistor, Gain, Distortion, Impedance, Bandwidth, Negative Feedback >> Operational Amplifier, Integrated Circuit, Hybrid Parameters, Y-Parameters, Direct Coupled Amplifier, Class A . . . Class AB . . . Class B . . . Class C Amplifier, Common-Emitter Connection, Preamplifier)

AMPLITUDE — simply an expression for the magnitude or value of an alternating waveform. Generally with regard to sine waves it is taken to mean the maximum or peak value while the amplitude at any instant is known as the *instantaneous amplitude.* Hence if a sine wave is expressed by $v = V_{max} \sin \omega t$, V_{max} is the amplitude and v is the instantaneous amplitude.
(* Sine Wave)

AMPLITUDE DISTORTION arises in a transmission channel or network from variation in gain or loss with the amplitude of the input signal, i.e. the system has a non-linear input-output characteristic. With high distortion it is possible for a signal to be clipped, e.g. a sine wave becomes "squared off" at the peaks. This results in the generation of harmonics which can be measured at the output of the network.
See Distortion
(* Sine Wave, Harmonic, Characteristic, Fourier Analysis)

AMPLITUDE MODULATION is a modulation technique in which the amplitude of a carrier wave is varied above and below its unmodulated level according to the amplitude of the modulating signal. Although it was the first type of modulation to be developed it is still very much in use today for both radio and line transmission.

The carrier wave, f_c, is most likely to be a single frequency sine wave but the modulating signal (the baseband) is more likely to be a

11

band of frequencies and complex, e.g. speech, music, tv or data. Here we first consider a single frequency for the modulating wave otherwise diagrams and explanations get out of hand. Call this frequency f_m. In practice f_c is many times f_m, say from 30 up to several hundred times. However, in Figure A4 we use a ratio of only 5 to avoid becoming entangled in an unmanageable diagram.

In the figure, (ii) represents the carrier wave, unmodulated for the first 50 μs, then modulated by the 20 kHz wave shown in (i). The amplitude variation of the carrier can be seen and it varies from $(V_c + V_m)$ to $(V_c - V_m)$. The carrier now contains the information from the modulating wave and clearly V_m cannot exceed V_c, hence carrier levels are comparatively high.

It can be shown by straightforward mathematics that if the carrier is represented by $V_c \sin \omega_c t$ volts and the modulating wave by $V_m \sin \omega_m t$ volts, then the result of modulation is:

$$v = (V_c + V_m \sin \omega_m t) \sin \omega_c t$$

where v is the instantaneous value of the modulated wave. Note that modulation results in the product of the two waves, not their addition.

On expansion the expression can be resolved into 3 components:

(i)   the original carrier
(ii) a lower *side frequency*, $V_m/2 \times \cos 2\pi(f_c - f_m)t$
(iii) an upper *side frequency*, $- V_m/2 \times \cos 2\pi(f_c + f_m)t$

or simply, the carrier plus lower and upper side frequencies ($f_c - f_m$) and ($f_c + f_m$) as shown in (iii) and (iv) of the figure.

When f_m is considered as a band of frequencies the theory above still holds good for each individual frequency but of course overall it becomes more complicated. We can sum it up however by saying that because f_m now widens out into a band, the result is that the modulation products can simply be expressed as the carrier plus lower and upper *sidebands*. This is illustrated graphically in (v) of the figure where the baseband is now, say, 100 Hz (f_1) to 4.5 kHz (f_2), f_c we take as 900 kHz. Now the modulated wave contains (i) the carrier, (ii) a lower sideband (l.s.b.) extending from ($f_c - f_2$) to ($f_c - f_1$) and (iii) an upper sideband (u.s.b.) extending from ($f_c + f_1$) to ($f_c + f_2$) as shown. The total bandwidth occupied by the modulated wave is therefore ($f_c + f_2$) − ($f_c - f_2$) = $2f_2$, i.e. twice the highest modulating frequency as shown in the figure to be in this case, 9 kHz.

The *modulation factor* (*m*) is a means of expressing the degree of depth to which the carrier is modulated and it is given by:

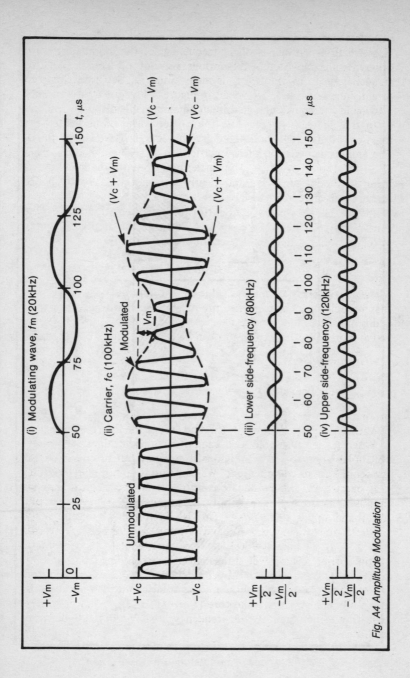

Fig. A4 Amplitude Modulation

13

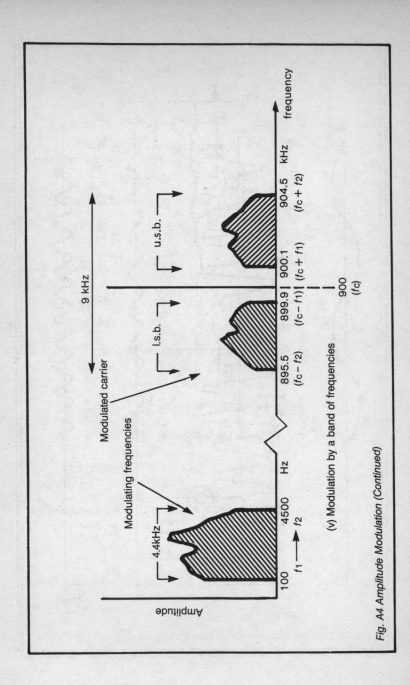

Fig. A4 Amplitude Modulation (Continued)

(v) Modulation by a band of frequencies

14

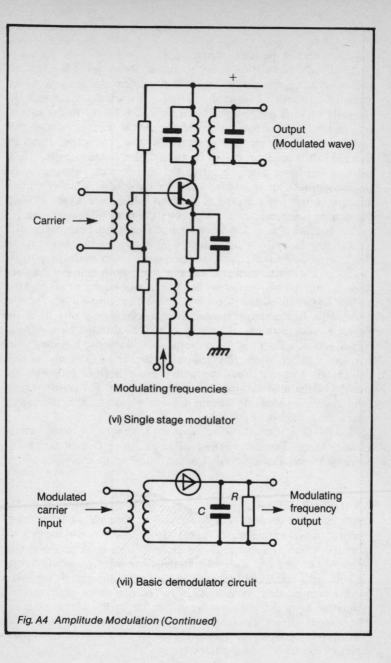

+

Output
(Modulated wave)

Carrier →

Modulating frequencies

(vi) Single stage modulator

Modulated
carrier
input →

C   R

→ Modulating
frequency
output

(vii) Basic demodulator circuit

Fig. A4 Amplitude Modulation (Continued)

$$m = V_m/V_c$$

and it can also be quoted as a percentage.

Amplitude modulation is accomplished by applying both carrier and modulating waves together to a non-linear system such as the input of a transistor, suitably biassed. Figure A4(vi) shows the elements of such a circuit. The transistor is biased to the square-law part of its characteristic. Mathematical analysis shows that components at $2f_c$ are also generated in the process but these are rejected in the collector circuit by the coupled tuned circuits. These act as a band-pass filter, selecting the carrier plus sidebands only.
Demodulation — it is evident that the modulated wave is quite a mixture so what is required is a circuit which effectively extracts the desired baseband signal and throws the remainder away. Such a circuit is known as a *demodulator* but sometimes, especially with regard to radio systems it is called a *detector*. Figure A4(ii) shows that the modulating frequencies are impressed on both the positive swings of the carrier and also the negative. Both contain the same information so only one is needed hence all positive or all negative half-cycles are discarded. This is a job which a simple diode rectifier does well. In the simple demodulator circuit shown in (vii) of the figure, a diode is followed by a capacitor, C, shunted by a resistor, R. C acts as a kind of reservoir capacitor to smooth out the carrier frequency pulses while R continually discharges C slowly so that the charge does not build up and prevent it from following the troughs of the modulation. The values of C and R have to be carefully chosen so that the output follows the modulating frequency waveform as closely as possible.
(* Modulation, Carrier Wave, Baseband, Coupled Circuit, Tuned Circuit, Filter, Transistor, Diode, Rectification, Demodulation >> Single Sideband Transmission, Common-Emitter Connection)

ANALOGUE SIGNAL   The term analogue is derived from the Greek meaning proportional to, similar or parallel to. It therefore refers to any electrical signal which has a similarity with the original quantity which it represents. The properties such as amplitude, frequency or phase of an analogue signal are therefore continuously variable with time within a certain range. Audio signals provide a good example, they vary in all three of the above parameters in sympathy with the sound wave which originally generated them. The output of an electronic temperature measuring device also provides an example for the amplitude of the signal at any instant directly represents the temperature.

Analogue signals may be contrasted with *digital* signals which have constant amplitude but can carry the same information in coded form.
See Digital Signal.
(* Signal >> Pulse Code Modulation, Analogue-to-Digital Conversion, Digital-to-Analogue Conversion)

ANDERSON BRIDGE is a modified form of the Maxwell bridge, capable of measuring a wide range of inductances against fixed values of capacitance. The circuit is shown in Figure A5. L is the unknown inductance connected in series with a variable resistor,

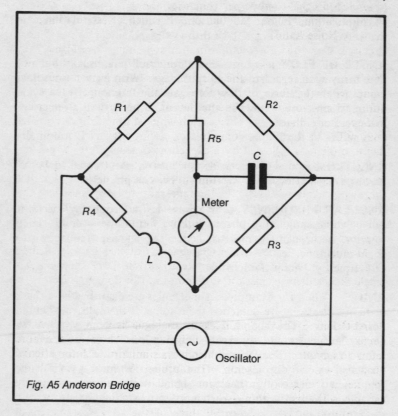

Fig. A5 Anderson Bridge

R_4. Compared with the Maxwell bridge, the Anderson has the additional component R_5. The bridge is balanced by adjusting R_4 and R_5. At balance (i.e. when there is no deflection on the meter), then:

17

$$R_1 R_3 = R_2 R_4 \quad \text{and} \quad L = R_1 R_3 C(1 + R_5/R_1 + R_5/R_2)$$

(* Bridge, Maxwell Bridge, Inductance, Capacitance)

ANGLE MODULATION is a term used for a modulation process in which the phase of the carrier wave is varied according to the instantaneous value of the modulating wave. Phase modulation is obviously an example of angle modulation but frequency modulation is also because when a carrier wave varies in frequency, its phase relative to the modulating wave must also be changing. Angle modulation has the significant advantage over amplitude modulation of improved signal-to-noise performance.
(* Modulation, Phase Modulation, Frequency Modulation $\gg$ Signal-to-Noise Ratio)

ANGLE OF FLOW is a term used with amplifiers, usually but not necessarily with regard to the output stage. With a given sinusoidal input signal, the angle of flow expresses the fraction of each cycle during which current flows in the output. The angle is given either in degrees or radians.
(* Sine Wave, Radian $\gg$ Class A . . . AB . . . B . . . C Amplifier)

ANGSTROM is a unit of wavelength measurement equal to 10^{-10} metres, named after A. J. Angström, a Swedish physicist.

ANGULAR FREQUENCY — if a wave has a frequency f hertz, it can be represented by a phasor rotating f times per second. Each rotation is through 2π radians, hence the angular frequency (ω) is $2\pi f$ radians per sec.
(* Frequency, Phasor, Radian)

ANION When for example, air molecules are disturbed by a spark or flame, electrons are detached from some of them, leaving behind positive ions. The liberated electrons soon become attached to nearby molecules and so create negative ions, these are the ones known as *anions.* Similarly in electrolysis anions are automatically produced by the dissociation of molecules. Within a gas-discharge tube or an electrolyte therefore, being negative, the anions are attracted towards the anode when a potential gradient exists.

A positive ion is called a *cation.*
(* Ion, Electrolyte, Charge, Anode, Cation, Positive, Negative)

ANODE — this is the electrode through which electron current flows out of a device. To attract electrons it is therefore held positive with respect to the cathode. Devices employing an anode are electrolytic cells, thermionic valves, rectifiers and gas-discharge tubes. See also Cathode.

(* Electron, Electrode, Positive, Negative)

ANODE FALL – see Plasma

ANODE SLOPE RESISTANCE – see Thermionic Valve

ANTENNA is an arrangement of conductors or conducting materials designed for transmission or reception of electromagnetic waves. Antennas are around in all shapes and sizes from a long wire suspended high above the ground, to a small slot in a flat sheet of metal. There is a reciprocity theorem for antennas which states that in most respects the characteristics of an antenna used for transmitting are similar to those when it is used for receiving. There is one obvious difference, a transmitting antenna handles much greater power, accordingly its conductors are larger. The wavelength of the transmission is a dominant factor in antenna design and generally antenna dimensions are related to it. The most important characteristics of an antenna are:

(i)   *Gain* – of course a passive lump of metal cannot have gain as with an amplifier, hence antenna gain is expressed relative to that of a generally accepted reference antenna. The simple dipole is sometimes used as a reference but one now commonly used is the *isotropic*, meaning that it produces the same radiation in all directions. The gain is therefore a figure expressing how well an antenna radiates or receives energy in or from a given direction compared with the reference. As an example the gain would be expressed as *x* dB relative to the isotropic.

(ii) *Directivity* – the *omnidirectional* antenna used as a reference for gain measurements is a theoretical consideration only, all practical antennas radiate or receive better to or from some directions than others. Very often they are designed specifically for their directional properties which are most easily displayed by a *polar diagram*.

(iii) *Efficiency* – not all the power delivered to a transmitting antenna is radiated (nor does all the wave power available to a receiving antenna find its way into the connecting cable), some is inevitably lost in the resistance of the conductors and in transmitting some may even be absorbed by the antenna structure. The efficiency of a transmitting antenna is therefore the ratio of the actual power radiated to the total power supplied at a specified frequency.

19

(iv) *Radiation resistance* – in a transmitting antenna this is a measure of the ability of an antenna to do its job. Some of the power flowing into an antenna is dissipated in the resistance of the metal, the remainder is radiated and it is this power which for convenience we express in terms of the *radiation resistance*. This is defined as the power radiated divided by the mean square value of the current at some specified reference point which is usually the feed point but sometimes at a current antinode (point at which the current is maximum). As an example a half-wave dipole (see below) has a radiation resistance of about 70 ohms.

(v) *Effective Height* – this is a term seldom used in connection with transmitting antennas but is a convenient measure of performance of a receiving antenna. The strength of a radio wave may be quoted as so many volts, millivolts or microvolts per metre, indicating that a straight piece of wire 1 metre high would have an e.m.f. induced in it of that value. However, even an antenna constructed in this way has an effective height less than its physical height so the effective height provides useful information as to the efficiency. Generally effective height has to be measured, especially with antennas of awkward shapes.

(*Electromagnetic Radiation, Electromagnetic Wave, Reciprocity Theorems, Microwave, Waveguide, Antenna Gain >> Polar Diagram, Artificial . . . Dipole . . . Ferrite Rod . . . Folded Dipole . . . Isotropic . . . Loop . . . Parabolic . . . Yagi Antenna, Broadside Array, End-Fire Array)

ANTENNA GAIN is measured by comparison with a reference antenna, either an elementary dipole or an isotropic. For a transmitting antenna the gain is the ratio of the signal power supplied to the antenna to that which would be needed by the reference antenna to produce the same field strength at some specified point. For a receiving antenna the gain is the ratio of the signal power delivered by the antenna to that which would be delivered by the reference antenna at the same location and for the same transmitted power. Gain is therefore a ratio and it may be quoted in decibels (relative to the reference antenna).

An example of high antenna gain is given by a satellite parabolic transmitting antenna which concentrates practically all its power into a narrow beam directed towards earth. Compared with the isotropic antenna which in the same position would radiate most of its power into space, the satellite antenna gain (in that particular direction) might be around 10 000 (40 dB) relative to the isotropic. On the other hand a simple dipole has a gain in the direction of

maximum radiation of a mere 1.64 (2.15 dB) relative to the isotropic.
(* Electromagnetic Radiation, Gain, Antenna, Decibel >> Dipole Antenna, Isotropic Antenna)

ANTIFERROMAGNETISM   In materials exhibiting this effect the magnetic dipoles tend to align so that neighbouring ones are in opposite directions rather than in parallel as with a ferromagnetic material.   At absolute zero temperature this results in an overall magnetisation of zero since the number of ions aligned in one direction is equal to the number in the opposite direction. However, as the temperature is increased atomic vibrations also increase and encourage the magnetic alignments to change until at a certain temperature, known as the *Néel temperature*, T_N the effect completely disappears.

If a magnetic field is applied to an antiferromagnetic material the magnetic susceptibility therefore varies with temperature. As the temperature is reduced below T_N the susceptibility decreases because the alignments in opposition increase.   Above T_N the material exhibits paramagnetism with the susceptibility falling again as temperature increases.
(* Magnetic Moment, Dipole, Ion, Ferrimagnetism, Ferromagnetism, Susceptibility Magnetic, Paramagnetism, Absolute Zero)

ANTINODE is a term used with standing waves and is a point at which the voltage or current reaches maximum value. Antinodes are shown in Figure S8 which also indicates the *nodes*, these are points of minimum or zero value.
(* Standing Wave)

APERIODIC CIRCUIT is one which has no natural resonance (Greek, a = *not*). The term aperiodic is generally used to describe a circuit containing inductance and capacitance yet is so heavily damped that resonance and free oscillations cannot arise. For an aperiodic circuit the degree of damping exceeds the *critical damping*, i.e. it is *overdamped*. Overdamping implies a high resistive component in the impedance, hence the impedance of an aperiodic circuit varies little with frequency.
(* Inductance, Capacitance, Resonance, Damping, Impedance)

APPLEGATE DIAGRAM   A special type of graph used to illustrate *bunching* in a velocity modulation process. It shows how those electrons with higher velocities than normal due to the additional energy provided by the positive half-cycles of an incoming microwave signal are able to catch up with the slower ones which have reduced energy due to the negative half-cycles — see Velocity Modulation.

ARBITRARY UNIT is a unit which is not based on existing physical phenomena but has at some time been chosen "arbitrarily", accordingly a prototype has to be maintained somewhere. The earliest units of measurement were all arbitrary. As an example the metre was originally defined as one ten millionth of the distance from the North Pole to the Equator (via Paris). In a way this was based on a physical phenomenon but not one which could easily be realised in practice. So that the unit would remain absolutely constant and could be copied easily, a prototype was constructed by which the metre was defined by the length between scratches on a platinum-iridium bar kept at the International Bureau of Weights and Measures at Sèvres. Subsequently the metre has been defined in terms of a number of wavelengths of orange light emitted by an isotope of the gas krypton, no prototype is therefore essential and the metre is no longer an arbitrary unit.

One unit however which remains arbitrary is the unit of mass, the kilogram and the prototype is a block of platinum, again preserved at Sèvres.
(* SI, Metre, Mass)

ARC is an electric discharge through an ionized gas which contains a *plasma*. A plasma is a concentration of approximately equal numbers of electrons and ions with an extremely low voltage gradient. This occurs within a gas-filled tube and accordingly only a small voltage is required to drive a large current. The discharge is visible and usually emanates from a small area on the cathode. This localized heating of the cathode increases the current density through thermionic emission so the arc is sustained. Arc currents in gas-discharge tubes may reach well over 10^6 A/m^2 at a low voltage of 20 or so.

Note that an arc occurs through an already ionized gas, a *spark* first creates its own ionization.
(* Gas Discharge, Cathode, Ionization, Plasma, Thermionic Emission >> Spark, Flashover, Arc Lamp)

ARGUMENT — see Polar Coordinate

ASTATIC GALVANOMETER — a very sensitive type of current measuring instrument. See Galvanometer.

ATOM   An atom is the smallest particle of an element which can take part in a chemical reaction, hence the derivation of the word

22

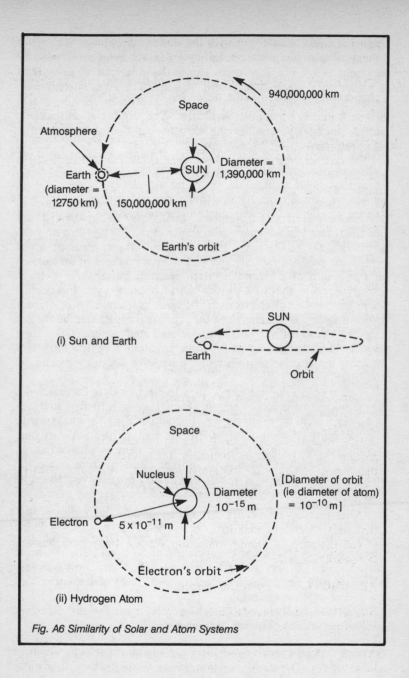

(i) Sun and Earth

(ii) Hydrogen Atom

Fig. A6 Similarity of Solar and Atom Systems

from the Greek, *atmos*, meaning indivisible. Atoms are like micro-miniature solar systems, each having a dense nucleus surrounded by electrons in orbits. Figure A6 shows the solar and atom systems together, very much alike except for size. The atom nucleus comprises mainly protons and neutrons. The neutron exhibits no charge but each proton has a positive charge. The number of protons (the atomic number) determines the element, e.g. the gas hydrogen has one proton only, iron 26, uranium 92.

The electrons are grouped together in *shells*, labelled as shown in the simplified sketch in Figure A7 for the element oxygen (atomic number 8) which happens to have two shells only (there can be up to 7). The maximum number of electrons in any shell is equal to $2n^2$ where n is the shell number. Shells may be sub-divided into sub-shells (see Fig. S4 where an example of the full labelling of shells and sub-shells is shown). Electrons circle the nucleus in orbits within the shells at fantastically high speeds (millions of revolutions in a millionth of a second!). Each electron carries or *is* a charge exactly equal to that of a proton but of opposite sign. In a normal atom the number of electrons is the same as the number of protons hence the net positive charge of the protons is neutralized by the net negative charge of the orbiting electrons and generally the atom appears electrically neutral. Within an atom it is the attraction between the positive protons and the negative electrons which hold the latter in orbit.

What is of paramount importance in electronics is that electrons in the outermost orbits of certain atoms, if given sufficient additional energy, can move to orbits even further out from the nucleus with the possibility of being released altogether from the atom. Anything moving possesses kinetic energy and when more is supplied to an electron (through collision with another electron, from an electric field, heat or light), it is enabled to change progressively to orbits further out, depending on the amount of energy it has gained. In some materials electrons in the outermost orbit are sufficiently far away from the nucleus that when they are "excited" by added energy, they are able to escape and become "free". Such free electrons are required for electric current to flow. The atoms of metals such as copper and silver part with their outermost (valence) electrons with no fuss, on the other hand atoms of insulators hold on to their electrons tightly.

(* Element, Electron, Orbit, Charge, Nucleus, Proton, Neutron, Shell, Current, Bohr Theory, Valency)

ATOMIC MASS UNIT   For many calculations it is more convenient to express the masses of atoms and molecules in a unit more

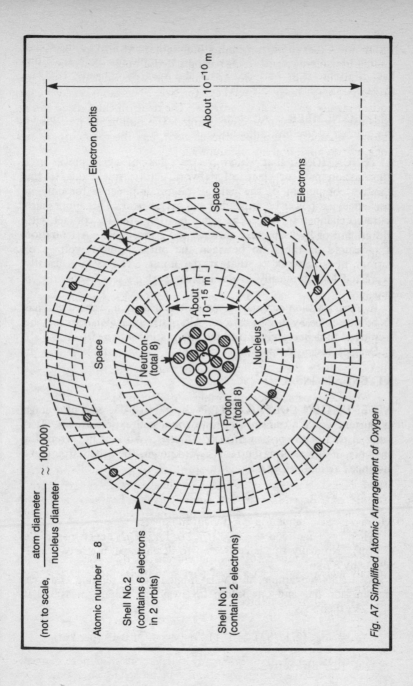

(not to scale, $\dfrac{\text{atom diameter}}{\text{nucleus diameter}} \approx 100{,}000$)

Atomic number = 8

Shell No.2
(contains 6 electrons
in 2 orbits)

Shell No.1
(contains 2 electrons)

Electron orbits

Space

Electrons

Neutron
(total 8)

About 10^{-15} m

Nucleus

Proton
(total 8)

Space

About 10^{-10} m

Fig. A7 Simplified Atomic Arrangement of Oxygen

25

commensurate with their sizes. The atomic mass unit (u) used has a value of 1.66043×10^{-27} kg. As an example the hydrogen atom has an atomic mass of $1.007\,825$ u and a water molecule, 18.02 u. (* Atom, Molecule, Mass, Mole)

ATOMIC NUMBER   All elements are given a number according to the number of protons in the nucleus — see Nucleus.

ATTENUATION is that which creates a loss of signal power in a transmission path or electrical network.   It is solely due to the resistive component of the path or circuit impedance for only in resistance can power be expended and lost as heat.   This applies also to radio channels in which the signal is attenuated by contact with the ground or by its passage through the atmosphere.   Attenuation is measured as the ratio between the output power, voltage or current of a network to that at the input.   The ratio is usually expressed logarithmically in decibels or perhaps less frequently, in nepers.

In a transmission channel attenuation is usually unwanted and has to be overcome by amplification.   Alternatively *attenuators* may be employed to deliberately introduce attenuation into a circuit.

(* Decibel, Neper, Propagation Constant $\gg$ Attenuator)

ATTENUATION BAND — see Filter

ATTENUATION COEFFICIENT is the rate of decrease of voltage or current down a transmission line, expressed exponentially.   It is the real part of the *propagation coefficient*.   Working in current for example, if the sending current, I_s is known, then the current, I a distance l along the line is:

$$I = I_s e^{-\alpha l}$$

where α is the attenuation coefficient in nepers.

When $l = 1$ metre, $\alpha = - \log_e (I/I_s)$ or $\log_e (I_s/I)$ nepers per metre (Np/m).   Normally this is converted to decibels per metre by multiplying by 8.686.

As a simple example, if 2 V is applied at the sending end of a transmission line and one kilometre away the voltage measured is 1.783 V, then:

$$\alpha = \log_e (2/1.783) = 0.115 \text{ nepers} = 1.0 \text{ dB (per km)}$$

i.e. $\alpha = 10^{-3}$ dB/metre.

Attenuation coefficient is also a feature of correctly terminated networks, the same considerations apply except that distance is not part of the equation.

See also Phase-Change Coefficient.

(* Transmission Line, Propagation Coefficient, Decibel, Neper, Network)

ATTENUATION CONSTANT — see Attenuation Coefficient.

ATTENUATION/FREQUENCY DISTORTION (ATTENUATION DISTORTION) (also known as *frequency distortion*) — this arises when there is a variation of gain or loss in a transmission channel or network with the frequency of the input signal. It is typified by the "tone control" of a radio receiver which deliberately introduces loss at the higher frequencies. See also Figure F1(iii) as an example of gain variation with frequency.

See Distortion.

(* Attenuation, Frequency)

AUDIO FREQUENCY (A.F.) "Audio" comes from Latin, to *hear*, so an audio frequency is simply one which can be heard. The full audio range is usually taken to be from 20 to 20 000 Hz, however human ears respond differently (even the pair we own) so the person with hearing over this range must be considered lucky.

When speech is transmitted electronically as for example, by telephone, it is intelligibility rather than fidelity which matters so then we manage with a range of only 300 — 3400 Hz. It is classed as "intelligible" and in fact it is reasonably so although with any distortion present, sibilants may be wrongly judged. For good quality speech transmission a range of from 200 to about 7 000 Hz is sufficient while for high quality music at least 30 Hz to 15 kHz should be transmitted.

(* Frequency ≫ Telecommunication System)

AVALANCHE Generally this is an activity in which there is an increase of something which becomes more and more rapid, an avalanche of rocks down a mountain is a good example. In this a single rock falling dislodges others which themselves start to fall. What is important in this process is that the falling rocks gain in kinetic energy as gravity accelerates them, hence each has the power to dislodge not just one rock but several. An avalanche cannot build up unless there is a constant supply of energy. Each of the rocks dislodged plays its part in displacing others so it is evident that in no time at all, many rocks are hurtling downwards.

In electronics an avalanche occurs on the same principles. A single particle or photon, given sufficient energy and therefore velocity by an external electric field can collide with several atoms in succession and ionize them. Electrons freed in the process and mobile ions in gases are charged particles and they also gain energy from the field so splitting further atoms into ions and electrons. The first single particle (or, of course, it could be several) is therefore able to create a large number of charged particles, all with increasing velocities if the field strength is sufficient. The effect is obviously cumulative as with the rocks above and clearly if allowed to continue something has to give and the destruction of the particular device is inevitable. Circuits are therefore designed to prevent such breakdown, on the other hand the effect can be used to good advantage as for example in the Geiger Counter.

(* Atom, Ionization, Electric Field, Electric Field Strength, Energy, Collision, Avalanche Breakdown, Zener Breakdown, Avalanche Photodiode)

AVALANCHE BREAKDOWN occurs in a p-n junction with reverse bias. As the applied reverse voltage is increased there comes a point where there is a rapid increase in reverse current. This is mainly due to the intense electric field of the reverse bias imparting sufficient velocity to electron minority carriers of the reverse saturation current to dislodge orbiting electrons. This results in the generation of electron-hole pairs by impact ionization. The continued action of the electric field on the newly released charge carriers creates further pairs, the effect is cumulative and an avalanche is formed, i.e. the current increases disproportionately. A typical reverse bias characteristic showing the avalanche point is given in Figure P10(iv).

The actual voltage at which breakdown occurs is controlled mainly by the doping level of the semiconductor material used.

(* Avalanche, Doping, P-N Junction, Reverse Saturation Current, Minority Carrier, Electron-Hole Pair, Impact Ionization)

AVALANCHE PHOTODIODE   A reverse biased p-n junction photodiode operated at a voltage near the breakdown voltage. There is photocurrent multiplication due to the avalanche process – see Photodiode.

B

BACK E.M.F. (BACK ELECTROMOTIVE FORCE) In an inductive circuit, if the current varies, the magnetic flux it produces also varies in direct proportion and accordingly itself generates an e.m.f. By Lenz's Law the induced e.m.f. e is in such a direction as to oppose the change which originally produced it. The e.m.f. is given by:

$$e = -L \frac{di}{dt}$$

where L is the self-inductance of the circuit and dt is an infinitesimally small interval of time during which the current changes by di. This opposing e.m.f. is known as the *back e.m.f.*

Back e.m.f.'s are also induced in d.c. motor armatures. When the armature rotates, the conductors cut the magnetic flux of the field coils, hence an e.m.f. is induced in the conductors even though the machine is acting as a motor. This induced or back e.m.f. opposes the flow of motor current, hence illustrating Lenz's Law.
(* Electromotive Force, Magnetic Flux, Inductance, Lenz's Law >> Electric Motor)

BAND-PASS FILTER Passes a predetermined range of frequencies only — see Filter and/or Figure F4.

BAND-REJECT FILTER (same as Band-Stop Filter) — see Filter and/or Figure F4.

BAND-STOP FILTER Passes all frequencies except a predetermined range — see Filter and/or Figure F4.

BANDWIDTH If a range or band of frequencies extends from the lowest, f_1 to the highest, f_2 then the bandwidth is simply $f_2 - f_1$ Hz, kHz, MHz, etc.

(i) For an amplifier the bandwidth is that range of frequencies over which the amplification falls within specified limits. Generally it is taken as the range between the frequencies at which the response is 3 dB down compared with that at mid-band.

(ii) Signals carrying intelligence have certain bandwidths, e.g. for speech over a telephone circuit, $f_1 = 300$ Hz, $f_2 = 3400$ Hz therefore the bandwidth is $3400 - 300 = 3100$ Hz.

(iii) A modulated wave occupies a range of radio frequencies and has a bandwidth which depends on the mode of transmission, e.g. for an amplitude modulated signal the bandwidth is twice the maximum modulating frequency, for a frequency modulated wave it is considerably greater.

(* Frequency, Amplifier, Decibel, Modulation >> Tuned Amplifier)

BARKHAUSEN EFFECT — so called because it was first noticed by a gentleman of that name. It was Barkhausen's work which produced the first experimental evidence of magnetic domains. In 1919 he discovered that when a specimen is being magnetised, it takes place by a series of discontinuous jumps. We now know that each jump corresponds to the reversal of saturation of some 10^{15} atoms, occupying a space of 5×10^{-5} mm^3 or less. Jumps are not in general due to a change in magnetisation of the whole domain (which typically might occupy some 10^{-3} mm^3) but correspond to a sudden displacement of a domain boundary from one stable position to another.

The effect adds support to the domain theory of ferromagnetism in that spin magnetic moments can only be in certain directions, hence the jumps are due to changes from one direction to another. If spins were allowed to be at random, this would not occur.

(* Ferromagnetism, Magnetisation, Domain, Magnetic Moment, Spin)

BASE usually refers to one of the regions of a bipolar transistor. It is a thin layer of doped semiconducting material sandwiched between the emitter and the collector. Minority carriers are injected into the base from the emitter — see Transistor.

BATTERY is a set of cells for the supply of electricity. Each cell consists of an electrolyte in contact with two electrodes, cylindrical, rod or flat. The cell has the capability of forcing electrons away from its positive terminal towards the negative terminal through chemical action. If a circuit is connected across the terminals, the difference in charge between them (the p.d.) causes electrons to flow from the negative terminal round the circuit and be attracted back to the positive terminal. The driving force of the battery is known as its electromotive force (e.m.f.), measured in volts.

Primary batteries are those in which during use some of the chemical constituents of the cells are used up, for example in a hand-torch battery, the so-called "dry cell'. This functions on the Leclanché principle but the electrolyte is in fact a moist paste, if it were completely dry the cell could not function. When discharged

the battery is discarded. *Secondary* batteries when discharged can be re-charged by passing a current through them in the opposite direction to that of the discharge current (e.g. car battery).
(* Electrolyte, Electron, Charge, Leclanché Cell, Secondary Cell, Potential Difference, Electromotive Force)

BEAT FREQUENCY is produced when two signals of slightly different frequencies are combined, they do not modulate (unless some non-linearity is present) but simply add. Consider two sine waves of equal amplitude, V and of frequencies f_1 and f_2 where f_1 is slightly greater than f_2. They are shown graphically in Figure B1, labelled $V \sin 2\pi f_1 t$ and $V \sin 2\pi f_2 t$. Adding these two waves together produces:

$$V (\sin 2\pi f_1 t + \sin 2\pi f_2 t)$$

as shown. Expanding by simple trigonometry leads to the conclusion that the resultant wave has an amplitude $2V$ and consists of a frequency $(f_1 + f_2)/2$ multiplied by a second, $(f_1 - f_2)/2$. The figure shows the result to be in the form of two overlapping sine waves consisting of the frequency $(f_1 + f_2)/2$ varying between its maximum levels at twice the frequency $(f_1 - f_2)/2$. There are therefore two beats per envelope cycle so that the number of beats per second (the beat frequency) is $f_1 - f_2$, i.e. the *difference frequency*.

As an example of an application of beat frequency generation, two audio frequency oscillators may be synchronized by mixing their outputs and detecting the beat frequency on headphones or on an a.c. meter. One oscillator is then adjusted in frequency until the beat is zero whereupon the two oscillator frequencies are equal.
(* Frequency, Sine Wave, Heterodyne, Modulation, Oscillator)

BEATING is the addition of two sinusoidal waves so that a periodic signal arises through interference of one wave on the other. The periodic signal generated is known as the *beat frequency* which is equal to the difference between the frequencies of the original waves. The amplitude of the beat frequency is equal to the sum of the original amplitudes.
(* Beat Frequency, Sine Wave, Heterodyne)

BEL is the basic logarithmic unit employed for expressing ratios of powers, especially in the measurement of transmission gains or losses. It is given the symbol B and is named after Sir Alexander Graham Bell (the Scottish-American inventor). If the power, current or

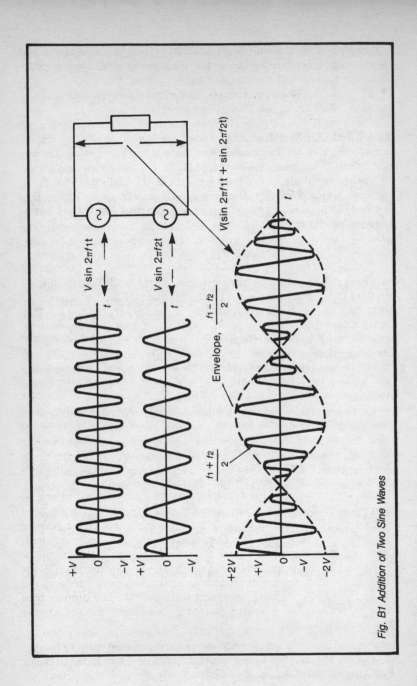

Fig. B1 Addition of Two Sine Waves

voltage input to a circuit is given by P_1, I_1 or V_1 respectively and the power output by P_2, I_2 or V_2, then the attenuation (or gain):

$$n = \log(P_2/P_1) = \log(I_2{}^2 Z/I_1{}^2 Z) = 2\log(I_2/I_1)\ \mathrm{B}$$

but note that I_1 and I_2 must be measured in the same terminating impedance, Z. Similarly:

$$n = 2\log(V_2/V_1)$$

and again the voltages must be measured in the same impedance.

The bel happens to be an inconveniently large unit (e.g. a power gain of one million is equivalent to only 6 B), hence in practice the *decibel*, which is one-tenth of a bel, is almost invariably used. (* Attenuation, Gain, Decibel)

BIAS, BIASING refers to a current, voltage or a.c. signal applied to a device to ensure that the required operating conditions are obtained. There are two main uses for these terms in electronics:

(1)   The most commonly found is with regard to establishing the optimum operating point for a transistor or thermionic valve. A *load line* is drawn on the output characteristics and typically for a small-signal transistor amplifier this might indicate that the optimum base bias current should be, say 0.6 mA. This means that in this case and with no signal applied, the bias consists of a steady current in the base circuit of 0.6 mA and this sets the operating point as required. Hence the bias controls the position of the operating point. This is also shown when we consider the various classes of amplification (Class A, AB etc.) for again in each case it is the bias used which basically controls the operating conditions.

Biasing a transistor for example, may be accomplished in one of several different ways. The simplest and one without frills is to obtain the base bias directly from the supply through a resistor (R_b) of such value that the base voltage or current is as required. The circuit is shown in Figure B2(i). Alternatively the circuit in (ii) may be used to provide some stabilization. Any rise in collector current (due to temperature, change of transistor etc.) reduces the collector voltage, hence the current through R_b. The drop in base current reduces the collector current so tending to compensate for the original change.

(2)   The term "bias" is also to be found in magnetic recording systems. It refers to an a.c. voltage at some 40 − 100 kHz superimposed on the input signal to improve linearity.

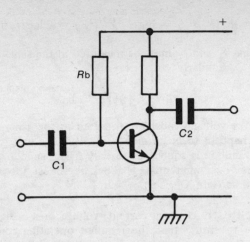

(i) Bias with no stabilization

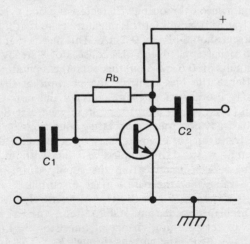

(ii) Bias with simple stabilization

Fig. B2 Biasing a Transistor

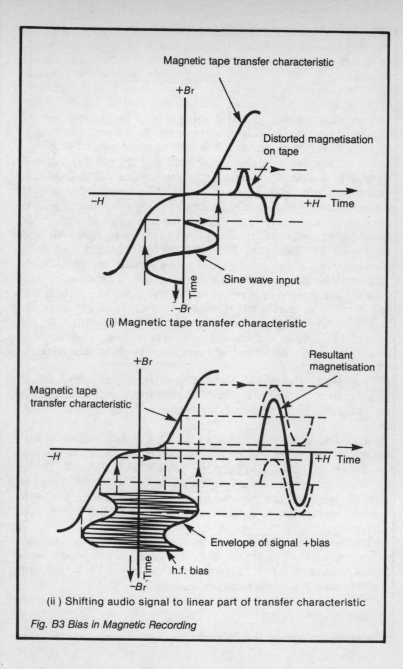

Magnetic tape transfer characteristic

Distorted magnetisation on tape

Sine wave input

(i) Magnetic tape transfer characteristic

Resultant magnetisation

Magnetic tape transfer characteristic

Envelope of signal +bias

h.f. bias

(ii) Shifting audio signal to linear part of transfer characteristic

Fig. B3 Bias in Magnetic Recording

Figure M3 shows a *B-H* magnetisation loop from which it is clear that non-linearity abounds. For values of *H* below the maximum, small *B-H* loops are produced, each resulting in a different value of remanence, B_r and a typical magnetic tape transfer characteristic might be as shown in Figure B3(i). The non-linearity in the recorded signal is evident. To operate only on the straight section of the transfer characteristic a constant value of *H* (+ or −) could be used as a bias (d.c. biasing), this however uses only the positive or negative half of the characteristic. The more satisfactory method of *h.f. biasing* is adopted as shown graphically in Figure B3(ii). A sine wave at 3−4 times the highest signal frequency is the bias and it is mixed linearly with the signal so that the bias frequency amplitude varies as shown. The h.f. bias, being well above the audio range is of no concern on replay and the positive and negative audio flux variations add together, resulting in an overall wave, relatively free from amplitude distortion. Note that the very non-linear section of the tape transfer characteristic as it passes through the origin is not used and also that an enhanced magnetisation is obtained because both the positive and negative sections of the tape transfer characteristic contribute. Figure B3(ii) reminds us that the amplitude of the bias is critical so because the tape transfer characteristics of, for example ferric oxide and chromium dioxide coatings are different, a recording machine may need adjustable bias levels to accommodate all types.

(* Transistor, Thermionic Valve, Characteristic, Beat Frequency, Magnetisation ≫ Operating Point, Stabilization, Load Line, Class A etc. Amplifier, Magnetic Recording, Magnetic Tape)

BINDING ENERGY   This results from the general statement that "atoms always have less mass than the combined mass of their constituent particles" (i.e. neutrons, protons and electrons). This is because some of the mass is employed as energy which is required to bind the neutrons and protons together in the nucleus. If it were not for this the protons would fly apart because of their like positive charges.

The most instructive way of illustrating this is by means of a set of calculations. Consider a single atom of helium which needs binding energy in the nucleus to keep its two protons entwined with the neutrons. It has two electrons. From:

mass of proton $= 1.672\,65 \times 10^{-27}$ kg

mass of neutron $= 1.674\,95 \times 10^{-27}$ kg

mass of electron $= 9.109\,53 \times 10^{-31}$ kg ,

we get:

> Total mass of helium atom (2 of each, neutrons, protons
> and electrons) $= 6.697\,02 \times 10^{-27}$ kg .

However, from its atomic weight the actual mass of the helium atom can be shown to be $6.647\,38 \times 10^{-27}$ kg. There is therefore a discrepancy, known as the *mass defect* of 4.964×10^{-29} kg.

Since energy and mass are interchangeable ($E = mc^2$, see Relativistic Effect), then:

$$E = (4.964 \times 10^{-29}) \times (9 \times 10^{16}) = 4.4676 \times 10^{-12} \text{ joules}$$

or: 2.79×10^7 eV ,   i.e. 27.9 MeV .

This is the binding energy holding the helium nucleus together and is the energy we would have to supply to a single nucleus to separate it into its constituent nucleons (neutrons and protons). Note that to separate the single electron from the hydrogen nucleus, a mere 13.6 eV is required.

(* Atom, Nucleus, Electron, Neutron, Proton, Energy, Relativistic Effect, Electron-Volt)

BIOT-SAVART LAW is concerned with the force between two conductors carrying a current — see Ampere-Laplace Law.

BIPOLAR TRANSISTOR is a junction transistor in which the main action is the result of the flow of two different types of charge carrier (electrons and holes) — see Transistor.

BOHR THEORY   This is the work of Niels Henrik Bohr (a Danish theoretical physicist). He extended Lord Rutherford's work on the atom to produce the first quantum theory of the hydrogen atom (this is the simplest atom because it comprises a nucleus with one orbiting electron only). He proposed the following:

(i) the electron rotates about the nucleus in circular orbits with angular momentum which is an integral multiple of $h/2\pi$ (h is Planck's constant);

(ii) the electron radiates or absorbs energy only when it moves from one orbit to another;

(iii) the energy difference between two orbits is radiated or absorbed as a single photon.

From Bohr's work the electron energy and radius of each of the various orbits of the hydrogen electron can be calculated. From this are derived the energy required for the electron to shift from one orbit to another further out from the nucleus (or the energy released by a shift further in) and the energy required for release from the atom altogether.

(* Atom, Electron, Energy, Orbit, Planck Constant, Ionization Potential)

BOLTZMANN'S CONSTANT   Heat is often referred to as a "form" of energy and one way of describing it is that in matter it can be perceived as the kinetic energy (k.e.) of atomic and molecular motion.   Temperature is a measure of the average of this energy (average because at any instant individual particles do not have the same energy).   Given the premiss that the average k.e. of the particles of a gas is directly proportional to the absolute temperature, Ludwig Boltzmann (an Austrian physicist) published his now well known formula which gives a precise relationship between the k.e. of a molecule and the temperature as:

$$\text{ke}_{av} = 3/2 \ kT \ \text{joules}$$

where T is the thermodynamic temperature and k is a constant, now known as Boltzmann's Constant of value $1.380\,54 \times 10^{-23}$ joule per (degree) kelvin (or equally 8.62×10^{-5} eV per kelvin). Note that the k.e. is independent of the mass of the molecule.

As an example the average k.e. of a single molecule at room temperature is $3/2 \times 1.38 \times 10^{-23} \times 293 \simeq 6 \times 10^{-21}$ J, a very small quantity of energy indeed but then this is for one molecule only.

Boltzmann's Constant appears in most formulae which involve both energy and temperature.

(* Atom, Energy, Kinetic Energy, Joule, Electron-Volt, Thermodynamic Temperature, Molecule, Mass)

BOND   In electronics a bond is the uniting force between atoms in a molecule.   Out of the 100 or so different atoms around, 6 have the highest number of electrons (8) in the valence shell (the outermost).   These are helium, neon, argon etc. and they are known as the *noble gases.* A particular feature which they have in common is that they are unlikely to combine with other elements. All other elements have less than 8 valence electrons and bonding theory assumes that they would like to gain the same stable electronic configuration of the noble gases.   This can be achieved by (i) emptying the valence shell by giving up one or more electrons or (ii) completing it by taking over one or more. When certain different elements meet in a chemical reaction therefore, it is possible for them to attain the stable configuration by interchange of electrons in this way.

The simplest example is perhaps that of sodium chloride (common salt). A sodium atom has 1 electron only in its outer (3rd) shell. If it gives this one up the 3rd shell is dispensed with and the 2nd shell becomes the outer, it has 8 electrons. Chlorine on the other hand has 7 electrons in its outer (3rd) shell. By taking on one, the shell is complete. Hence sodium and chlorine atoms reacting together do what is obvious, resulting a positive sodium ion and a negative chlorine. These are particles carrying unlike charges and so are attracted powerfully to each other, this is the bond which links the two atoms and keeps the molecule stable. The process is known as *electrovalent, electrostatic* or *ionic* bonding, basically through the *transfer* of electrons.

Covalent bonding occurs, not when electrons are transferred but when they are shared. As an example, an atom with 4 valence electrons may form a covalent bond with a neighbouring atom. The 8 shared electrons are attracted simultaneously to both atoms and move in orbit round them. This produces the bond and by this technique of sharing, in a way gives both atoms the stable configuration of 8 electrons in the outermost shell.

There are other techniques of bonding but these are of more interest to chemists than to electronics engineers.

(* Atom, Electron, Molecule, Shell, Ion, Valency)

BRANCH   In a network a *node* is a point where 3 or more of the elements are connected together. A *branch* is a conducting path between two nodes as shown in Figure N3 which uses the Wheatstone bridge as an example.

(* Network, Node)

BREAKDOWN is a process occurring in insulators and dielectrics in which there is a change from the insulating to a conducting state, sometimes with noticeable physical damage. When the voltage across an insulator reaches breakdown, firstly the conductivity increases slightly at some point because the energy provided by the high voltage releases a few electrons to act as charge carriers. Subsequently, in the dielectric of a capacitor for instance, the current increases as the stored electrostatic energy discharges through the breakdown path. The material then has low resistance and can no longer be classed as an insulator.

Breakdown in insulators requires some 10^5 to 10^9 volts per metre thickness of the material. Much depends on the time for which the voltage is applied, temperature, surface leakage, frequency etc.

Air also has its breakdown voltage. Down here on earth it is of the order of 3—5000 kilovolts per metre. Up in the clouds different conditions apply and when the air there does break down with a lightning discharge, we can certainly appreciate that breath-taking voltages must be present.

Certain gases are used in gas-discharge tubes for their "breakdown" properties. In this case there is no costly physical damage, "breakdown" merely implies a chain reaction in which the whole of the gas is ionized.

(* Dielectric, Energy, Conductivity, Ionization, Insulator, Gas Discharge >> Lightning)

BRIDGE (BRIDGE NETWORK) is an assembly of elements connected as four sides of a square as shown in Figure B4(i). Each side is known as an *arm* of the bridge and consists of one or more components such as resistor, capacitor etc. Here we consider them as impedances Z_1, Z_2 etc. For measurement purposes a d.c. or a.c. supply is connected to one pair of opposite corners of the square, a detector or meter is connected to the other pair. Not immediately recognizable as such but nevertheless identical electrically, is the lattice network shown in Figure B4(ii).

It is instructive to consider first the important underlying feature of this very useful network. In Figure B4(iii) is shown a general network of impedances, hardly recognizable as a bridge but more as the lattice network. The feature (which can easily be proved) is that if a generator is connected in place of any one of the impedances, then the current in one of the others can be made zero by suitable arrangement of the values of the other four, the value of the generator impedance being unimportant. As an example, by connecting a generator or battery in the Z_5 arm and suitably adjusting Z_1 to Z_4 the current in Z_6 can be made zero and in fact Z_6 can then be disconnected without affecting the power absorbed by the network. The bridge is then said to be "balanced". In practice we substitute some sort of indicating device such as an a.c. or d.c. meter for Z_6, connect the supply in place of Z_5 and then balance the bridge by aiming for zero deflection on the meter.

How to balance the bridge is easily determined using Ohm's and Kirchhoff's Laws, but the principle can be seen simply from (iv) from which it is clear that for equal voltage drops across Z_1 and Z_2 so that there is no potential difference between a and b:

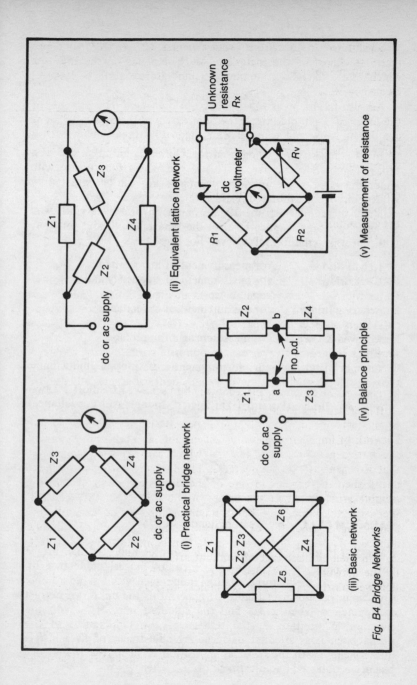

(i) Practical bridge network

(ii) Equivalent lattice network

(iii) Basic network

(iv) Balance principle

(v) Measurement of resistance

Fig. B4 Bridge Networks

41

$$Z_1/Z_3 = Z_2/Z_4$$

from which also:

$$Z_1/Z_2 = Z_3/Z_4 \quad \text{and} \quad Z_1Z_4 = Z_2Z_3$$

from which it is worth noting that the products of the two sets of impedances looking across the square must be equal.

In its simplest form when used for measuring an unknown resistance, Figure B4(v) applies. This is the Wheatstone bridge with which the value of the unknown resistance, R_x can be obtained by adjustment of the calibrated resistor, R_v.

Many measuring instruments are based on bridge networks and are usually more complicated than the Wheatstone bridge but they still conform to the formula above. For these see:

Kelvin Bridge — for measurement of low resistances
Wien Bridge — for measurement of frequency and capacitance
Schering Bridge — for measurement of capacitance
Anderson, Hay, Maxwell & Owen Bridges — for measurement of inductance
Campbell Bridge — for measurement of mutual inductance.

(* Network, Resistance, Impedance, Ohm's Law, Kirchhoff's Laws, Wheatstone Bridge, Potential Difference, Inductance, Capacitance)

C

CADMIUM CELL – see Weston Standard Cell

CAMPBELL BRIDGE is one of the more complicated a.c. bridge networks designed for the measurement of mutual inductance by comparison of the unknown mutual inductance with a standard one. The circuit is shown in Figure C1 and in this the unknown mutual inductance is labelled M_x and the standard one, M_s. With the switches in position 2, the resistances and inductances of the primary windings are first balanced by adjustment of L_1 and R_1. Subsequently with the switches in position 1, the mutual inductance balance is obtained by adjustment of M_s. Then:

42

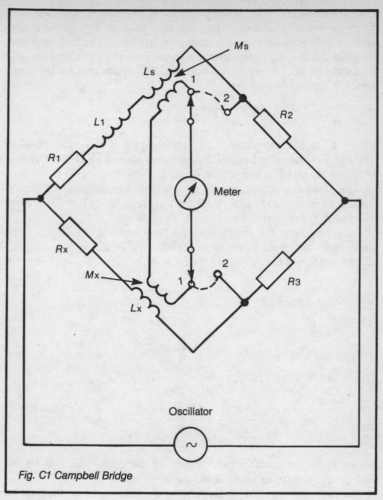

Fig. C1 Campbell Bridge

$$M_x = M_s \times R_3/R_2$$

$$L_x = \frac{R_3(L_1 + L_s)}{R_2}$$

$$R_x = \frac{R_1 R_3}{R_2}$$

(* Bridge, Inductance, Transformer)

CAPACITANCE   This is the property of two conductors, insulated from each other, whereby they are able to store an electric charge when a potential difference is connected to them. A conductor may be of any form, e.g. wire, metal plate or even the earth may be one. The ratio of the charge to the potential difference (p.d.) is constant, hence it is possible to write:

$$C = Q/V$$

where C is the capacitance in farads (symbol F — named after Michael Faraday, the English chemist and physicist), Q is the charge in coulombs and V is the p.d. in volts.

The farad is a comparatively large unit so generally capacitance is quoted in microfarads (μF = 10^{-6} F), nanofarads (nF = 10^{-9} F) or picofarads (pF = 10^{-12} F).

In a *capacitor* the conductors are frequently in the form of flat plates and the capacitance depends on their effective area (A), the thickness (t) and permittivity (ϵ) of the dielectric:

$$C = \epsilon A/t$$

but since

$$\epsilon = \epsilon_0 \times \epsilon_r$$

and

$$\epsilon_0 = 8.854 \times 10^{-12}$$

(see Permittivity), then:

$$C = \frac{8.854 \times 10^{-12} \times \epsilon_r A}{t} \text{ farads}$$

where ϵ_r is the relative permittivity or dielectric constant of the dielectric, t is in metres and A in square metres.

Because the farad is a large unit a more practical formula is:

$$C = \frac{8.854 \times \epsilon_r A}{100t} \text{ picofarads}$$

where t is in cm and A is in sq. cm.

The simplest forms of connection of two or more capacitances (generally as capacitors) are the series and parallel. Consider the parallel connection first because it is the least complicated. As shown above for a capacitor, C is proportional to the area of the

44

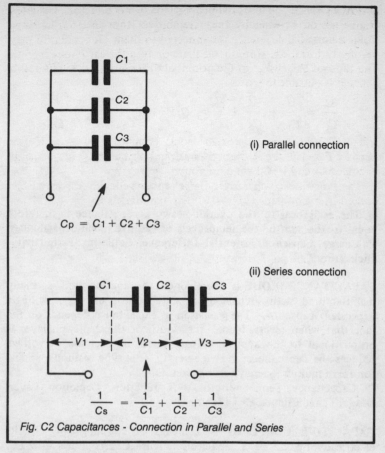

Fig. C2 Capacitances - Connection in Parallel and Series

plates, hence if several capacitors are connected in parallel, the total plate area is the sum of the individual areas. Accordingly, the equivalent capacitance of two or more parallel-connected capacitors is the sum of their individual capacitances, i.e.:

$$C_p = C_1 + C_2 + C_3 + \ldots$$

as shown in Figure C2(i).

In Figure C2(ii) is shown a series arrangement of three capacitors. If a voltage, V_s is connected to the network terminals then the same value of charging current flows through each capacitor for the same time. Each capacitor therefore receives the same amount of charge irrespective of its size. Let this value of charge be Q, then

$Q = CV_1 = CV_2 = CV_3$ where $V_1 + V_2 + V_3 = V_s$. The same charge would be stored by the equivalent capacitor C_s, i.e. $Q = C_s V_s$, hence:

$$V_s = Q/C_s \quad V_1 = Q/C_1 \quad V_2 = Q/C_2 \quad V_3 = Q/C_3$$

$$\therefore \quad \frac{Q}{C_s} = \frac{Q}{C_1} + \frac{Q}{C_2} + \frac{Q}{C_3} \text{ , i.e. } \frac{1}{C_s} = \frac{1}{C_1} + \frac{1}{C_2} + \frac{1}{C_3}$$

or
$$C_s = \frac{C_2 C_3 + C_1 C_3 + C_1 C_2}{C_1 C_2 C_3}$$

The reciprocal of the overall network capacitance is therefore equal to the sum of the reciprocals of the individual capacitances. (* Charge, Capacitor, Potential Difference, Coulomb, Permittivity, Dielectric)

CAPACITANCE DIODE is a semiconductor junction diode specially manufactured with enhanced capacitance for use as a voltage-dependent capacitor. The variation in capacitance depends on the fact that when reverse-biased the width of the depletion layer is proportional to the applied voltage hence an increase in voltage reduces the capacitance and vice versa. This type of diode is ideal for use in radio frequency tuning circuits.
(* Capacitance, Semiconductor, P-N Junction, Depletion Layer, Diode, Tuned Circuit >> Varactor)

CAPACITIVE COUPLING is a means of coupling two circuits electrically by use of a capacitor. Figure C12(i) shows how C_m is connected in series with circuits 1 and 2 and therefore couples them. Alternatively a shunt arrangement can be used —see Coupled Circuits.

CAPACITIVE REACTANCE   This is a means of expressing the opposition offered by a capacitance to the passage of an alternating current in Ohm's Law terms. The unit is therefore the ohm. The reactance is denoted by the symbol X_c. Hence by Ohm's Law, $I = V/X_c$ where I and V are current through and voltage across a capacitance (C).
    The quantity of charge in a capacitor is given by $Q = I \times t$ coulombs where I is the current in amperes and t the time in seconds.

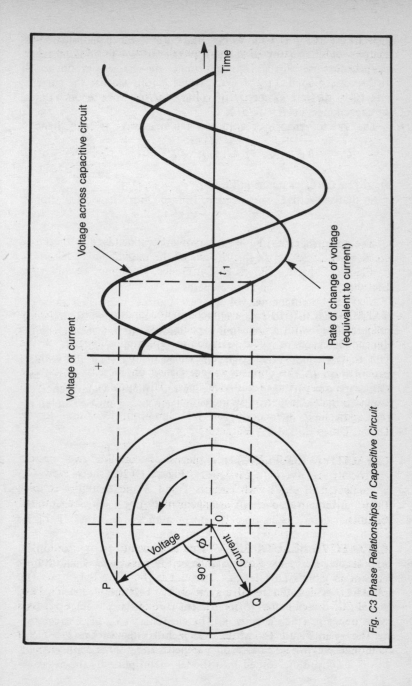

Fig. C3 Phase Relationships in Capacitive Circuit

Rearranging as $I = Q/t$ shows that the current can be considered as the rate of charge (or discharge) at any instant in coulombs per second. However, for a given capacitance the charge is proportional to the voltage applied ($Q = V/C$), hence it follows that the current is equal to the rate of change of voltage (in volts per second) times the capacitance, i.e. $I = dv/dt \times C$.

The rate of change of voltage for a sine wave $= 2\pi f V$, hence:

$$I = 2\pi f V \times C$$

where C is the capacitance in farads.

So that capacitive reactance can fit into Ohm's Law calculations:

$$\text{capacitive reactance}, X_c = \frac{V}{I} = \frac{1}{2\pi f C} \text{ or } \frac{1}{\omega C} \text{ ohms}$$

($\omega = 2\pi f$, V is in volts and I in amperes).

Next, if instantaneous voltages are plotted with their rates of change (which in effect are related to the instantaneous currents), curves as in Figure C3 are obtained. Because the rate of change of voltage reaches its maximum one quarter of a cycle before the voltage itself does, then clearly in a capacitive circuit the voltage lags on the current by an angle $\phi = 90°$ as shown by the rotating voltage phasor OP lagging on the current phasor OQ. Hence to complete the formula for capacitive reactance, a j must be added to express this phase difference, i.e.:

$$\text{reactance of a capacitance } C \text{ farads} = \frac{-j}{2\pi f C} = \frac{-j}{\omega C} \text{ ohms}.$$

By convention, capacitive reactance is given a negative sign. The above considerations assume that no resistance is present. If this is not the case then ϕ is no longer 90° but something less.

(* Charge, Capacitance, Sine Wave, Voltage, Current, Coulomb, Ohm's Law, Complex Notation, Phase, Phase Angle, Quadrature)

CAPACITOR A device having the ability to store electric charge, basically two conductors (often in the shape of flat plates) separated by an insulator (the *dielectric*). The elements of a 2-plate capacitor are shown in Figure C4 which also includes the various graphical symbols used. When a battery (or other generator) is connected as shown, electrons are forced into the left hand plate by the negative

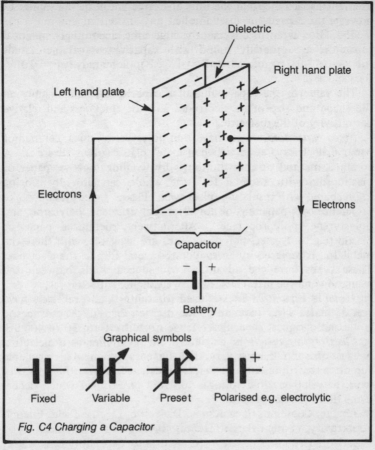

Fig. C4 Charging a Capacitor

In the figure above, the following labels appear:

Dielectric

Right hand plate

Left hand plate

Electrons

Electrons

Capacitor

− + Battery

Graphical symbols

Fixed   Variable   Preset   Polarised e.g. electrolytic

pole of the battery and equally removed from the right hand plate by the attraction of the positive pole. Momentarily therefore a current flows until the potentials on the plates are equal to those of the battery. The capacitor is then said to be *charged* and if the battery is disconnected, it remains so. There is no flow of electrons through the dielectric but because there is a potential across it, an electric field exists through it. Hence energy supplied by the battery is now stored in the dielectric.

The capacitance is expressed as the ratio of electric charge gained to the voltage applied. A capacitor has a capacitance of one farad (F) if it receives a charge of one coulomb (C) for a potential of one volt (V), hence: $C = Q/V$ farads, where Q is the quantity of charge in coulombs and V is the voltage applied. (Note that the symbols used for capacitance and the unit of charge are both the capital C, however the capacitance C is in italic.

The farad is an inconveniently large unit, accordingly practical capacitors are generally found with capacitances of microfarads ($\mu F = 10^{-6}$ F), nanofarads (nF = 10^{-9} F), picofarads (pF = 10^{-12} F).

The value of the capacitance of a capacitor depends mainly on the shape and size of its electrodes and the thickness and relative permittivity of the dielectric.

Fixed capacitors usually have thin polystyrene, mica, ceramic or paper dielectrics pressed between metal plates (often silvered). A common method of construction is by winding together paper or plastic film with a metal foil, the whole capacitor then being impregnated with insulating oil or wax. Plastic dielectrics now take preference over paper e.g. of polyester, polyethylene, polycarbonate, polystyrene, polypropylene. Alternatively, metallized paper or plastic (e.g. polyester, polypropylene) are available, with these the metal foil is replaced by an evaporated metal film as the electrode. These types have the advantage of reduced voids between the insulation and the metal hence relatively higher capacitances.

Variable capacitors as are used for tuning radio receivers have sets of plates which overlap to the degree required. The dielectric is air and a typical capacitance range might be from 30 to 400 pF.

Electrolytic capacitors employ a chemical film as a dielectric. Because the film can be very thin, large capacitances are available (up to many thousands of microfarads). However, these usually work at relatively low voltages to avoid *breakdown* which occurs if the film becomes punctured.

(* Charge, Coulomb, Capacitance, Dielectric, Electric Field, Energy, Permittivity, Potential Difference, Breakdown >> Electrolytic Capacitor, Ceramic Capacitor, Silvered Mica Capacitor, Loss Angle, Residual Charge)

CARRIER is a shortened form of two different terms (1) charge carrier and (2) carrier wave – see these terms.

CARRIER CONCENTRATION is a term used to express the number of charge carriers available per unit volume in a semiconductor. It is related to electric current only when these charges move. The mathematics can only be shown in outline. We consider intrinsic semiconductors first.

The carrier concentration of electrons, n is limited by the density, N_c of the energy levels in the conduction band. Each level accommodates only one electron, hence:

$$n = N_c\, P(E_c)$$

where $P(E_c)$ is the probability that a level of energy, E_c, will be occupied by an electron and E_c is the energy at the bottom of the conduction band. These probabilities are extremely small, for example at room temperature, for silicon, less than 2×10^{-10}, for germanium, less than 2×10^{-6}. From this:

$$n = N_c \exp\left(-E_g/2kT\right)$$

where E_g is the energy gap (i.e. the difference in energy levels between conduction and valence bands), k is Boltzmann's constant and T is the thermodynamic temperature. Clearly n increases with temperature.

The probability of a hole (p) occurring where N_v is the number of energy levels in the valence band is obtained similarly, i.e.:

$$p = N_v \exp\left(-E_g/2kT\right)$$

For an intrinsic semiconductor, $n = p = n_i$, the number of electron-hole pairs. Next, taking the product of n and p from the above:

$$np = n_i{}^2 = N_c N_v \exp\left(-E_g/kT\right)$$

i.e.
$$n_i = \sqrt{(N_c N_v)} \exp\left(-E_g/2kT\right)$$

showing that the carrier concentration depends only on the type of semiconductor and the temperature as might be expected.

For n and p-type semiconductors things change because of the doping. As an example, for the n-type, the greater the density of impurity atoms, the greater is the probability of an electron being in the conduction band. In any doped semiconductor material there may be both donors and acceptors together so that if N_d represents the concentration of donor atoms and N_a of acceptors, then if $N_d > N_a$, the material overall is n-type, conversely if $N_a > N_d$ it is p-type. Total charges must balance, hence:

$$p + N_d = n + N_a$$

In an n-type semiconductor let the concentration of electrons $= n_e$ and that of holes $= n_h$. In a p-type semiconductor let the concentration of electrons $= p_e$ and that of holes $= p_h$.

Then it can be shown that for an n-type material, approximately:

$$n_e = N_d$$

where N_d is the concentration of donor atoms, and

$$n_h = n_i^2/N_d$$

For a p-type material:

$$p_e = n_i^2/N_a$$

where N_a is the concentration of acceptor atoms and

$$p_h = N_a .$$

From these equations we can begin to see the order of things. Take n-type silicon as an example and suppose that the concentration of donors, N_d is $10^{21}/m^3$, the electron concentration is therefore approximately the same. If the concentration of electron-hole pairs (n_i) is, say, $10^{15}/m^3$, then the hole concentration is $(10^{15})^2/10^{21} = 10^9/m^3$. There are therefore 10^{12} as many electrons as there are holes. No wonder we call the electrons in n-type the *majority* carriers.
(* Semiconductor, Electron, Energy Levels, Probability, Thermodynamic Temperature, Hole, Electron-Hole Pair, Doping)

CARRIER STORAGE occurs in a p-n junction when switched from forward to reverse. The diode cannot immediately reach the full reverse condition because of the presence of stored minority carriers at the junction. The effect of these is to produce a small reverse current but initially greater than the normal reverse saturation current, depending on the external circuit conditions. The carriers are rapidly removed by recombination and by being forced back across the junction by the reverse bias. When all carriers are removed the diode is then in its normal reverse state and the time taken for this to happen is known as the *storage time*.
When a reverse current suddenly ceases as shown above, damaging voltages may occur in inductive circuits, hence diodes used in power rectification circuits may need special overvoltage protection.
(* Charge, Charge Carrier, Recombination, P-N Junction, Diode, Reverse Saturation Current)

CARRIER WAVE is a continuous, single frequency wave of constant amplitude, generated specifically for modulation so that a baseband signal can be transmitted at a higher frequency. The modulation

process generates *side frequencies* if the modulating wave is at a single frequency, or *sidebands* if for a range of frequencies. The side frequencies or bands are classed as upper or lower according to whether they are above or below the carrier frequency. In a modulated wave the term is also used to describe the carrier frequency component. This component is usually transmitted as an integral part of the modulated wave, however in certain systems (e.g. single-sideband) it can be suppressed before transmission.
(* Modulation >> Baseband, Single-Sideband Transmission)

CARTESIAN COORDINATE   It was first shown by Renée Descartes (a French mathematician) that any point in a plane can be defined relative to two axes by two numbers, now known as *cartesian coordinates.* In electronics the two axes are almost invariably at right angles as shown in Figure C5. In this figure it is shown

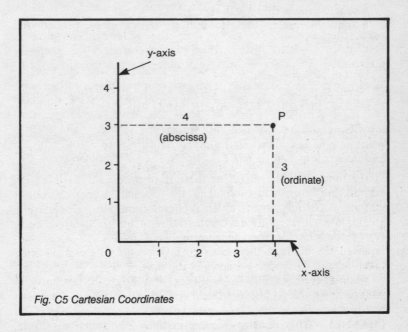

Fig. C5 Cartesian Coordinates

that relative to the x and y axes, the position of the point P can be expressed by the two numbers 4, 3. These are known as the *abscissa* (coordinate measured parallel to the x-axis) and *ordinate* (coordinate measured parallel to the y-axis). It is of course by such coordinates that we normally plot graphs. (See also Polar Coordinate.)

CATHODE   This is the electrode through which electron current enters a device. The electrons are ejected from the cathode through thermionic emission or the photoelectric effect (photocathode). The current flows towards the anode which is held at a positive potential relative to the cathode. Devices employing a cathode are electrolytic cells, thermionic valves, rectifiers and gas-discharge tubes. See also Anode.
(* Electron, Thermionic Emission, Photoelectric Effect)

CATHODE FALL – see Plasma

CATION   When electrons are liberated from atoms or molecules, the latter become positive ions. This occurs in a gas by ionization also in an electrolyte by dissociation. The positive ions are known as *cations* and being positive are attracted towards the cathode when a potential gradient exists.

   A negative ion is called an *anion*.
(* Atom, Molecule, Ion, Ionization, Dissociation, Electrolyte, Charge, Anion)

CELL   This is a device which produces electricity from chemical or other non-mechanical means. It is a two-terminal, direct voltage unit in which electrons are driven away from the positive terminal towards the negative terminal. Most cells have an electromotive force (e.m.f. – the "open circuit" voltage) of between 1 and 2 volts. When a load is connected the potential difference across the cell terminals is less than its e.m.f. owing to the voltage drop across the cell internal resistance. Cells relying on chemical reaction usually contain an electrolyte and are known as *electrolytic*.
(See also Primary Cell, Secondary Cell)
(* Electromotive Force, Potential Difference, Resistance, Internal Resistance, Electrolyte)

CELSIUS – the name given to the scale of temperature on which water freezes at 0° and boils at 100° under specified conditions (also known as the *Centigrade* scale) – see also Kelvin.

CHANNEL   This is a term frequently used in electronics, especially with regard to field-effect transistors. The channel is that part of the semiconductor through which the majority carriers flow from source to drain as shown in Figure F3(i). The conductivity of the channel is controlled by the gate voltage.
(* Field-Effect Transistor, Conductivity >> Channel)

CHARACTERISTIC   This is the relationship between interdependent quantities peculiar to a device, network or system. A characteristic is usually expressed as a curve on a graph relating the two quantities under examination. The complete term is therefore "characteristic curve" but for convenience it is usually shortened to "characteristic". Note that even straight lines on a graph come under the general description of "curve". An example of a component characteristic is given in Figure F3(iv), it shows graphically one of the relationships existing in a particular type of transistor. Many such component characteristics are the result of measurement, others are calculated, e.g. for the simple resistor, Ohm's Law enables us to draw the characteristic relating voltage with current with little effort.

The wide scope of electronics naturally generates a profusion of characteristics, hence they are subdivided:

(i) *electrode characteristics* − show the relationship between current and voltage at one of the electrodes of a component, e.g. between collector current and collector voltage of a bipolar transistor. These are sometimes divided again into *input* and *output* characteristics.

(ii) *transfer characteristics* − show how an effect is transferred *through* a device and they therefore show the relationship between the conditions on one electrode and those created on a different electrode. The example given above (Fig. F3(iv)) is that of a transfer characteristic.

(iii) *static characteristics* − refer to active devices (e.g. transistors and thermionic valves) and show relationships between current and voltage either at the same or between different electrodes under *static* conditions, i.e. with all other applied voltages maintained constant.

(iv) *dynamic characteristics* − these again refer to active devices and relate the current on one electrode to the voltage on a different electrode under specified working conditions. Frequently this involves drawing a *load line* over a set of static characteristics. This allows examination of changes in voltage or current under *working* conditions.

(* Transistor, Electrode, Hybrid Parameters ≫ Load Line)

CHARACTERISTIC IMPEDANCE is a feature of 4-terminal symmetrical networks and of 2-wire transmission lines. There is a common factor in that a transmission line may be considered to consist of a large number of tiny similar 4-terminal networks in

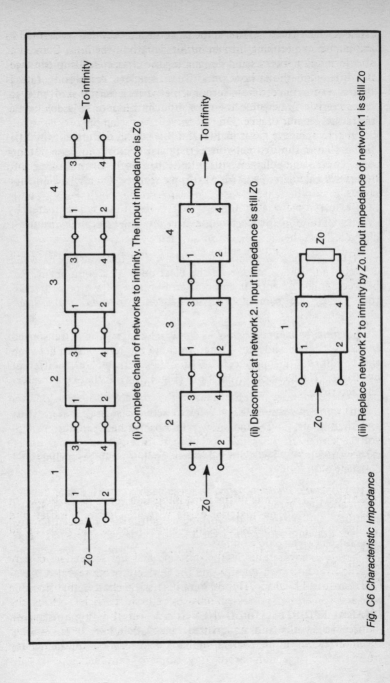

(i) Complete chain of networks to infinity. The input impedance is Z0

(ii) Disconnect at network 2. Input impedance is still Z0

(iii) Replace network 2 to infinity by Z0. Input impedance of network 1 is still Z0

Fig. C6 Characteristic Impedance

tandem. The characteristic impedance of a 2-wire line is defined as the impedance looking into an infinite length of the line. Looked at as 4-terminal networks and designating the characteristic impedance, Z_0, Figure C6 shows how we arrive at a second definition. This is that if any symmetrical 4-terminal network is terminated with its characteristic impedance then the input impedance will also be the characteristic impedance.

In (i) of Figure C6 is shown the theoretical definition while (ii) shows that if the first network is removed, then because the number of networks remaining is still infinite, the impedance looking into terminals 1 and 2 is also Z_0. At (iii) we see how the above definition arises.

Being symmetrical it follows that if the input is terminated by Z_0, then the impedance looking back into the output terminals is also Z_0.

The characteristic impedance (Z_0) of a 2-wire transmission line can be calculated from the four primary coefficients, R, L, G and C (see Transmission Line):

$$Z_0 = \sqrt{\frac{R + j\omega L}{G + j\omega C}} \text{ ohms}$$

where each has the value per unit length. For j see Complex Notation.

In practice, for short lines, Z_0 can be measured, for if Z_{oc} is the impedance looking into the line with its distant end open-circuited and Z_{sc} that measured when the distant end is short-circuited, then:

$$Z_0 = \sqrt{Z_{oc} \times Z_{sc}} .$$

(* Network, Impedance, Complex Notation, Iterative Impedance, Transmission Line)

CHARGE   This is one of the most important terms in the book. In the whole world no material exists without charge. Gravity and charge hold the universe together and charge is the basis of all present day electronic wonders.

Nature is mysterious in the extreme and her secrets are closely guarded for although one by one the laws are being revealed, never are the reasons why. This is how it is with charge, that invisible certain something possessed only by atomic particles. It is the fundamental driving force of electricity yet it is a phenomenon which we do not fully understand. Nevertheless we have certainly been successful in developing methods of measuring and harnessing it.

It was not until 1897 that the English physicist, J. J. Thomson, was able to prove that charged particles (which we now know as electrons) actually existed. Then it was left to R. A. Millikan (an American physicist) to refine earlier measurements and produce a reasonably accurate idea of the charge carried by a single electron. We now give charge the symbol Q and the unit is the *coulomb*. The electron charge is sometimes called the *elementary charge* because so far nothing smaller has been confirmed. It has a value of 1.6021×10^{-19} coulombs. Since Millikan's work it has been discovered that the atom nucleus contains *protons*, each of which has exactly the same amount of charge as the electron but in one important way it is very different. Whereas similar charges dislike each other intensely and repel, the proton and electron charges exhibit great attraction for each other. The whole phenomenon is summed up by the golden rule:

"Like charges repel, unlike attract".

We label the proton charge, *positive* and the electron charge, *negative.*

A charge is therefore defined as a quantity of electrical energy. Charges give rise to fields and in the field of one charge another charge experiences a force on it, of attraction if the two charges are of different types but of repulsion if the same. See Figure C7.

The way in which the force between two charges varies is:

$$F \propto \frac{Q_1 Q_2}{d^2}$$

where Q_1 and Q_2 represent the magnitudes of the charges and d is the distance between them.

The charge of a single electron may seem insignificant but when millions of them get together (as is normally the case), the total charge is mighty and powerful. It is charge which can move massive trains at high speed for our convenience yet generate thunderstorms for aggravation.

It is also most instructive to calculate for ourselves the magnitude of the forces which are locked up in matter. Such a calculation has no practical use whatsoever but it does enable us to appreciate how exacting Nature is where charges are concerned.

Imagine two cubes of copper of side a mere one millimetre and let them be one metre apart. Assume that in both cubes all protons (the positive charges) are removed. There are some 8.5×10^{19} atoms

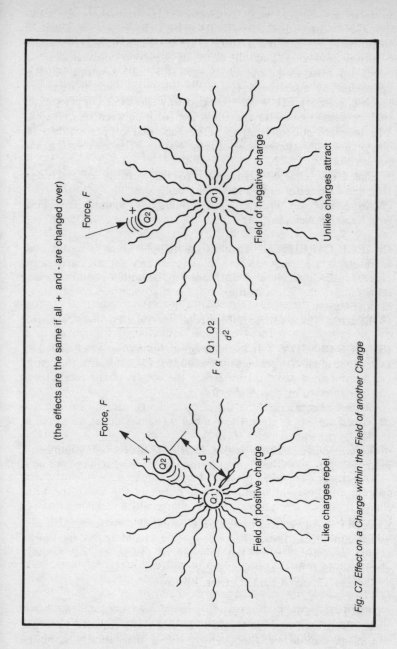

Fig. C7 Effect on a Charge within the Field of another Charge

(the effects are the same if all + and - are changed over)

Force, F

Q2 +

Field of negative charge

Unlike charges attract

$$F \propto \frac{Q_1 \, Q_2}{d^2}$$

Force, F

Q2 +

d

Field of positive charge

Q1 +

Like charges repel

in each tiny cube so with 29 electrons per atom there are about 2.5×10^{21} altogether. The total negative charge per 1mm cube is therefore $(2.5 \times 10^{21}) \times (1.602 \times 10^{-19})$, i.e. some 400 coulombs.

From Coulomb's Law the force of repulsion between the two cubes 1m apart works out to about 1.4×10^{15} newtons which is approximately equal to 1.4×10^{11} tonnes (or tons, there is not much difference). Thus we have two tiny specks of copper (minus their protons) one metre apart and the force between them is some 140 thousand million tonnes! The fact that copper exhibits no charge normally shows how *exactly* Nature balances electron and proton charges.

The term "charge" also refers to the quantity of electricity stored in a capacitor or in a secondary cell.

(* Atom, Electron, Proton, Field, Coulomb, Coulomb's Law, Positive, Negative, Newton)

CHARGE CARRIER   An electron or hole which is mobile and therefore is a moving charge. Electrons carry (or are) a negative charge, holes, positive and both are mobile within conductors and semiconductors. When in motion these charge carriers constitute an electric current.

(* Electron, Hole, Current, Electron-Hole Pair, Positive, Negative)

CHARGE DENSITY   If we consider a region of space occupied by many individual charges closely spaced, then at a distance the charge can be imagined as uniform. Hence the effects of the total charge can be expressed by *charge density*.

Surface charge density is the electric charge per unit surface area of a medium. It is given the symbol σ (sigma) and is measured in coulombs per square metre (C/m^2).

Volume charge density is the electric charge per unit volume of a medium. It is given the symbol ρ (rho) and is measured in coulombs per cubic metre (C/m^3).

(* Charge, Coulomb)

CIRCUIT   An electrical circuit is a complete conducting path over which current can flow. There cannot be a build-up or depletion of charge anywhere, hence the number of charge carriers (usually electrons) must be the same at every point around it.

(* Current, Charge, Charge Carrier, Electron)

COERCIVE FORCE   This is a term used with ferromagnetic materials, it is the reverse magnetic field strength required to reduce the magnetisation or flux density of a magnetically saturated

specimen to zero, i.e. to demagnetise it.
See Magnetic Hysteresis.
(* Magnetism, Magnetisation, Magnetic Field Strength, Ferro-magnetism >> Saturation)

COERCIVITY is a characteristic of a ferromagnetic material, it is a measure of the magnetic field strength required to demagnetise a sample of the material from magnetic saturation.
See also Coercive Force.
(* Ferromagnetism, Magnetic Field Strength, Magnetic Hysteresis >> Saturation)

COHERENCE is a wave property in which corresponding points on the wavefront are in phase. It is possible therefore to look upon a coherent beam as comprising a wave with its spatial and time pro-perties predictable. In a more practical way a coherent wave is one at a single frequency and a non-coherent wave, although having a predominant wavelength, is basically a mixture of different waves of random phases and varying amplitudes.

Coherent oscillations have the property that if interrupted, the wave will recommence at a phase which it would have had with no interruption. Generally lasers are coherent oscillators.
(* Electromagnetic Radiation, Phase, Wavefront, Laser)

COLD CATHODE is one which emits electrons at ambient tempera-tures, i.e. it is not heated. For emission a sufficiently high voltage gradient must exist at the surface. Also light can have the effect of releasing those electrons from a cold cathode which receive suffici-ent energy from incident photons to exceed the work function. Electronic emission is also possible from a cold cathode in a gas-filled tube for example with neon at moderately low pressure. The normal space charge surrounds the cathode and electrons may be drawn from it depending on the strength of the electric field existing between the anode and cathode.

Cold cathodes are preferably of, or coated with, materials of low work function.
(* Cathode, Space Charge, Work Function, Photoelectric Effect, Photoemission, Gas Discharge)

COLLECTOR is one of the regions of a bipolar junction transistor. Minority carriers in the base region are swept into the collector region where they become majority carriers — see Transistor.

COLLISION is the sudden encounter of a moving body with another or with a stationary body. It is something experienced so often in daily life. We know the rules which govern such clashes and the rules are no different in the microscopic world of atomic particles.

In a way *momentum* is an expression of the power lurking in the velocity of a body. It is a function of both the mass and the velocity, i.e.:

$$\text{momentum}, p = mv \text{ kg m/s}$$

where m is the mass of the body in kilograms and v its velocity in metres per second. The *Law of Conservation of Momentum* states that: "provided that no external force acts, the total momentum of a group of objects is constant."

This can be examined in a practical way by using the classic example of rifle and bullet. These two form a "group of objects" and while the rifle is being aimed the total momentum is zero because neither rifle nor bullet has velocity. When the trigger is pulled the explosion forces the bullet forward with a certain momentum. Because the total momentum must remain at zero, the rifle recoils, i.e. it acquires a momentum in the opposite direction. The forward momentum of the bullet equals the backward momentum of the rifle. This is when things fly apart. In the atomic world we are more interested in what happens when they collide. For collisions the Law still holds good, the total momentum is unchanged after the event.

Another illustration which brings us one step nearer in understanding particle collisions is given by the game of billiards. The player strikes a ball with the cue whereupon all the momentum of the cue is transferred to the ball because the cue comes to rest ($v = 0, \therefore p = 0$ — friction is neglected of course). With luck, the moving ball then collides with another, they bounce off each other with the momentum of the striking ball now shared between the two.

Things get easier when we consider collisions between two electrons for the "bodies" have exactly the same mass so it is evident that there is simply a redistribution of velocity but we must not lose sight of the fact that velocity embraces both speed and direction. Collisions are subdivided into two types, *elastic* and *inelastic*. Firstly we recall the formula for kinetic energy:

$$E_k = \tfrac{1}{2}mv^2 \text{ joules}.$$

Elastic Collisions: the rule governing these is that the total kinetic energy after collision is the same as that before, simply

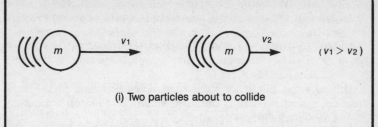

(i) Two particles about to collide

(ii) After collison the velocities are exchanged

Fig. C8 Elastic Collision in a Straight Line Between Two Similar Particles

implying that because the collision is elastic, no kinetic energy is lost (in fact in physics this is how elasticity is defined, i.e. that in a collision there is no decrease in kinetic energy). Collisions in a straight line are the least complicated, consider therefore two particles about to collide as in Figure C8(i). Velocity denoted by a lower case v is that before collision, after collision a capital V is used.

Equating the momenta before with after collision:

$$mv_1 + mv_2 = mV_1 + mV_2$$

$\therefore$
$$(v_1 - V_1) = (V_2 - v_2) \qquad (1)$$

also equating the kinetic energies:

$$\tfrac{1}{2}mv_1{}^2 + \tfrac{1}{2}mv_2{}^2 = \tfrac{1}{2}mV_1{}^2 + \tfrac{1}{2}mV_2{}^2$$

from which:
$$(v_1 + V_1)(v_1 - V_1) = (V_2 + v_2)(V_2 - v_2) \qquad (2)$$

and dividing equation (2) by equation (1):

$$(v_1 + V_1) = (v_2 + V_2) \qquad (3)$$

or:

$$v_1 - v_2 = -(V_1 - V_2) \qquad (4)$$

showing that the *relative* velocities before and after are the same. Note here that the m's have disappeared from the equation as might be expected.

Adding equations (1) and (3) brings the important conclusion that $v_1 = V_2$, i.e. on collision the two particles simply exchange their velocities (see Fig. C8(ii).

Although the figure shows two particles travelling in the same direction, a similar result is obtained when the collision is head-on, i.e. one of the velocities is negative.

This is a highly simplified explanation for seldom do particles meet in a straight line. However, the law of conservation of momentum applies equally to the separate components of velocity, i.e. momentum in the x direction before collision = momentum in the x direction after collision and similarly for the y and perhaps z directions (see Fig. C5). This enables us to calculate not only the velocities after collision but also the angle at which the bodies part.

From the above explanation, limited in scope though it may be, it is possible to appreciate how in secondary emission, resident electrons at the surface of a material are able to escape when they exchange velocities with high velocity ones bombarding them from an external source.

Inelastic Collisions: in these some of the original kinetic energy is lost in doing work or producing heat. Everyday collisions are of this form and range between the completely elastic (which in fact is not a practical condition because some friction is always around) and the completely inelastic in which the colliding objects actually stick together.

Although we may picture electron collisions in terms of those of billiard balls, there is more to consider. Electrons carry negative charges and as two get close to each other there is an increasing force of repulsion — a complicated affair altogether.

(* Energy, Momentum, Mass, Electron, Kinetic Energy, Secondary Emission)

COLOUR is a sensation produced in the brain when the eye reacts to electromagnetic radiation at a certain frequency. Figure E5 shows the "rainbow" colours on a basis of radiation wavelength. On a frequency basis the range is approximately from 4×10^{14} Hz (lowest red) to 7.9×10^{14} Hz (highest violet).

In television any colour is defined by its *luminance* which expresses the level of brightness of a picture element and its *chrominance*. The latter term which tells about the colour, itself has two components, *hue* which is the dominant electromagnetic frequency and *saturation* which can best be explained as the colour *intensity* or "colourfulness". A colour with 0% saturation in fact contains no colour at all but is entirely grey. At the other extreme 100% saturation indicates a colour which has no dilution by white.

A characteristic of the human eye is that certain primary colours can be combined to produce a multitude of others, in electronics we use red, green and blue. For example, blue and red mixed together give purple. Red and green together give yellow and with a little blue added the result is a pastel green, not necessarily the same as the primary green on its own. It is on this basis that colour television is so successful, allowing us to enjoy its exquisite reproduction that we all now take for granted.

(* Electromagnetic Spectrum >> Television, Television Signal, Television Receiver)

COMPENSATION THEOREM This is a theorem used as an aid in network analysis. It is one of the few theorems which is not restricted to linear networks only. In simple terms it states that any impedance in a network can be replaced by the voltage across it. In full it states that any impedance can be replaced by a zero impedance generator having an e.m.f. equal to the instantaneous p.d. which existed across that impedance.

A simple circuit can be used to demonstrate this as in Figure C9(i). By Ohm's Law (plus Kirchhoff's when necessary), the current in resistor R is 0.025 A, hence the p.d. across R is 0.025 × 20 = 0.5 V. By the Compensation Theorem therefore R can be replaced by a zero impedance generator of e.m.f. −0.5 V as in (ii) of the figure. The minus sign arises because this e.m.f. must be in opposition to E for if not, some voltage has been gained from somewhere which of course is impossible. It can be shown by use of Kirchhoff's Laws that the network in (ii) produces the same currents in each branch as does the original network in (i).

(* Network, Impedance, Ohm's Law, Kirchhoff's Laws, Electromotive Force, Potential Difference)

COMPLEX CONJUGATE – see Rationalization

COMPLEX NOTATION (COMPLEX NUMBERS, COMPLEX ALGEBRA) is a method of handling phase differences in a.c. networks mathematically instead of by graphic or phasor diagram. Basically the method enables manipulation of the rectangular components of phasors by keeping all horizontal components together and similarly all vertical components. To do this a phasor

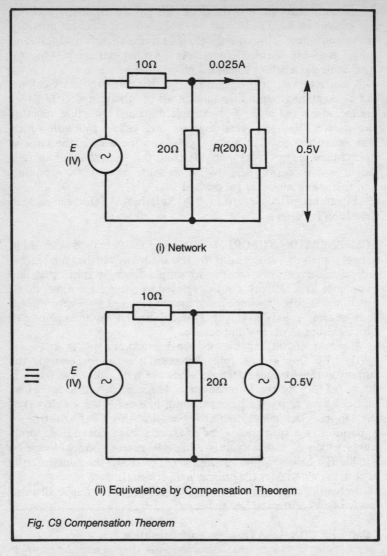

(i) Network

(ii) Equivalence by Compensation Theorem

Fig. C9 Compensation Theorem

is first resolved into its components as shown in Figure C10. The components and axes are labelled *real* and *imaginary* (a misleading label which has been handed down from early mathematicians). The phasor OP in the figure is resolved into:

real component = OPcos ϕ and imaginary component = OPsin ϕ .

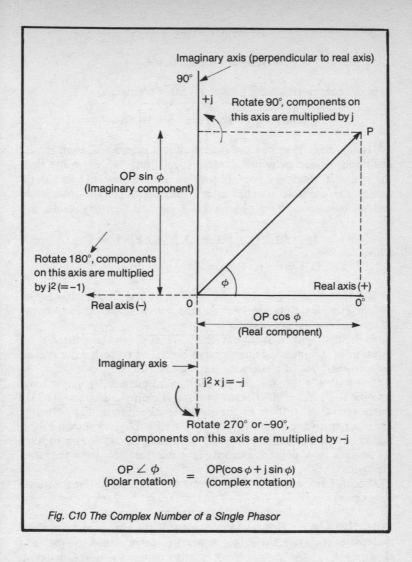

Fig. C10 The Complex Number of a Single Phasor

To keep the components apart (because they cannot be manipulated in this form by normal algebra), an "operator" is used, denoted by the letter j (for electronics only, mathematicians used "i"). j is said to rotate any phasor or component through 90° anticlockwise, hence the phasor OP can now be expressed by OP(cos ϕ + j sin ϕ), for example, if OP has a magnitude of 10 and $\phi = 60°$ (i.e. in polar coordinates, OP = 10∠60°), then:

$$\text{OP}\cos\phi \ = \ 10 \times 0.5$$

$$\text{OP}\sin\phi \ = \ 10 \times 0.866$$

so in complex notation the phasor $10\angle 60°$ becomes:

$$10(0.5 + j\,0.866) \quad \text{or} \quad 5 + j\,8.66 \ .$$

Having done this, phasors can be added, subtracted, even multiplied and divided as required using special rules which ensure that the real and imaginary components do not become entwined until finally the complex number is reformed as a phasor. Addition and subtraction of two phasors $(a + jb)$ and $(c + jd)$ results in:

$$(a + jb) + (c + jd) \ = \ (a + c) + j(b + d)$$

and

$$(a + jb) - (c + jd) \ = \ (a - c) + j(b - d) \ .$$

Multiplication and division of phasors are less frequently carried out in complex notation because the job is more easily accomplished using polar coordinates.

Capacitive and inductive circuits readily lend themselves to solution by complex algebra because reactance in both cases is conveniently 90° out of phase with the resistance.

If rotating a phasor through 90° multiplies it by j, then by rotating it a further 90° (i.e. to 180°), it is multiplied by $j \times j \,(= j^2)$. But a phasor at 180° is in the opposite direction and is normally given a negative sign, hence $j^2 = -1$ or $j = \sqrt{-1}$ as shown in the figure. In mathematics there is no such thing as the square root of -1 so it is now perhaps possible to come to terms with the label "imaginary".

(* Phasor, Cartesian Co-ordinate, Polar Co-ordinate, Rationalization, Reactance)

CONDUCTANCE This is a term expressing the ability of a specified material of a certain shape (e.g. a wire) to carry an electric current. It depends on the *conductivity* of the material and the material dimensions. As an example, for a given uniform length of wire, the conductance is inversely proportional to the length and directly proportional to the area of cross-section. Conductance is given the symbol G and for any purely resistive circuit:

$$G \ = \ I/V \text{ siemens (S)}$$

where I is the current in amperes and V, the voltage applied, is in volts.

Conductance is the reciprocal of resistance, hence a resistance of 10Ω is equivalent to a conductance of $0.1\,\text{S}$. Conductance is also the real component of admittance (Y), i.e. $Y = G + \text{j}B$ where B is the susceptance and all units are in siemens. The relationship between conductance and the components of impedance is given by:

$$G = \frac{R}{R^2 + X^2} \text{ siemens,}$$

where R and X are in ohms.

Most circuit analysis is conducted using the concept of resistance, however there are occasions when conductance may be more useful, especially for parallel combinations for if the conductance of each branch is known then the total conductance is simply the sum of the individual branch conductances.

(* Conductivity, Siemens, Complex Notation, Admittance, Susceptance, Reactance)

CONDUCTION BAND   The range of energy levels possessed by electrons in a solid which have been released from the orbits of parent atoms and are therefore available as charge carriers (i.e. for conduction). On an energy-level diagram this range of levels appears as a band as shown in Figure E12 — see Energy Bands.

CONDUCTIVITY expresses the ease with which charge carriers (current) can flow through a given material. Generally it varies:

(i)   directly with the average number of free electrons (n)
(ii) directly with the electron mean free path (d)
(iii) for most materials, inversely as the square root of the absolute temperature (T), i.e.

$$\sigma \simeq nd/\sqrt{T}$$

where σ is the conductivity.

Consider a length of wire as in Figure C11 in which we find that:

(i)   the current is proportional to the cross-sectional area (a)
(ii) the electric field strength varies inversely with length (l).

The conductivity is then expressed by the electric field strength required to produce a given current density, i.e.:

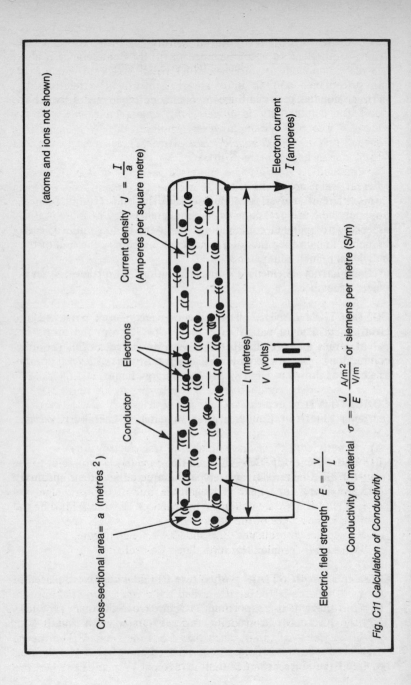

Fig. C11 Calculation of Conductivity

(atoms and ions not shown)

Electron current I (amperes)

Current density $J = \dfrac{I}{a}$ (Amperes per square metre)

Electrons

Conductor

l (metres)

V (volts)

Cross-sectional area $= a$ (metres^2)

Electric field strength $E = \dfrac{V}{L}$

Conductivity of material $\sigma = \dfrac{J}{E} \dfrac{A/m^2}{V/m}$ or siemens per metre (S/m)

$$\sigma = \frac{\text{current density } (J)}{\text{electric field strength } (E)}$$

J is in amperes per square metre, E is in volts per metre, hence the unit for conductivity is *amperes per square metre per volt per metre*. The S.I. system however simplifies this by bringing in a special unit for *conductance*, the *siemens* (S), accordingly the unit for σ is siemens per metre (S/m).

Conductivity can also be expressed in terms of a unit cube (1 metre sides) of the material. If a current I (amps) flows between opposite faces and the voltage across them is V (volts), then the conductivity, $\sigma = I/V$ siemens per metre.

(* Charge, Conductance, Electron, Mean Free Path, Current Density, Electric Field Strength, Siemens)

CONDUCTOR   This is a material which contains sufficient "free" electrons so that an electric field pervading the material can accelerate them towards the positive pole, so causing a relatively large current to flow. Most metals are good conductors, a particularly useful non-metal one is carbon.

Materials used for conductors have low resistivities (high conductivities). Copper for example has a resistivity of 1.72×10^{-8} ohm-metres (Ω m). Silver is even better as a conductor at 1.62×10^{-8} Ω m. Generally conductors have resistivities in the range 10^{-8} to 10^{-6} Ω m.

(* Atom, Electron, Conductivity, Conductance, Resistivity, Copper, Silver)

CONJUGATE IMPEDANCE   Two impedances are said to be *conjugate* if their real (resistive) parts are equal and their imaginary (reactive) parts are equal in magnitude but of opposite sign, i.e. $R + jX$ and $R - jX$ are conjugate impedances. Each is said to be the conjugate impedance of the other.

Using polar co-ordinates, $ZL\phi$ and $ZL-\phi$ are conjugate.

(* Impedance, Complex Notation, Polar Co-ordinate)

CONTACT POTENTIAL   When two dissimilar metals are placed in contact, a potential difference called the *contact potential* appears between them. This arises from the difference in the work functions of the two metals. Consider two dissimilar metals A and B with work functions ϕ_A and ϕ_B such that ϕ_A is the greater. This means that more energy is required in metal A to encourage a free electron to jump the surface barrier than is required in metal B. When the

71

two metals are placed in contact therefore the electron emission B→A will exceed that A→B. A therefore becomes negatively charged and B positive, this difference in potential is the contact potential.

The phenomenon can also be explained via Fermi levels. If metal B has the higher Fermi level, then A must have more lower energy levels available than B. Accordingly electrons from B are free to move into A and the latter becomes negative with respect to B. The process continues until the two Fermi levels become equal and it follows that the contact potential is equal to the difference in the Fermi levels of the metals (when they are not in contact).

Contact potentials are usually no more than a small fraction of one volt.

(* Electron, Work Function, Fermi Level)

CONTACT WORK FUNCTION – see Work Function

CONVENTIONAL CURRENT   One would imagine that when dealing with quantities, a positive amount would be greater than a negative amount and any movement would be from positive to negative. Generally this holds true so it is unfortunate that names for the two types of electric charge were decided on long before the electron was discovered. Accordingly it was considered that electricity flowed from positive to negative but the subsequent discovery that most current flow is by electrons has proved this to be a bad guess. Current flow is from negative to positive except in a few cases, for example with positive ions in gases or liquids. These do flow from positive to negative although much more slowly than electrons because of their greater mass. The original idea has remained with us simply because changing it would cause confusion for some time. To distinguish between this generally incorrect direction of current flow and electron flow the former is labelled "conventional current" (i.e. following tradition).

Fearful of the complications arising from a changeover, the experts have decided that current direction on semiconductor graphical symbols shall remain conventional but note that the artful device known as "hole current" is used so that we moderns cannot be accused of being incorrect. To sum up, it is suggested that it is usually better not to think in terms of conventional current but to "see" current flow as pictured in Figures C11 or C15, remembering the golden rule, "like charges repel, unlike attract".

(* Charge, Current, Electron, Semiconductor, Hole Current, Positive, Negative)

COPPER is an element, symbol Cu, atomic number 29, which is extensively used in electronics as a conductor. Copper has one

electron only in its outer (4th) shell which it readily gives up for conduction purposes. Its resistivity is therefore very low (only bettered by silver) at $1.724\,\Omega m \times 10^{-8}$ (at 20°C).
(* Element, Atom, Conductivity, Shell, Resistivity, Silver)

CORE usually refers to the soft ferromagnetic material which is part of the magnetic circuit of for example, a generator, electric motor or transformer. Important qualities required of such a core are high permeability, low coercivity and low remanence. At the lower end of the frequency range, laminated cores are used. These consist of thin laminations of a ferromagnetic material such as iron, each coated with an insulating film so that when built up as a core the magnetic properties remain but electrically the resistance between adjacent laminations is high. This reduces the magnitude of eddy currents. At radio frequencies, ferrite cores are more likely to be employed, these are cast into the core shape required and the ceramic mix can be such that both high permeability and high electrical resistance are obtained — again eddy current losses are minimized.
(* Ferromagnetism, Permeability, Coercivity, Remanence, Eddy Current, Core Loss, Transformer >> Ferrite, Lamination, Electric Motor, Generator)

CORE LOSS refers to the dissipation of electric power in a ferromagnetic core. From the circuit point of view such a power loss is wasted energy. The total loss is mainly that due to eddy currents and magnetic hysteresis.
(* Core, Eddy Current, Magnetic Hysteresis)

COULOMB   A single electron (or ion) carries a tiny electric charge. When more than one congregate, their charges are additive, hence a unit of electric charge is needed rather than attempting to quote how many electrons are involved. The S.I. unit of charge is the coulomb (symbol C — after Charles Augustin de Coulomb, a French engineer and physicist). In fact the number of elementary charges (usually electrons) gathered together which constitute a charge of one coulomb is 6.242×10^{18}. When this quantity of electric charge is conveyed past a given point in one second, then one ampere of current is said to flow. From this the definition of the coulomb follows, i.e. it is the charge transported in one second by a constant current of one ampere. Hence:

$$\text{Charge, } Q = I \times t \text{ coulombs (C)}$$

where I is the current in amperes and t is the time in seconds.

The charge per electron is equal to:

$$1/(6.242 \times 10^{18}) = 1.602 \times 10^{-19} \text{ C}.$$

(* Electron, Charge, Ampere, S.I.)

COULOMB'S LAW   A law concerned with the force between charges at rest from Charles Augustin de Coulomb. The law states that the mutual force of repulsion between like charges or of attraction between unlike charges concentrated at points in an isotropic medium (the same throughout) is (i) proportional to the product of the charges, (ii) inversely proportional to the square of the distance between them and to the permittivity of the medium. As a formula:

$$F = \frac{Q_1 Q_2}{4\pi\epsilon d^2} \text{ newtons}$$

where Q_1 and Q_2 represent the charge magnitudes in coulombs, d is the distance between their centres in metres and ϵ is the permittivity of the medium.
(* Charge, Force, Newton, Coulomb, Permittivity)

COUPLED CIRCUITS are those between which power can be transferred by some means of coupling between them. Basically there are two ways in which coupling is arranged, (a) by components common to both circuits (*common impedance coupling*) or (b) by transference of power by means of a magnetic field.

For (a) the components can either be in series between the two circuits as shown for the capacitor C_m in Figure C12(i) which is linking two resonant circuits or for the inductor L_m in (ii) which is doing the same thing in a different way. For the capacitor any voltage across it produces a current from circuit 1 into circuit 2. For the inductor, current through it as part of circuit 1 gives rise to a voltage across it which is injected into circuit 2. These forms of coupling are frequency dependent, *resistance* (or *direct*) coupling can similarly be used and in this case the coupling itself is not frequency dependent although the individual circuits may be.

For (b) the term *mutual inductance coupling* is used. Here the only coupling is via the magnetic flux generated in, say L_1 which also embraces L_2 [see Fig. C12(iii)]. If all the flux generated by L_1 cuts L_2, then the mutual inductance:

$$M = \sqrt{L_1 L_2} \text{ henries}$$

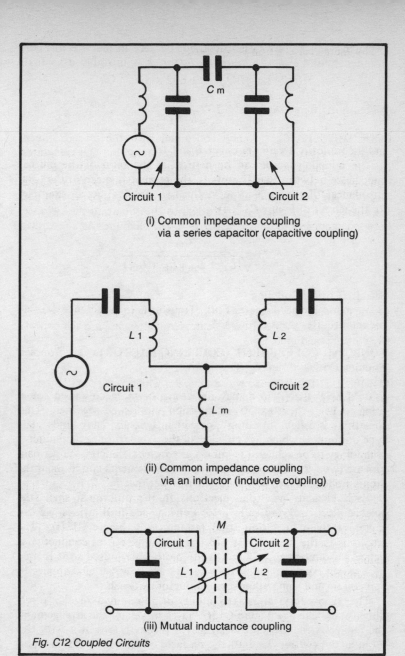

(i) Common impedance coupling
via a series capacitor (capacitive coupling)

(ii) Common impedance coupling
via an inductor (inductive coupling)

(iii) Mutual inductance coupling

Fig. C12 Coupled Circuits

(when L_1 and L_2 are in henries), but because in practice this condition cannot be met, a *coupling factor,* k is introduced so that:

$$k = \frac{M}{\sqrt{L_1 L_2}}$$

and theoretically k varies between 0 and 1.

The coupling factor can be defined as the ratio of the mutual impedance between two circuits to the geometric mean of the total impedances of the same type in the two circuits. As an example, for the circuit of Figure C12(ii):

$$k = \frac{L_m}{\sqrt{(L_1 + L_m)(L_2 + L_m)}}$$

See also Critical Coupling.
(* Magnetic Field, Magnetic Flux, Transformer, Inductance, Mutual Inductance, Resonant Circuit)

COUPLING COEFFICIENT (COUPLING FACTOR) – see Coupled Circuits, Critical Coupling, Transformer.

COVALENT BOND in a material atoms or molecules need something to keep them exactly in position and locked together. That something is called "bonding", of which there are many kinds. The type of bonding which has enabled all the wonders of semiconductor technology to be achieved is known as *covalent.* Silicon and germanium are two very important semiconductor elements and in them the atoms are locked into the lattice by this method.

Each element has four electrons in the outermost shell (the valence electrons) and purely for convenience in drawings, we can represent them in a simplified fashion as in Figure C13(i). The electrons in the inner orbits play no part in electrical conductivity, hence we omit them. Silicon is the more widely used so it is used here as an example, much of what is said however also applies to germanium and some other semiconductor materials.

The silicon crystal has its atoms disposed in a regular three-dimensional cluster. Figure C13(ii) gives an idea of the arrangement, the cubical structure of the lattice for atom 1 is shown with this atom at the centre. Each of the six faces of the cube has two atoms at the corners, diagonally opposed. Every atom has therefore four immediate neighbours (except at the surface of the material) and the

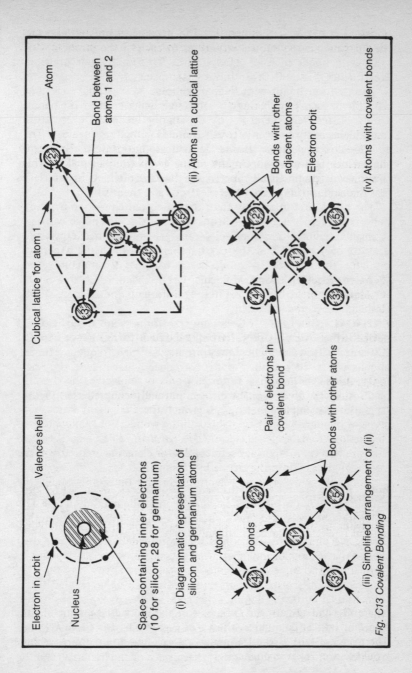

Electron in orbit   Valence shell

Nucleus

Space containing inner electrons
(10 for silicon, 28 for germanium)

(i) Diagrammatic representation of
silicon and germanium atoms

Atom

Bond between
atoms 1 and 2

(ii) Atoms in a cubical lattice

Cubical lattice for atom 1

Bonds with other
adjacent atoms

Electron orbit

(iv) Atoms with covalent bonds

Pair of electrons in
covalent bond

Bonds with other atoms

Atom

bonds

(iii) Simplified arrangement of (ii)

Fig. C13 Covalent Bonding

bonds each has are as indicated. The drawing therefore leaves to the imagination the cubical structures of each of the atoms 2 – 5, again with bonds to four other atoms. To simplify our drawings even further, Figure C13(iii) shows this in plan.

Atoms form bonds with their neighbours by "pairing" electrons with them, each pair sharing an orbit embracing both of the parent atoms. Effectively therefore, by the sharing technique every atom has 8 electrons in orbit in 4 covalent bonds with atoms nearby. The additional four electrons enable the atom to complete its final sub-shell which is a move that many atoms are anxious to make. This is shown diagrammatically in (iv) of the figure which in fact is a development of (iii) to show the electrons and their orbits.

The bonds are sufficiently tight that at absolute zero temperature none is broken hence no electrons are available as charge carriers. At higher temperatures some electrons gain sufficient energy from heat to be released and the crystal changes from being a perfect insulator to one not so good, i.e. it becomes a semiconductor. (* Atom, Electron, Bond, Molecule, Orbit, Valency, Crystal, Shell, Absolute Zero)

CRITICAL COUPLING   Generally transformers are thought of as devices which transmit power from one circuit to another a single frequency. However, when they are part of high frequency tuned circuits where the overall response is frequency dependent, they can in fact be used as band-pass filters.

Consider the two resonant circuits mutually coupled as in Figure C12(iii). The coupling factor, k, is given by:

$$k = \frac{M}{\sqrt{L_1 L_2}}$$

Both circuits are tuned to the same resonance frequency (f_r) and *critical coupling* (k_c) is reached when there is the maximum transfer of energy between the two circuits. Under this condition the current in circuit 2 is maximum and it can be shown that:

$$k_c = \frac{1}{\sqrt{Q_1 Q_2}}$$

where Q_1 and Q_2 are the Q-factors of the individual circuits. The effect of critical coupling is shown in Figure C14 for curve $k = k_c$. The response falls as the frequency varies above and below f_r as one would expect from resonance.

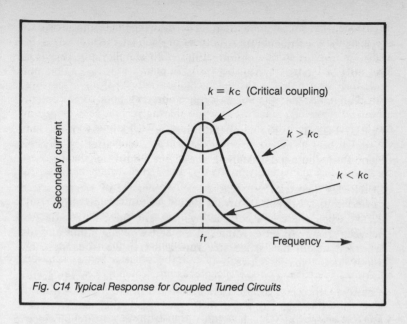

Fig. C14 *Typical Response for Coupled Tuned Circuits*

As k is reduced below the critical value, the response again falls as shown for the curve $k < k_c$. When k exceeds k_c however, the maximum current is actually lower than that for critical coupling but now exhibits a "double hump" (curve $k > k_c$). By careful adjustment of the value of k to something slightly above the critical value a reasonably flat-topped band-pass characteristic can be obtained. This is especially useful in intermediate frequency amplifiers for example those used in amplitude modulation radio receivers where maximum transfer of energy at the resonance frequency is required but with a bandwidth of some 9 kHz. In such transformers k may be as low as 0.01, very different from the mains transformer where 0.95 may be expected.
(* Transformer, Tuned Circuit, Coupled Circuits, Filter, Q-Factor, Intermediate Frequency)

CRITICAL DAMPING is the degree of damping in an oscillatory circuit at which the system just fails to oscillate — see Damping.

CRYOGENICS is the branch of physics dealing with extreme cold and its effects (from Greek, *frost*).
(>> Cryotron)

CRYSTAL The arrangement of atoms or molecules of a substance into a regular framework (the *lattice structure*). Externally a crystal has the form of a solid enclosed by symmetrical plane faces. All the crystals of a particular substance have the same shape. A simple form is the cube of common salt (sodium chloride), this is an example of a crystal having all its faces alike. Most are much more complex.

(* Atom, Molecule >> Crystal Filter, Crystal Oscillator)

CURIE POINT is the temperature above which a ferromagnetic material loses its magnetic properties. It is named after the physicist Pierre Curie (husband of Marie Curie) — see Ferromagnetism.

CURRENT (electric)   This is the movement of electric *charge carriers* round a circuit. Current flow between two points normally occurs when there is a conducting path and an electrostatic field between them. As an example, in a metal wire the atoms and ions are fixed within the lattice structure and free electrons move randomly in the spaces between them. If a positive charge is applied to one end of the wire and a negative charge to the other (e.g. from a battery), the electrostatic field set up from end to end within the wire causes the electrons to drift away from the negative charge towards the positive. Such a flow of electrons constitutes an electric current. The rate of flow depends on the magnitude of the field applied (i.e. on the potential difference). The magnitude of the current itself is the rate at which charge passes a given point. In terms of the unit of charge, one ampere is the current when one coulomb of charge flows per second.

Charge carriers may also be positive as for example in the case of ions within a gas, these drift towards a negative region.

Because current is the framework on which all electronic activity is based, Figure C15 is added to gather together the various terms associated with it and to illustrate the process in greater detail:

(i)   a conductor contains "free" electrons, i.e. they have accumulated sufficient energy to be able to break away from atoms;

(ii)   chemical action within the battery forces electrons away from the positive terminal towards the negative, i.e. it generates an electromotive force;

(iii)   as there is a complete circuit connected to the battery terminals, a potential difference is created across points A and B. An electric field is therefore applied across the ends of the conductor and is propagated from end to end at almost the speed of light;

(iv)   the electric field contains energy and is therefore capable of doing work. It imposes a force on all free electrons and

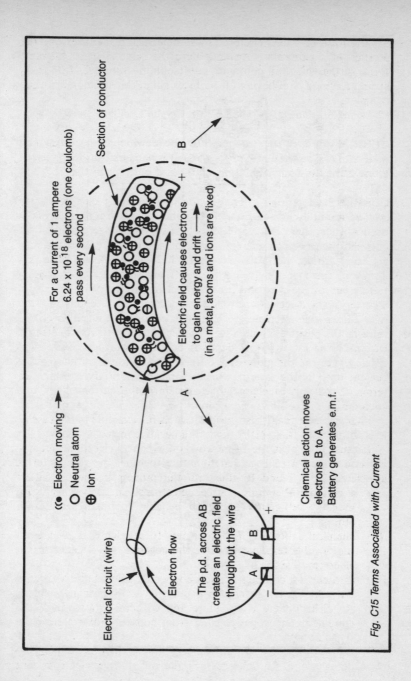

Electron moving →
Neutral atom
Ion

For a current of 1 ampere
6.24 x 10^{18} electrons (one coulomb)
pass every second

Section of conductor

B

+

Electric field causes electrons
to gain energy and drift →
(in a metal, atoms and ions are fixed)

−

A

Electrical circuit (wire)

Electron flow

The p.d. across AB
creates an electric field
throughout the wire

B

+

A

−

Chemical action moves
electrons B to A.
Battery generates e.m.f.

Fig. C15 Terms Associated with Current

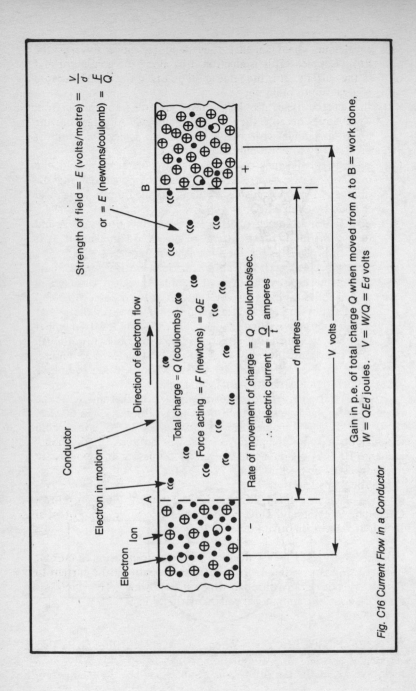

Fig. C16 Current Flow in a Conductor

accelerates them so that they tend to move towards the positive pole. This is electron drift along the conductor and is the current. It is the same at all points in the circuit because charge cannot build up;

(v)   the electric field also helps more electrons to escape from their orbits because they also gain energy. Also fast moving electrons collide with attached ones and knock them out of orbit. They too become charge carriers;

(vi)   the current depends on the strength of the electric field, the mobility of the electrons in that particular material and the number of them available. This is summed up in a practical manner by Ohm's Law;

(vii)   now if, for example, 6.24×10^{18} electrons flow into A and out at B, this is one coulomb of charge on the move. If it happens in one second, the current is one ampere;

(viii)   although electrons enter at A and electrons leave at B, these are not necessarily the same ones. Electron drift commences at all points along the wire (even if many kilometres long) immediately the electric field is present. However the rate at which they move along the wire is surprisingly low (remember they are moving in all directions but with a bias towards B). The rate is usually only one or two centimetres per minute.

Figure C16 is added to show how the various formulae linking charge, electric field strength, work etc. fit in.

Practical currents vary over a wide range. In the middle of the range a motor car headlamp bulb operates with some 3 A, a 60 watt light bulb on 240 V mains, 0.25 A. The current flowing in a radio antenna or in some computer circuits may be down in the nano-ampere (10^{-9} A) region while conversely thousands of amperes are needed to start an electric train.

(See also Ohm's Law)

(* Charge, Electric Field, Electric Field Strength, Electron, Force, Coulomb, Ion, Energy, Drift Velocity, Lattice Structure, Potential Difference, Electromotive Force)

CURRENT DENSITY   A measure of the concentration of current passing through a material. It is equal to the ratio of the current to the cross-sectional area through which it is flowing. The symbol is J and the unit, the ampere per square metre (A/m^2).
(* Current)

CUT-OFF FREQUENCY   When referring to a filter, it is that frequency at which the attenuation changes from a low value to a high one, i.e. at the transition from the pass band to the attenuation

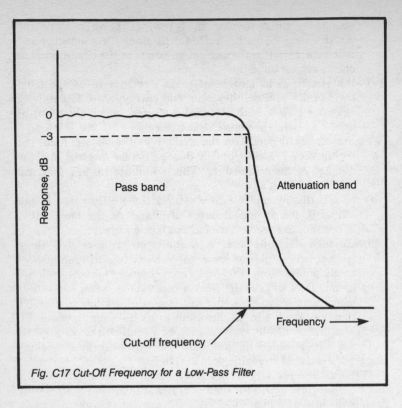

Fig. C17 Cut-Off Frequency for a Low-Pass Filter

band. The change in attenuation is not abrupt hence the cut-off frequency has to be defined in some way, this is generally as the frequency at which the attenuation has changed by 3 dB when the filter is connected between specified impedances. Figure C17 gives an example for a low-pass filter.

If the term refers to a waveguide, the cut-off frequency is the frequency below which transmission fails for any particular mode — see Waveguide.

(* Frequency, Attenuation, Filter, Decibel)

CYCLE is that part of a wave between two successive points having the same value and at which the wave is varying in the same direction. This is illustrated in Figure S5 and one cycle is equivalent to rotation of the phasor OP through a complete circle, irrespective of its starting point.

(* Sine Wave, Phasor)

D

DAMPING is that property of an electrical or mechanical system which reduces the amplitude of free oscillations. Once oscillation commences an ideal resonant circuit should continue to oscillate indefinitely. The fact that it does not arises from resistance losses etc. in the electrical circuit and from friction and other losses in mechanical systems. In both cases energy is extracted from the oscillation and dissipated in the form of heat. How the system functions depends on the degree of damping, it is termed *critical* if the system just fails to oscillate, *overdamped* if the damping is greater.

When damping is less than the critical, it is said to be *underdamped* and free oscillations can arise but because of damping will slowly decay. This is illustrated by the graph of Figure F7 which shows an example of how the current in a free oscillation circuit decays. A measure of the rate of the decrease in amplitude of an oscillation is given by the *damping coefficient,* δ. This is defined as the ratio of the amplitude of any one of the damped oscillations to the amplitude of the one following. When this ratio is expressed as a natural logarithm it is known as the *logarithmic decrement.*

Damping is also the term used when oscillations of for example, a measuring instrument pointer are reduced by some electrical or mechanical means.
(* Resonance, Oscillation, Free Oscillation, Logarithmic Decrement ≫ Magnetic Damping, Regeneration)

DAMPING COEFFICIENT (DAMPING FACTOR) A measure of the rate of decrease in amplitude of an oscillation due to damping – see Damping.

DANIELL CELL is a primary cell and is an improvement on the *voltaic cell* which suffers from polarization. It is named after John Frederic Daniell, an English chemist. In the Daniell cell two different electrolytes are separated by a porous pot. The positive electrode is copper, immersed in an electrolyte of copper sulphate, the negative electrode is amalgamated zinc (surface coated with mercury) immersed in dilute sulphuric acid. Cell e.m.f. is just over 1 volt. The cell is "reversible" because if an external voltage slightly greater than the normal output voltage is applied to the terminals in the opposite direction, the chemical reactions are reversed.
(* Cell, Voltaic Cell, Electrode, Electrolyte, Polarization, Electromotive Force)

DARAF   The unit of *elastance* − see this term.

D.C. − see Direct Current

D.C. COMPONENT is the mean value of a signal. Fourier analysis shows that any recurring waveform can be analysed into a d.c. component to which is added an alternating function. D.C. component applies to asymmetrical waves only for the mean value of a symmetrical wave (i.e. equal above and below the time axis) is zero.
(* Direct Current, Fourier Analysis)

D.C. VOLTAGE is a lax way of expressing *direct voltage*, in reality the term is saying *direct current voltage*, but "current" is superfluous.

de BROGLIE WAVES   In 1924 Louis Victor de Broglie (a French physicist) published a hypothesis suggesting that any moving object had an associated wave motion. He based this on the argument that if light can act both as a particle and also as waves, then why should not electrons act similarly? He called them *matter* or *pilot* waves in the sense that the wave guides or steers the particle. To de Broglie's credit, he produced these ideas long before there was any experimental evidence.

To appreciate that particles behave like waves and vice versa needs quite a stretch of the imagination but less if we develop the de Broglie formula in terms of the photon:
Einstein gave us:

$$E = mc^2$$

where E is the energy, m, the mass and c, the velocity of light.
Planck gave us:

$$E = hf$$

where h is Planck's Constant = 6.626 J s, f is the wave frequency, hence:

$$hf = mc^2 \quad \therefore \quad m = hf/c^2 .$$

Now the wavelength, $\lambda = c/f$ and the momentum (p) of a photon travelling at the speed of light = mass (m) × velocity (v) is equal to:

$$\frac{hf}{c^2} \times c = \frac{hf}{c}$$

and since

$$f/c = 1/\lambda, \text{ then } p = h/\lambda, \text{ i.e. } \lambda = h/p$$

and since

$$p = mv$$

then

$$\lambda = h/mv$$

– this is the expression for the "de Broglie Wavelength".

Next consider the single hydrogen electron which has an orbital velocity, $v = 2.187 \times 10^6$ m/s, an orbit radius of $r = 5.295 \times 10^{-11}$ m and a mass, m of 9.109×10^{-31} kg: length of hydrogen orbit is equal to:

$$2\pi r = 2\pi \times 5.295 \times 10^{-11} = 3.3 \times 10^{-10} \text{ m}$$

"de Broglie Wavelength equals:

$$\frac{h}{mv} = \frac{6.626 \times 10^{-34} \text{ J s}}{9.109 \times 10^{-31} \text{ kg} \times 2.187 \times 10^6 \text{ m/s}} = 3.3 \times 10^{-10} \text{ m}$$

both exactly the same. This makes sense so that a wave "guiding" a hydrogen electron in its orbit has its end joined to the beginning of the next wave. If this does not happen then subsequent waves do not reinforce the earlier ones and the wave loses its form. An electron therefore can only accept exactly the amount of energy which satisfies this condition. This might be illustrated as in Figure D1 which shows in an exaggerated fashion a normal orbit modified by 3 cycles of a waveform. Here the 1st, 4th, 7th . . . waves start at exactly the same point. If the number of complete waves is n, then the circumference of the orbit $= n\lambda = 2\pi r$. n must be a whole number otherwise the wave does not join back to itself. It is called the orbit *quantum number*.
(* Atom, Electron, Orbit, Frequency, Wavelength, Energy, Photon, Planck Constant, Momentum, Quantum Theory)

DECIBEL   Using logarithmic units to express power, current or voltage ratios has two distinct advances: (i) large numbers are reduced and so become more manageable, and (ii) in a complex system with a large number of circuits, each contributing a gain or loss, calculation of the overall power etc. ratio by multiplying

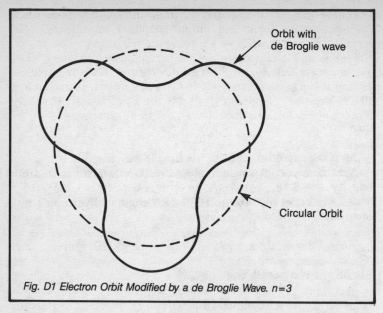

Fig. D1 Electron Orbit Modified by a de Broglie Wave. n=3

fractions is unwieldy. By expressing each ratio in a logarithmic unit, addition takes the place of multiplication, a more manageable process altogether. Hence the *bel* came on the scene (after Alexander Graham Bell, the Scottish-American inventor) which is simply the common logarithm (to the base 10) of the power ratio. This gives rather low figures so an offshoot soon appeared, the *decibel* (symbol dB) which is one tenth of one bel. If the power, current or voltage input to a circuit is given by P_1, I_1 or V_1 respectively and the power output by P_2, I_2 or V_2, then the attenuation (or gain):

$$n = 10 \log \frac{P_2}{P_1} = 10 \log \frac{I_2^2 \times Z}{I_1^2 \times Z} = 20 \log \frac{I_2}{I_1} \text{ dB}$$

but note that I_1 and I_2 must be measured in the same terminating impedance, Z. Similarly:

$$n = 20 \log \frac{V_2}{V_1} \text{ dB}$$

and again the voltages must be measured in the same impedance. (Note however that we often deliberately go astray when quoting the voltage gain of an amplifier by using the above formula while ignoring differing input and output amplifier impedances. No problem if we realize what we are doing and tell others.)

If gains and attenuations are being considered together, then signs become necessary. If P_2 is greater than P_1, there is amplification and n is positive, conversely if P_1 is the greater, there is a loss and n is negative. Suppose $P_1 = 1$ mW and $P_2 = 0.5$ mW, obviously there is a power loss so n should work out to be negative:

attenuation in dB:

$$(n) = 10 \log (P_2/P_1) = 10 \log 0.5 = 10(-0.3010) = -3.01$$

Absolute values can be quoted in decibel notation provided that a *reference* or *zero* level is stated or known. As an example, the reference level of a quantity such as signal power or sound pressure is chosen and this is given the decibel value of 0. The reference level is usually indicated by an added letter to the symbol. One commonly used in electronics is one milliwatt for which the symbol now becomes dBm. Thus a power level of 100 mW may be expressed as +20 dBm because a power gain of 20 dB on 1 mW results in 100 mW. No reference level need be quoted because it is indicated by the "m". Equally −30 dBm is the same as 1 μW. Another commonly used reference level is one volt for which the symbol used is dBV and there are several used for sound and noise levels [e.g. dB(A)].

Note that the practice of quoting noise levels directly in decibels used by the general public is technically wrong, but it works.

There is an alternative unit, the *neper* but the decibel is more likely to be used in practical situations. The neper comes into its own in line transmission theory.

(* Transmission Line, Power, Attenuation, Gain, Neper, Bel)

DECINEPER is a transmission unit equal to one-tenth of a neper — see Neper.

DEGENERATE SEMICONDUCTOR is one which has lost the properties normally expected of a semiconductor. This occurs when the impurity density is increased greatly. As the doping level of an n-type semiconductor is increased the Fermi level moves towards the conduction band [see the energy level diagram of Fig.D10(i)]. With a p-type semiconductor the Fermi level moves towards the valence band [see Fig.D10(ii)]. For n-type silicon the donor density is of the order of $10^{22}/m^3$ and calculations show that when the density reaches about $10^{26}/m^3$ the Fermi level actually falls within

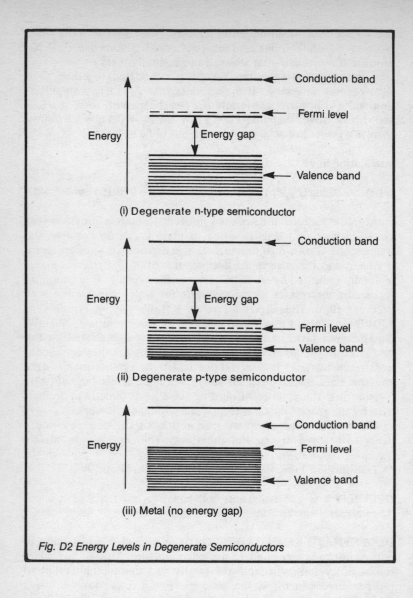

Fig. D2 Energy Levels in Degenerate Semiconductors

the conduction band as shown in Figure D2(i). Similarly the Fermi level comes within the valence band for p-type as illustrated in Figure D2(ii). For comparison (iii) shows the energy diagram for a metal which of course has no energy gap. Both types of semi-conductor now have so many majority carriers that they have almost the same conductivity as a metal. We say that the semiconductor has *degenerated* into a metal and it is no longer a true semiconductor. (* Semiconductor, Energy Diagram, Energy Levels, Impurity, Doping, Fermi Level)

DELAY DISTORTION occurs when the time of propagation of the signal through a system varies with frequency. This occurs especially in transmission lines in which the wave velocity varies with fre-quency. This shifts the phase of some frequencies relative to others and it is possible for the output waveform, which is the sum of all frequencies together, to differ appreciably from the input waveform.

The term *delay/frequency distortion* is also used.

See Distortion.

(* Transmission Line, Waveform, Frequency, Phase Shift, Group Delay >> Delay Equalizer)

DEMODULATION In the modulation process a signal which con-tains the information to be transmitted is impressed upon a higher frequency carrier wave. It is then transmitted over a line or radio channel in this form, i.e. as a modulated wave. Demodulation or *detection* is the final process in the chain and is the one in which the baseband signal is regained from the modulated wave. The technique used depends on the type of modulation.

For demodulation of amplitude modulated waves two practical methods are (i) use of a *diode detector* followed by a resistance-capacitance network for separating out the modulating frequencies, or (ii) use of a *square-law detector* which employs the non-linear part of the input characteristic of a transistor.

Demodulation of frequency modulated waves is more compli-cated. It was originally accomplished by two American engineers, Foster and Seeley, who produced a *phase-difference discriminator* circuit which bears their names. Subsequent improvements, especially with regard to integration, now give us a transistor stage which provides limiting to remove noise in conjunction with a frequency sensitive circuit. This first expresses the f.m. deviation as a phase-shift, then as an amplitude variation, i.e. the original modulating signal.

See also Amplitude Modulation, Frequency Modulation, Phase Modulation, Pulse Modulation.

(* Carrier Wave, Modulation, Baseband, Characteristic, Non-Linearity, Phase Shift, Noise >> Detector, Diode Detector, Frequency Discriminator)

DEPLETION LAYER   This is a region in a semiconductor material (usually at a p-n junction) in which there are very few charge carriers [see Fig.P10(i)]. This condition applies even when there is no applied voltage. When a reverse bias is connected, the width of the depletion player and its resistivity increase. For a forward bias the width is reduced and the layer conductivity increases.   See P-N Junction. (* Semiconductor, Doping, Charge Carrier, Bias)

DEPLETION MODE is a way of operating field-effect transistors. In this mode there is an appreciable drain current when the gate potential is zero.   To reduce the drain current therefore a reverse gate bias is required — see Field-Effect Transistor.

DEPOLARIZER is a chemical for removing the gas which collects on an electrode of a primary cell — see Primary Cell, Leclanché Cell.

DERIVED UNITS   These are part of the S.I. system and are developed from the S.I. *base* units.   As an example the three base units for length, mass and time are the metre (m), kilogram (kg) and second (s).   A derived unit from these is that for force, the newton (N) which has a unit symbol $kg\,m/s^2$.   Going one step further, the derived unit for work or energy is the joule (J) which has a unit symbol $N\,m$ — see S.I.

DEVIATION RATIO is a term used in frequency modulation systems. It is defined as the ratio between the maximum frequency deviation and the maximum modulating frequency —see Frequency Modulation.

DIAMAGNETISM is a property exhibited by materials resulting in a relative permeability very slightly less than 1.   The relative permeability, μ_r can be used as a guide to the effect a magnetising field has on a material.   For μ_r less than 1, the indication is that the magnetisation produced is in such a direction as to oppose the applied field. Two examples only of diamagnetic materials are required to demonstrate how weak the effect is, silver has a relative permeability of 0.999 999 81, that for bismuth is 0.999 998 6.

Diamagnetism arises from the orbital motions of electrons, hence the effect is common to all substances.   When placed in a magnetic field the electron velocities (and therefore orbits) change in such a

92

way that as a magnetic dipole, the electron opposes the applied field, overall therefore a diamagnetic material reduces the flux density of an applied field but only to a minute degree. Diamagnetism is not affected by temperature as is *ferromagnetism.*
See also Ferromagnetism, Paramagnetism.
(* Magnetism, Magnetic Field, Magnetisation, Permeability, Dipole, Electron, Orbit)

DIELECTRIC   This is an insulating medium which is capable of sustaining an electric field. If an insulating material is subjected to an electric field, its molecules (or atoms) become elongated in the direction of the field, the electrons being pulled one way, the nuclei the other as illustrated pictorially for an atom in Figure D3.

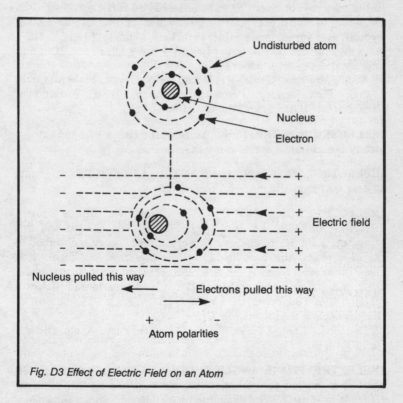

Fig. D3 Effect of Electric Field on an Atom

The molecules are therefore aligned in the direction of the field so giving rise to a redistribution of charge within the material, hence an electric field persists after the actuating field has been removed.

Because the electric charges within a molecule are unbalanced, the molecule is *poled*, i.e. it has ends which are oppositely charged (dipoles). If when no external field is applied, each molecule acts as a dipole, the material is said to be *polar*, if the molecules are electrically balanced, the material is *non-polar*. Losses occur in dielectrics because energy is absorbed from the electric field in aligning the molecules. In this respect polar and non-polar materials have different loss/frequency characteristics.

The *permittivity* of a dielectric is a measure of the electric flux density developed in it by a given electric field strength, measured in farads per metre.

Dielectric strength indicates the maximum voltage a sample can withstand before *breakdown*, i.e. when sufficient energy is imparted to the material for electrons to be released and current to flow. It is measured in volts per metre of thickness of the sample tested. Typical, very approximate values (V/m) are: ceramics ($4-12 \times 10^6$), polyethylene and polystyrene (4×10^7), ruby mica (4×10^7) and impregnated capacitor paper ($2-4 \times 10^7$).

(* Atom, Molecule, Insulator, Electric Field, Electric Field Strength, Electric Flux Density, Permittivity, Dipole, Polar, Breakdown, Capacitor >> Loss Factor, Microwave Heating)

DIELECTRIC ABSORPTION   Some of the charge of a capacitor is lost by absorption — see Absorption.

DIELECTRIC CONSTANT (DIELECTRIC COEFFICIENT)   Same as Relative Permittivity — see Permittivity.

DIELECTRIC LOSS ANGLE   Application of a voltage across a dielectric results in the displacement of electric charges and this represents a storage of energy. However, some energy is absorbed in the process and this is indicated by the *dielectric loss angle*. It is given the symbol δ and is the difference between the *dielectric phase angle* and 90° as shown in Figure D4. Clearly the more efficient a material is as a dielectric, the smaller is its loss angle. The tangent of the loss angle is the *dissipation factor*.

(* Dielectric, Energy, Phase Angle, Dielectric Phase Angle, Dissipation Factor)

DIELECTRIC PHASE ANGLE   When a sinusoidal alternating voltage (V) is applied across a dielectric material, the resulting current (I) leads in phase by the dielectric phase angle ϕ. This is shown as a phasor diagram in Figure D4. The cosine of the dielectric phase angle is the *dielectric power factor*.

(* Dielectric, Dissipation Factor, Phase Angle)

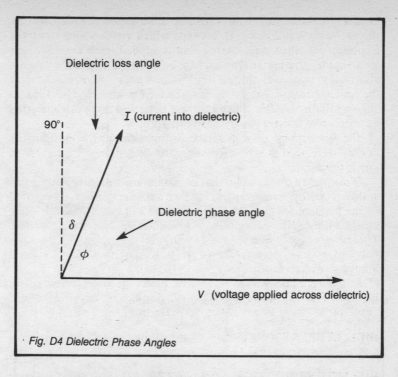

Fig. D4 Dielectric Phase Angles

DIELECTRIC POLARIZATION – see Electric Polarization

DIELECTRIC POWER FACTOR is the cosine of the dielectric phase angle – see this term.

DIELECTRIC STRAIN refers to the rearrangement of charges within the atoms in a dielectric – see Displacement.

DIELECTRIC STRENGTH   The maximum voltage a dielectric can withstand – see Dielectric.

DIFFRACTION is the phenomenon which allows electromagnetic waves to bend around the edge of an opaque object in their path. It can be illustrated by using light from a point source as shown in Figure D5. At the upper edge of the shadow it will be found that light has spread in, in fact there is a narrow pattern of light and dark fringes.   The wavefront of the light beam produces *secondary wavelets* and it is because not all of the wavelets are obstructed that an interference pattern is able to arise at the edge of the shadow.

95

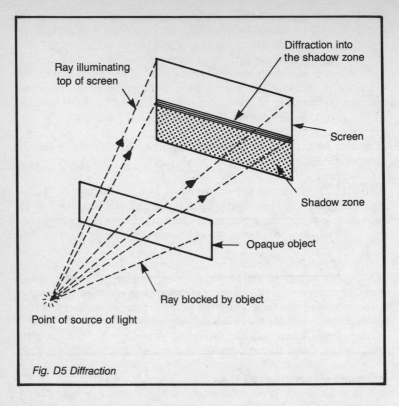

Ray illuminating top of screen

Diffraction into the shadow zone

Screen

Shadow zone

Opaque object

Ray blocked by object

Point of source of light

Fig. D5 Diffraction

Light is used here as an example but the same phenomenon occurs with all electromagnetic waves, there is a slight bending at any discontinuity in the medium through which the wave is travelling. The effect is found similarly with electron beams for each electron has an associated wave pattern as shown by de Broglie. (* Light, Electromagnetic Wave, Wavefront, de Broglie Waves)

DIFFUSION CURRENT   In a p-n junction, due to thermal energy, electrons and holes diffuse from one side of the junction to the other so giving rise to the junction potential barrier. Such a flow of charge carriers constitutes a flow of current and this is known as the *diffusion current*.
See P-N Junction.
(* Semiconductor, Hole, Charge Carrier, Current, Potential Barrier)

DIGITAL SIGNAL is one which can only take certain discrete values, usually few in number and most frequently, two only. Change between the values occurs only momentarily and for any given system no other values are allowed. One significant advantage of digital working is found in the *binary* system (2 values only, "on" or "off"). In this the difference between the two states can be detected with extremely small likelihood of error. Such signals are therefore virtually unaffected by normal variations in supply voltages, by temperature changes or circuit noise. All of these have an adverse effect on the alternative type of signal, the *analogue*. See Analogue Signal.

(* Signal, Binary, Binary Code >> Logic Level, Analogue-to-Digital Conversion, Digital-to-Analogue Conversion)

DIODE   This is simply any device which has two electrodes. There are many different types, most have a high resistance to the flow of current in one direction but a low resistance in the opposite direction.   Of these the current/voltage characteristic determines the application.

The *thermionic valve diode* consists of a heated cathode with an anode in an evacuated glass envelope (see Fig.T2). Electrons escape from the cathode by thermionic emission, they can flow across the space to the anode only when the latter is positive with respect to the cathode, hence the diode is a one-way device.

The *semiconductor diode* is simply a p-n junction. With forward bias, current flows through the diode, increasing exponentially with voltage applied [see Fig.P10(iv)]. With reverse bias there is only a minute (reverse saturation) current.

Diodes of both types are used for rectification of alternating current. The non-linear portion of the current/voltage characteristic is employed in signal demodulation and the device is used extensively in digital circuits.

See also Schottky Diode, Photodiode, Tunnel Diode, Zener Diode.

(* Thermionic Emission, P-N Junction, Carrier Storage, Characteristic, Non-Linearity >> Peak Inverse Voltage, Light-Emitting Diode, Varactor, Fast-Recovery Diode)

DIPOLE   This is an object oppositely charged or magnetized at two points, known as "poles" (di = 2). The *electric dipole* is a system of two point charges of equal magnitude and opposite polarity at a distance apart small compared with the distance the field is theoretically considered to extend.   In many molecules for example, the electric charges are distributed in such a way that the effective centre of the positive charges and that of the negative charges coincide.   If however the centres do not coincide, the molecule is said to be *polar* and it has a *dipole moment*, meaning that a torque will be exerted on it when an electric field is present.

The dipole moment is the product of the magnitude of either charge and the distance between the two charges (for the reasoning behind this, see Magnetic Moment). It is given the symbol p which is related to the electric field strength (E) and to the torque (T) the field produces on the dipole by:

$$p = T/E \text{ coulomb metres}$$

(E in volts per metre and T in newton metres).

There are also *magnetic dipoles*, each of which consists of a pair of North and South poles (see Magnetic Moment).

"Dipole" is also used as a shortened form of *Dipole Antenna*. (* Charge, Molecule, Dielectric, Field, Electric Field, Magnetism, Magnetic Moment >> Dipole Antenna)

DIPOLE MOMENT is a feature of a molecule which is polar — see Dipole.

DIRECT CURRENT is an electric current which flows in one direction only. As an example, it is the current through a resistor which is connected to a unidirectional voltage source such as a primary or secondary battery.

The term is frequently abbreviated to d.c. and used as an adjective, e.g. d.c. motor, d.c. bell, d.c. supply.
(* Current, Battery)

DIRECT-GAP SEMICONDUCTOR is important in the functioning of lasers, light-emitting diodes and all devices relying on *radiative recombination*, i.e. the recombination of electrons with holes which produces the radiation of a photon. This is something which does not occur equally in all semiconductors and to what extent a semiconductor is capable of emitting light depends on a rather complex quantity known as the *momentum vector, k*. Here care must be taken not to get momentum and energy mixed.

On an energy diagram [e.g. Fig.E12(iv)] the energy gap (the forbidden band) is the difference between the maximum energy level in the valence band and the minimum energy level in the conduction band. Taking gallium arsenide as an example, we find that its energy diagram is not as shown generally for semiconductors (Fig.E12) because the energy gap changes its form according to the value of k as sketched in Figure D6(i). It is seen that irrespective of the value of k the maximum valence band energies and minimum

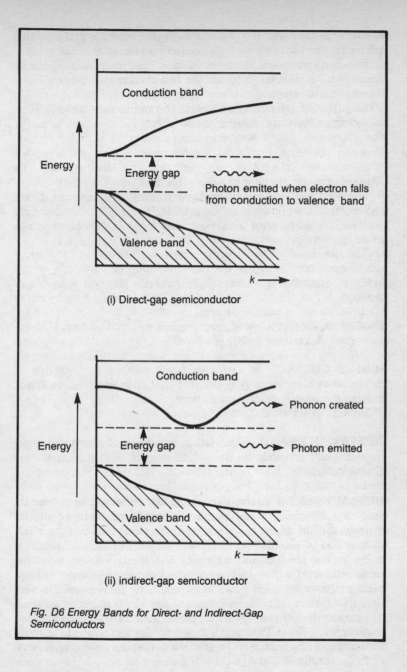

Fig. D6 Energy Bands for Direct- and Indirect-Gap
Semiconductors

conduction band energies are the same and occur together. This allows an electron with the right amount of energy to make a direct transition from conduction to valence band with accompanying emission of a photon. Accordingly gallium arsenide is known as a *direct-gap semiconductor*.

In (ii) of the figure the diagram for germanium and silicon is shown and clearly the value of k now affects electron transitions for the maximum and minimum energies occur at different values. However, the fact that k is a momentum vector indicates that transitions can take place provided that the electron loses the required amount of momentum. This is accomplished by release of a phonon (or for transition from valence to conduction band, by absorption of phonon). Germanium and silicon are therefore classified as *indirect-gap semiconductors* since the transition is not made directly.

The likelihood of an electron emitting a phonon of the correct momentum coupled with the emission also of a photon makes radiative recombination less likely to take place in indirect-gap semiconductors than in direct-gap ones, hence we find that gallium arsenide is a better emitter of light.

(* Electron, Semiconductor, Energy, Energy Bands, Laser, Momentum, Photon, Phonon, de Broglie Waves)

DIRECT VOLTAGE is a unidirectional voltage for example as produced by a battery. It is the potential difference created across a resistance when a direct current flows through it.

(* Voltage, Potential Difference, Direct Current)

DISPERSION arises when the constituent waves of a group of waves travel through a medium or over a line with different velocities — see Group Velocity.

DISPLACEMENT is a term used regarding the effects of an electric field on a dielectric. When an electric field is applied to a dielectric or insulator, the atoms are stretched out as indicated in Figure D3. Polarization of the material follows as shown in Figure D7 resulting in the surface charges as also shown. The small displacement of the electron charges within each atom, all in the same direction constitutes a minute current, known as the *displacement current*, but note that this current only flows while polarization is being established.

Consider two charges q_1 and q_2 separated by a distance d within a dielectric. From Coulomb's Law and the fact that the electric field strength, E, is defined so that the force on a charge q_2 is given by F/q_2, it follows that:

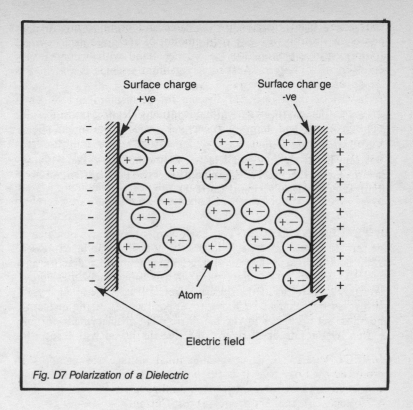

Surface charge +ve

Surface charge -ve

Atom

Electric field

Fig. D7 Polarization of a Dielectric

$$E = \frac{q_1}{4\pi\epsilon d^2}$$

where ϵ is the permittivity of the dielectric.

The quantity $q_1/4\pi d^2$ is constant and equal to ϵE showing that the electric field is dependent on the permittivity. It is convenient in calculations concerned with dielectrics to consider the quantity $q_1/4\pi d^2$ as the *displacement* or *electric flux density*, symbol D and in practical work the unit is in coulombs/m^2. Hence:

$$D = \epsilon E$$

and if there is no dielectric,

$$D = \epsilon_0 E$$

where ϵ_0 is the permittivity of free space.

With a dielectric however there will be additional flux arising from its surface charge and it can be shown that the displacement inside the dielectric becomes:

$$D = \epsilon_0 E + P$$

where P is the electric polarization. This expression is the one more likely to be used in defining D. The displacement is also referred to as the *dielectric strain*.

(* Atom, Electron, Charge, Dielectric, Coulomb's Law, Permittivity, Electric Field, Electric Field Strength, Electric Polarization, Susceptibility Electric, Displacement Current)

DISPLACEMENT CURRENT   Each elementary charge in a dielectric sets up its own electric field and the net effect can be expressed as an electric flux. When a varying voltage is impressed across the dielectric we are able to determine what is called the *displacement current,* I_{dis} in terms of the applied electric flux. The applied voltage causes free charges to move to opposite sides of the dielectric and these set up a flux in the dielectric. The displacement current is given by the rate of change of the electric flux, ψ with respect to time, i.e.

$$I_{dis} = \frac{d\psi}{dt}$$

and because $\psi = D \times s$ where D is the displacement and s is the surface area:

$$I_{dis} = \frac{d(Ds)}{dt} = \frac{s\,dD}{dt} = \frac{s\epsilon\,dE}{dt}$$

since $D = \epsilon E$ where ϵ is the permittivity and E the electric field strength.

Thus the displacement current can also be expressed as a function of the rate of change of the electric field strength.

Note that if the electric flux remains constant, the displacement current is zero. It is also important to note that displacement current is not the normal conduction current because no charge carriers actually flow through the dielectric.

(* Charge, Dielectric, Electric Field, Electric Flux, Displacement, Electric Field Strength, Permittivity, Charge Carrier)

DISSIPATION is mainly the dispersal of energy as heat when current flows through a resistance; it is the power *loss*. Resistance is present in all electronic circuits, hence there is always some dissipation. In an electric fire for example, there is full dissipation of energy which is required. In a circuit containing free oscillations however, although dissipation is very much less, it is the factor which damps the oscillatory current and causes it to die out.

Non-resistive dissipation occurs for example, in dielectrics when energy is absorbed from the electric field in aligning the molecules and also in circuits carrying radio frequency currents for they radiate energy which is a loss to the circuit.

In equivalent circuits the total dissipation may be represented by insertion of an *effective series resistance* which would dissipate the same power.

(* Energy, Resistance, Current, Power, Dielectric, Dissipation Factor, Damping)

DISSIPATION FACTOR   Although this applies to both inductors and capacitors, it is used mainly with the latter. With capacitors the dissipation factor (d.f.) is the ratio of the effective series resistance, R to the capacitive reactance, X_c, i.e.:

$$\text{d.f.} = R/X_c = \omega CR$$

where $\omega = 2\pi \times$ the frequency, f.

Since the quality factor, Q for a capacitor $= 1/\omega CR$, then clearly the d.f. is the reciprocal of Q and vice versa. In general therefore, while Q is considered as a figure of merit, d.f. is a measure of imperfection.

Also since in general in an a.c. circuit, d.f. $= R/X$, then d.f. $=$ cotangent ϕ where ϕ is the phase angle [see Fig.13(i)]. The power factor (p.f.) and the dissipation factor are essentially equal when the p.f. is 0.1 or less (e.g. when $\cos \phi = 0.1$, $\cot \phi = 0.1005$), hence in low loss components such as good quality capacitors, the d.f. can be taken as $\cos \phi$.

(* Dissipation, Reactance, Phase Angle, Q-Factor, Power Factor, Impedance, Capacitance)

DISSOCIATION is the term used when certain metallic salts divide into charged ions when dissolving in water. Examples are sodium chloride (common salt) which dissociates into Na^+ and Cl^- ions and copper sulphate which dissociates into Cu^+ and SO_4^- ions. In the solution ion production and recombination goes on continually but the solution exhibits no overall charge because positive and negative charges balance. If a voltage is applied across the solution the ions act as charge carriers. When a solution contains a dissociated salt it is known as an *electrolyte*.

(* Ion, Charge, Charge Carrier, Electrolyte, Recombination)

DISTORTION is the change in form or character (other than in magnitude) of a signal during transmission through a component or system. In television distortion refers to deviations in any way of the picture from the original. Such changes are usually unwanted and the signal quality is therefore *impaired*. There are several different types of distortion in non-visual systems, one way of classifying them is as follows:

(i)   distortion which occurs when the transmission properties of a system vary with the *instantaneous magnitude* of the applied signal. In this category are *amplitude, harmonic* and *intermodulation* distortions. These are also classified as *non-linear* distortions because each arises from the effects of non-linearity somewhere in the system;

(ii) distortion which occurs when the transmission properties of a system vary with the *frequency* of the applied signal. There is only one type in this category, appropriately known as *attenuation/frequency* distortion. The terms *attenuation distortion* and *frequency distortion* are also used;

(iii) distortion due to phase shift moving out of line with frequency. In this category are *delay distortion* and *phase distortion*, these are generally associated with line transmission;

(iv) there is also *crossover distortion* which is peculiar to Class B amplifiers.

(* Attenuation, Non-Linearity, Phase Shift, Amplitude . . . Harmonic . . . Delay . . . Attenuation/frequency Distortion >> Intermodulation, Phase Distortion, Class B Amplifier)

DOMAIN   Modern theory suggests that it is electron spins which are mainly responsible for magnetism (see Fig.M5). This results in certain atoms having a net magnetic moment, i.e. the atom itself exhibits weak magnetic properties. In a complicated way, neighbouring atoms of certain materials interact magnetically so that overall a group of them develops N and S poles. Each of these groups is known as a *domain*, hence a domain might be regarded as a microscopic elementary magnet. Normally within an unmagnetised material the domains are distributed randomly and their overall magnetic effects cancel. When a magnetising force is applied

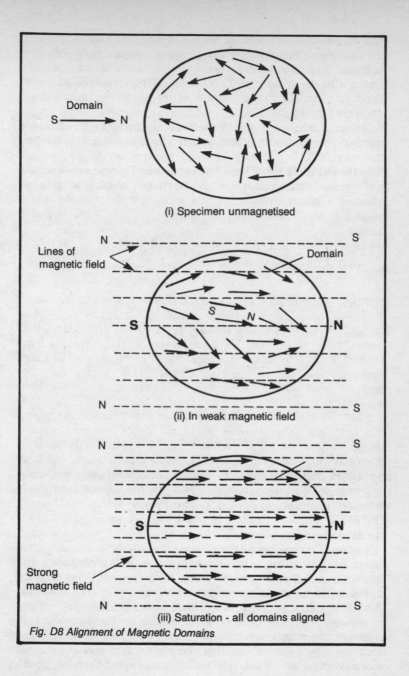

Fig. D8 Alignment of Magnetic Domains

however the domains tend to turn into the direction of the field (see Fig.M4) so the whole specimen becomes magnetically polarized. Materials reach magnetic saturation when all domains are fully aligned with the applied field. If the latter is reversed the alignment breaks up according to the strength of the field. The process might be pictured as in Figure D8.

(* Atom, Electron, Spin, Magnetism, Magnetic Field, Magnetic Moment, Ferromagnetism, Barkhausen Effect >> Magnetic Bubble)

DONOR IMPURITY is a term used in semiconductor manufacture. It is a pentavalent element such as arsenic or phosphorus, so called because it replaces tetravalent atoms within a lattice, completing the bonds but at the same time making electrons available as charge carriers.
See Doping.

DOPANT – see Doping

DOPING (IMPURITY SEMICONDUCTORS) is a process by which an intrinsic (pure) semiconductor is made extrinsic (i.e. not belonging naturally). It is an ingenious way of adding free electrons or creating holes to improve conductivity and therefore making semiconductor action possible. Because silicon is the most widely used semiconductor material, here we consider this element only but much of what is said also applies to germanium and other tetravalent elements.

Electrons cannot be forced into silicon and left there as happens in a capacitor for in this case the silicon would take on a negative charge, only to discharge the electrons when electrically possible. Doping on the other hand can add or subtract electrons, yet leave the silicon electrically neutral. One of the two methods is to add a tiny amount of another element which has five valence electrons in its outer shell (pentavalent, e.g. phosphorus, arsenic, antimony). The added element is called an *impurity*, it is the *dopant* and the process is known as *doping.*

Figure D9(i) represents the silicon crystal structure in simplified form. Each atom has four covalent bonds with its immediate neighbours. It so happens that the atoms of the impurity link into the crystal lattice of the silicon and it is evident from (ii) of the figure that when this happens, one electron of the five valence electrons of the impurity atom (shown as arsenic) has no home to go to. It therefore moves into orbit round the now positive arsenic ion and it can be shown that this orbit is at a radius much greater than that normally expected of the arsenic atom. Because of the large orbit

106

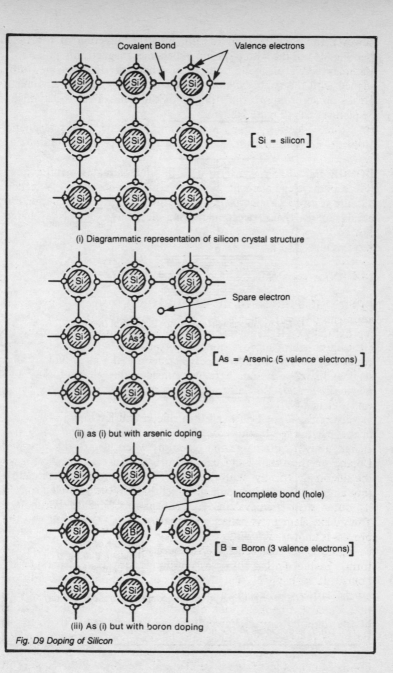

(i) Diagrammatic representation of silicon crystal structure

[Si = silicon]

(ii) as (i) but with arsenic doping

[As = Arsenic (5 valence electrons)]

(iii) As (i) but with boron doping

[B = Boron (3 valence electrons)]

Fig. D9 Doping of Silicon

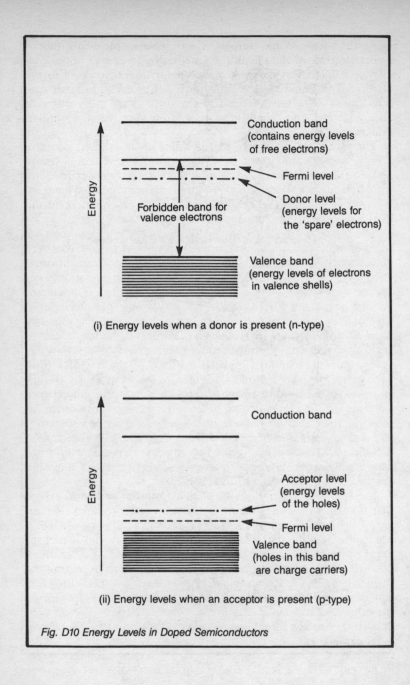

Fig. D10 Energy Levels in Doped Semiconductors

radius the energy of this "surplus" electron is only just below that of a free electron in the silicon (i.e. one having an energy in the conduction band). This is shown on an energy level diagram in Figure D10(i). The Fermi level is also shown as it is useful in other considerations. The valence band is seen to contain many different energy levels, this condition arises from the Pauli Exclusion Principle.

The figure clearly shows that, given a small amount of extra energy from say, an electric field, the "spare" electrons easily move up into the conduction band whereas those in the valence band have the whole of the forbidden band to jump. Hence at normal temperatures we can assume that nearly all electrons in the conduction band have been excited from the donor level.

The silicon is still electrically neutral because the added atoms are themselves neutral, all that happens is that some electrons are moved out of orbit. In practice the impurity is added by special diffusion techniques and would be of the order of only one impurity atom per 10^8 or more silicon atoms. The silicon becomes a better conductor because of the extra free electrons available and it is known as *n*-type because current is carried by *negative* electrons. The impurity is called a do*n*or because it donates electrons to the host element.

The second method involves doping with a trivalent element (e.g. boron, gallium, indium). Again the atoms of the impurity form bonds with the silicon atoms as shown for boron in Figure D9(iii). However, a trivalent element does not have sufficient valence electrons for the completion of four covalent bonds, hence, as shown, one bond is incomplete, leaving a hole. We call the impurity an *acceptor* because it accepts electrons from the host element and the silicon is classed as *p*-type. Its improved conductivity arises from the holes generated which for convenience (and with tongue in cheek) we class as mobile positive charges.

The energy considerations are similar to those for donors except that the acceptor level in Figure D10(ii) now refers to holes. We can regard the hole created when an acceptor atom settles in as though it were orbiting around the now negative boron ion. This is perhaps more difficult to appreciate but the hole needs to be "excited" downwards into the valence band because an electron leaving the valence band leaves an empty energy level there and this is therefore equivalent to a hole entering it. When this happens it is freed from the boron ion and can then move as a charge carrier. The trivalent impurity therefore produces an energy acceptor level as shown.

The charge carriers which predominate in either type of semiconductor are known as *majority carriers* (electrons in n-type, holes in p-type). The remaining carriers (holes in n-type, electrons in p-type) are *minority carriers*).

In the intrinsic semiconductor the number of electrons is equal to the number of holes. After doping it is obvious that this equality no longer applies and the relative numbers of electrons (n_e) and holes (n_h) will vary depending on the type and degree of doping introduced. It can be shown that, at a given temperature, if n_i is the total number of charge carriers (electrons and holes) in the pure material, then:

$$n_e n_h = n_i^2$$

for any level of doping.

This again shows that doping does not introduce additional charges, instead it changes the ratio between electrons and holes, i.e. for n-type material $n_e > n_h$ and for p-type, $n_h > n_e$.

(* Semiconductor, Charge Carrier, Electron, Orbit, Bond, Covalent Bond, Hole Valency, Fermi Level, Pauli Exclusion Principle, Ion Implantation >> Diffusion)

DRAIN is one of the electrodes of a field-effect transistor. It is coupled to the channel and is the electrode by which charge carriers leave — see Field-Effect Transistor.

DRIFT MOBILITY is given the symbol μ and it is the average drift velocity achieved by charge carriers in a semiconductor per unit electric field. The conductivity σ is given by:

$$\sigma = q(\mu_n n + \mu_p p)$$

where q is the electron charge, μ_n and μ_p are the mobilities and n and p are the numbers of the two types of charge carrier — see Conductivity and Drift Velocity.

DRIFT VELOCITY is the rate at which electrons or other charge carriers move along a conductor under the influence of an electric field. An understanding of it is best approached through the simplified mathematical reasoning below.

Free electrons in a conductor always have random motion due to their thermal energy. Random implies motion in *all* directions hence there is no net electric current. Under the influence of an electric field however, the electrons for example, are accelerated towards the positive end of the field. Each electron carries a charge of $e = 1.602 \times 10^{-19}$ coulombs and if the strength of the field is denoted by E (newtons per coulomb), then the force acting on each electron is eE newtons. According to the normal rule, force is equal to mass × acceleration, the acceleration of each electron is eE/m where m is its mass (9.109×10^{-31} kg).

Now the average distance travelled by an electron between collisions is known as the *mean free path*. The average velocity can also be calculated, hence the time between collisions which is known as the *relaxation time:*

$$\tau = \frac{\text{mean free path}}{\text{average velocity}} .$$

For metals τ is of the order of 10^{-14} s (for copper it is actually 2×10^{-14} s) and for semiconductors which have a higher density of free electrons, about 10^{-12} s.

The average or *mean drift velocity,* v = acceleration × time = $eE/m \times \tau$, which we can write as $v = \mu E$ where $\mu = e\tau/m$, known as the *mobility*, i.e.:

$$\text{mobility}, \mu = v/E$$

which is the *drift velocity per unit electric field* and since drift velocity is expressed in metres per second and electric field strength in volts per metre, the mobility has the rather unnerving dimension, metre squared per volt per second (m^2/Vs). Since the mobility is inversely proportional to m, the mass of the particle, it is clear and perhaps obvious anyway that the mobility of electrons is very much greater than that of positive ions owing to the much smaller mass of the electron.

A practical calculation shows what to many engineers is a surprising result. Consider a fine piece of copper wire, 0.04 mm diameter and 1 metre long. It has a resistance of 13.7 Ω. If a current of 1 mA flows through it as might be found in a computer, then the voltage across the wire is 0.0137 V and $E = 0.0137$ volts per metre. Then:

$$\text{drift velocity}, v = \frac{eE\tau}{m} = \frac{1.602 \times 10^{-19} \times 0.0137 \times 2 \times 10^{-14}}{9.109 \times 10^{-31}}$$

which is equal to 4.8×10^{-5} metres per second or about 1 mm in 20 seconds.

This shows just how comparatively slow electron flow is along a conductor even though individual electron velocities are extremely high. To illustrate this further, the wire can be shown to contain some 1.26×10^{20} electrons. In one second, 1 mA is equivalent to

111

the movement of 6.24×10^{15} electrons hence in one second this number has entered at one end of the wire and the same number has been removed from the other end, nevertheless this represents only 1 in 20 000 of the free electrons in the wire.

(* Electron, Electric Field, Electric Field Strength, Energy, Charge, Force, Newton, Current, Mean Free Path, Collision, Random)

DRIVING POINT IMPEDANCE is the impedance measured across a pair of terminals at any point in a network. It is most frequently measured at the network input terminals and is given by the ratio between the applied (r.m.s.) voltage to the resulting (r.m.s.) current flowing between the terminals.

(* Network, Root Mean Square, Impedance)

DYNAMIC refers generally to motive forces in actual operation as opposed to *static* where all is at rest. In electronics therefore dynamic indicates that the parameters of any device or circuit are in motion, i.e. changing.

See also Dynamic Characteristic.

DYNAMIC CHARACTERISTIC must be of an active device and is simply the relationship between the voltage on one electrode and the current through another electrode under specified operating conditions. The particular importance of most dynamic characteristics is that when the characteristic is curved, the relationship between the two quantities is not constant but depends on the instantaneous operating position on the curve. Two such characteristics are shown in Figure F3(iv) and (v).

(* Electrode, Characteristic)

DYNAMIC IMPEDANCE is the impedance of a parallel resonant circuit. The impedance, Z_0 is given by L/CR ohms where L is the inductance in henries, C, the capacitance in farads and R, the resistance in ohms. There is no frequency component in this equation hence Z_0 is purely resistive (but only at resonance). The term *dynamic resistance* therefore also applies.

(* Resonance Frequency, Resonant Circuit, Impedance, Inductance, Capacitance)

DYNAMIC RESISTANCE is the resistance of a parallel resonant circuit — see Dynamic Impedance.

E

EDDY CURRENT   When the magnetic flux linking with a conductor changes, an electromotive force (e.m.f.) is induced in the conductor. The "conductor" need not be part of the electrical circuit giving rise to the magnetic flux, it could, for example, be the iron in the magnetic circuit of a transformer or electric rotating machinery. As stated by Lenz's Law the e.m.f. sets up a current the effect of which is to oppose the original change in magnetic flux. This current is known as an *eddy current* and in flowing through the resistance of the conductor it creates a power loss known as the *eddy current loss*. Generally induced e.m.f.'s are proportional to the flux frequency hence because power loss varies as the voltage squared, the eddy current loss varies as the square of the frequency.

Eddy currents are troublesome in transformer and rotating machinery cores but their effect can be minimized by increasing the resistance of their paths. One way is by laminating the core, i.e. building it up with thin strips arranged parallel to the flux and insulated from each other. In radio frequency transformers eddy current loss is reduced by powdering the core so that the individual grains are insulated from each other. This increases the electrical resistance but affects the magnetization only slightly. Ferrites may also be used with the same aim, these are special magnetic materials which are non-conductive.

On the other hand, eddy currents are frequently employed to advantage, for example for heating metals to which heat cannot be applied directly such as electrodes in thermionic valves after they have been assembled in the glass envelope (degassing).
(* Electromagnetic Induction, Electromotive Force, Lenz's Law, Ferrite >> Degassing, Induction Heating, Lamination)

EDDY CURRENT LOSS is the power loss created when eddy currents flow in a conductor — see Eddy Current.

EFFECTIVE RESISTANCE   The "normal" resistance of say, a length of copper wire is simply calculated from the resistivity of copper and when a voltage is applied across the wire, the current is determined by Ohm's Law. This current is distributed uniformly throughout the wire. When the current is alternating, the normal d.c. rules do not apply especially at the higher frequencies. Several effects add up to increase the resistance:

(i)   skin effect – arises from the fact that a wire has inductance which is greatest in the centre, hence the wire impedance decreases from the centre outwards. Because of this, current flow is greatest near the surface (or skin) of the conductor. Effectively therefore the resistance of the wire increases, more so at the higher frequencies;

(ii) eddy currents, the byproduct of induced e.m.f.'s generate unwanted heat which consumes power from the applied current. This therefore represents an increase in the resistance equal to the power lost divided by the (current)^2;

(iii) in devices employing magnetic cores such as transformers and electrical machines, magnetic hysteresis (i.e. where the magnetization of the material lags on the magnetic field strength) also causes a power loss. Again this is equivalent to an increase in resistance.

These resistances add up to a single value at any given frequency which we call the *effective resistance.*

Effective Resistance is also known as *a.c. resistance*, sometimes as *r.f. resistance.*

(* Resistance, Ohm's Law, Skin Effect, Eddy Current, Magnetic Hysteresis)

EFFECTIVE VALUE of a sine wave – see Root Mean Square.

EINSTEIN MASS-ENERGY RELATIONSHIP – see Relativistic Effect.

EINSTEIN PHOTOELECTRIC EQUATION   Einstein explained the emission of electrons from certain materials when illuminated in terms of the energy transferred to an electron by a light photon. The photon energy is given by hf where h is the Planck constant and f the frequency. Provided that this energy exceeds the work function (ϕ) of the particular material, an electron having absorbed a photon receives sufficient energy so that not only can it cross the surface potential barrier but will have some left over in the form of kinetic energy. The maximum kinetic energy possessed by an electron which has crossed the barrier is denoted by $E_{K(max)}$ and the Einstein photoelectric equation is therefore:

$$E_{K(max)} = hf - \phi \text{ joules} .$$

See also Photoelectric Effect.

(* Light, Photon, Frequency, Planck Constant, Work Function, Energy, Kinetic Energy, Potential Barrier)

ELASTANCE We probably meet this term less frequently than some of the others ending in "ance" but it is the one attached to capacitance, used as an expression of the facility of charge storage. It is simply the reciprocal of capacitance and is given the symbol S. Hence since $C = Q/V$, then $S = V/Q$ indicating that for high charge storage in a capacitor, a low elastance is required. The unit is the reciprocal farad, i.e. F^{-1}, also referred to as a *daraf*.
(* Capacitance, Charge)

ELECTRIC AXIS is the axis of maximum conductivity in a piezo-electric crystal — see Figure P8(i).

ELECTRIC CHARGE The stuff electricity is made of — see Charge.

ELECTRIC CONSTANT is synonymous with Permittivity of Free Space. It has a value of 8.854×10^{-12} farads per metre — see Permittivity.

ELECTRIC DIPOLE Two equal point charges of opposite polarity at a distance apart — see Dipole.

ELECTRIC DISPLACEMENT is concerned with the effect of an electric field on a dielectric — see Displacement.

ELECTRIC FIELD This exists in the space surrounding a charge. Charge gives rise to a condition in the space around it known as an electric field and in this space another charge experiences a force on it. Apart from this an electric field cannot be detected by any other means, this is a fundamental condition Nature has bestowed on us. Consider the two conductors A and B as shown in Figure E1. Conductor A has a positive charge on its surface because some atoms have lost electrons, B has a negative charge because the surface has surplus electrons. There is therefore an electric field between A and B which we usually picture as dotted lines, arrowed to show the direction the force would act on an isolated small positive (test) charge. Since like charges repel and unlike attract, a positive test charge would experience a force tending to move it away from A and towards B as shown, hence the lines are so arrowed. In fact a free positive charge would trace out a "line of electric flux". However, such lines do not really exist, they simply make explanations easier.

Not only does a test charge experience a force on it but the conductors themselves do also since the electric field from A attracts B and vice versa. Note too that there is a difference in electric

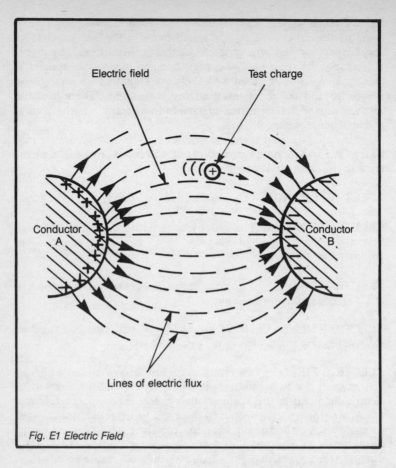

Fig. E1 Electric Field

potential between A and B depending on the magnitudes of the charges and the shapes of the conductors. An electric field therefore has a *potential gradient* running between the charges from which it arises.

When the charges which give rise to a field are at rest, the field is called *electrostatic.*

(* Charge, Field, Force, Potential Difference)

ELECTRIC FIELD INTENSITY – see Electric Field Strength.

ELECTRIC FIELD STRENGTH   This is a quantity expressed by the force acting on a unit charge at a point within an electric field. Coulomb's Law gives us the formula for the force between two electric charges as:

$$F = \frac{Q_1 Q_2}{4\pi \epsilon d^2} \text{ newtons}$$

where Q_1 and Q_2 represent the charge magnitudes in coulombs, d is the distance between their centres in metres and ϵ is the permittivity of the medium.

If the electric field is due to a charge of Q coulombs and the unit charge is that of the electron (normally designated by e), then the foce acting on the unit charge is:

$$F = \frac{Qe}{4\pi \epsilon d^2} \text{ newtons}$$

The electric field strength is the force *per unit charge* and is given the symbol E, hence:

$$\text{electric field strength}, E = \frac{Q}{4\pi \epsilon d^2} \text{ newtons per coulomb}$$

and the force acting on the unit charge is therefore:

$$F = eE .$$

Electric fields arise from charge differences which have the potential to do work on a charge within the field. This potential is measured in volts and it is clear that there is a *potential gradient* along the field, hence the electric field strength can most conveniently be expressed in volts per metre, i.e.

$$\text{electric field strength}, E = F/e \text{ volts per metre}$$

where F is the force acting on a unit charge at a point in the field and e is the unit charge (of the electron $= 1.602 \times 10^{-19}$ C).
(* Electron, Charge, Coulomb's Law, Electric Field, Electric Field Strength, Force, Work, Coulomb, Permittivity)

ELECTRIC FLUX is the sole constituent of an electric field. Because it is invisible, we normally depict it as a group of lines of force. In the S.I. system the total electric flux emanating from a charge, Q coulombs itself is equal to Q (coulombs).
(* Charge, Electric Field, Force)

ELECTRIC FLUX DENSITY shows the concentration of electric flux over a given area. Since the electric flux emanating from a charge of Q coulombs is itself equal to Q, then:

electric flux density, $D = Q/a$ coulombs per square metre (C/m^2)

where a is the area under consideration and is normal to the direction of the lines of force — see Displacement.

ELECTRIC IMAGE is a technique developed for analysis of certain electrostatic problems. Its use can be illustrated by consideration of an electron freed from the surface of a material. When an electron escapes it leaves behind a positive charge which exerts a force tending to pull the electron back. Calculation of the magnitude of the force can be made on the basis that if the escaping electron of charge $-e$ is at a distance x from the surface, then the force is that due to an *image charge* of $+e$ at the same distance x below the surface. The distance between the two charges, $d = 2x$, hence from Coulomb's Law, the force between the two charges which is actually the force tending to pull the electron back to the surface:

$$F = \frac{Q_1 Q_2}{4\pi\epsilon d^2} = \frac{e^2}{16\pi\epsilon x^2}$$

The idea of the electric image is useful in such theoretical calculations, nevertheless as can be seen from this particular example, the permittivity of the medium, ϵ cannot be stated exactly. It is in fact a mixture of that of the material and that of the surrounding medium.
(* Charge, Electron, Coulomb's Law, Force, Work Function, Permittivity)

ELECTRICITY is a form of energy possessed by atomic particles. That of the proton is labelled positive, for the electron it is negative. The two types create a force of attraction between them and atoms are so arranged that proton and electron charges cancel, hence an atom is normally electrically neutral. It is when this condition is disturbed by separation of one electron or more from an atom (ionization) that electricity comes into existence. On their own the electrons constitute a negative charge while the atom becomes positively charged because it has lost some of its balancing negative charge.

118

When these charges remain stationary they give rise to *static electricity*, when they are caused to flow through a material or gas they are known as *current electricity*.
(* Atom, Proton, Electron, Charge, Energy, Ionization, Current, Static Electricity, Positive, Negative)

ELECTRIC POLARIZATION   This occurs in a dielectric through which there is an electric field. The nucleus, being positive is displaced in the direction of the field (see Fig.E1) whereas the electrons are displaced in the opposite direction. The atom therefore develops polarities as shown in Figure D3, i.e. it becomes a dipole and has a dipole moment.

Electric polarization is given the symbol P and it is defined as the electric dipole moment per unit volume. It is related to the electric field strength (E) by:

$$P = \chi_e \epsilon_0 E \text{ coulombs per metre squared (C/m}^2) ,$$

where χ_e is the electric susceptibility and ϵ_0 is the permittivity of free space (E is in volts per metre, ϵ_0 in farads per metre and χ_e is dimensionless).
(* Dielectric, Electric Field Strength, Coulomb, Dipole, Susceptibility Electric, Permittivity, Relaxation Time)

ELECTRIC POTENTIAL   Anything possessing potential energy has the capacity to do work. In an electric circuit potential energy has the ability to move an electric charge (usually electrons) round the circuit, i.e. create an electric current. Electric potential energy is measured in volts (V). The *potential difference* or *voltage* between two points in a circuit is a measure of the energy required to move a given amount of charge between those points, hence the potential difference:

$$V = \frac{\text{energy or work (joules)}}{\text{charge (coulombs)}} \text{ joules per coulomb or volts .}$$

Since from Ohm's Law, voltage = current × resistance and the power expended = current² × resistance, i.e.

$$V = I \times R \text{ and } P = I^2 \times R$$

then

$$V = I \times P/I^2 = P/I$$

119

hence the potential difference, V, can be expressed in watts per ampere, i.e. a volt can also be defined as the difference of electric potential between two points in a circuit carrying a constant current of one ampere when the power dissipated between these points is equal to one watt.

(* Charge, Energy, Work, Joule, Ohm's Law, Coulomb, Power)

ELECTRIC POTENTIAL ENERGY — see Potential Energy.

ELECTRIC SUSCEPTIBILITY — see Susceptibility, Electric

ELECTROCHEMICAL EQUIVALENT is the mass of any ion deposited from an electrolyte by one coulomb of electricity. Thus the mass deposited by a current of I amperes flowing for t seconds is Izt where z is the electrochemical equivalent of the ion being deposited. As an example, silver nitrate ($AgNO_3$) ionizes into Ag^+ and NO_3^-, the ion deposited from the solution is the Ag, i.e. pure silver.

The ampere was originally defined in these terms as that current which flowing uniformly for one second would deposit 0.001118 grams of silver from a solution of silver nitrate. 0.001118 is therefore the electrochemical equivalent of silver although this is more likely to be quoted as 0.248 ampere-hours per gram.

(* Current, Electrolyte, Coulomb, Ionization, Mass, Ampere)

ELECTRODE   This is a conductor through which electric charge carriers enter or exit from an electrolyte, vacuum, gas or other medium such as a semiconductor or dielectric.

(* Charge Carrier)

ELECTRODE CHARACTERISTIC shows the relationship between current and voltage at an electrode — see Characteristic.

ELECTROKINETICS is the theory concerning the force components of moving charges. As an example, this leads to calculation of the force between two current-carrying conductors so to the definition of the ampere.

(* Charge, Current, Ampere, Force)

ELECTROLUMINESCENCE is concerned with the emission of light by certain phosphors when under the influence of a strong electric field. The phenomenon was first observed by G. J. Destriau and is therefore occasionally referred to as the *Destriau Effect*. Electron-hole pairs are created by the field and light arises from recombination with excess energy emitted as photons. Electroluminescence occurs with both a.c. and d.c. excitation and typically a thin layer of the phosphor (less than $50\,\mu m$) is sandwiched between two electrodes, one of which must be transparent for the light to escape. Several hundred volts may be required. Colour of the light depends on the phosphor.

(* Light, Electric Field, Electron-Hole Pair, Energy, Recombination, Photon, Visible Spectrum)

ELECTROLYSIS is the chemical decomposition of a solution (the electrolyte) when an electric current is passed through it. A simple example is given by a common salt solution (sodium chloride, NaCl). When a current flows between two electrodes in the solution the salt dissociates into sodium and chlorine which are liberated at the electrodes — see Electrolyte.

ELECTROLYTE has two meanings: (i) a substance which can dissolve in a liquid to produce a solution capable of conducting an electric current, (ii) the solution itself. Electrolytes are essential in cells (*electrolytic cell*) and in electroplating processes.

The substance used is a compound which when dissolved in a liquid allows some or most of its molecules to dissociate into separate ions, some positively charged, an equal number negatively charged. Because the ions are charged particles and mobile they are capable of transporting electricity. This is best explained by an example, e.g. that of sodium chloride (common salt) in water. Water, when pure, happens to be a poor conductor of electricity.

The sodium chloride molecule is the product of the two elements, sodium and chlorine [see Fig.E2(i)]. The sodium atom has one electron only in its valence shell, the chlorine has 7 but to complete its shell would like 8. It seizes the single sodium electron and the molecule forms by the bond between the two ions. The sodium atom is not unhappy about this arrangement because it too prefers to have its outer shell complete (i.e. 8 electrons in Shell 2).

When the sodium chloride is dissolved in water the ions separate as shown in Figure E2(ii), a positive sodium and negative chlorine. These ions bear no relationship to the original elements and exist only in the solution. While free in the solution they follow the normal rules for charges and the electrolyte acts as an electrical conductor as demonstrated in Figure E2(iii).

(* Atom, Molecule, Bond, Shell, Charge, Ion, Faraday Law of Electrolysis, Cell >> Electroplating)

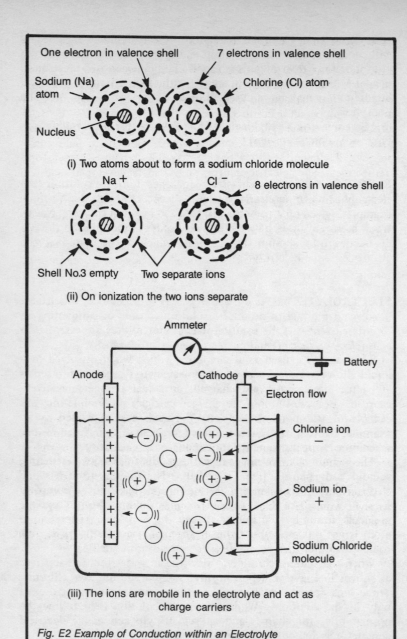

One electron in valence shell

7 electrons in valence shell

Sodium (Na) atom

Chlorine (Cl) atom

Nucleus

(i) Two atoms about to form a sodium chloride molecule

Na +

Cl −

8 electrons in valence shell

Shell No.3 empty

Two separate ions

(ii) On ionization the two ions separate

Ammeter

Battery

Anode

Cathode

Electron flow

Chlorine ion −

Sodium ion +

Sodium Chloride molecule

(iii) The ions are mobile in the electrolyte and act as charge carriers

Fig. E2 Example of Conduction within an Electrolyte

ELECTROLYTIC CELL – see Cell

ELECTROMAGNETIC INDUCTION was discovered by the English physicist, Michael Faraday in 1831. Knowing that an electric current produces a magnetic field, he reasoned that a magnetic field might produce an electric current. This he found to be true although it became evident that whereas a steady current gives rise to a steady magnetic field, only a *changing* magnetic field could produce a current. From Faraday's work dynamos, generators, transformers and electric motors were soon developed and an electricity supply into homes became a reality.

Faraday found that an electromotive force (e.m.f.) was produced in a conductor while there was a change of magnetic flux through it. The moving magnetic flux releases electrons and accelerates them in one particular direction. He also found that the e.m.f. induced in a conductor was proportional to the *rate of change* of magnetic flux linking with it, i.e.:

$$\text{e.m.f. induced, } e = \frac{\text{total flux cut (webers)}}{\text{time (seconds)}} \text{ volts}$$

i.e.

$$e = -\frac{d\phi}{dt} \text{ volts}$$

where $d\phi/dt$ is the rate of change of flux with time in Wb/s.

In S.I. terms it can therefore be stated that the e.m.f. induced is one volt when the magnetic flux changes at the rate of one weber per second. The minus sign shows that e is in opposition to the change which produces it.

If a conductor of length l metres moves a distance of d metres through a magnetic field, then the area of flux "cut" by the conductor $= l \times d$.

The total flux cut, $\phi = Bld$ webers where B is the flux density in tesla.

$$\text{Rate of change of flux, } \frac{d\phi}{dt} = \frac{\phi}{t} = \frac{Bld}{t}$$

Now if the conductor moves at a constant velocity, $v = d/t$ metres per second, then:

$$\text{induced e.m.f., } e = \frac{Bld}{t} = Blv \text{ volts .}$$

123

If, however, the conductor moves at an angle θ to the "lines" of magnetic flux:

$$e = Blv \sin \theta \text{ volts}.$$

The *direction* of the induced e.m.f. and resultant current flow can be determined using Fleming's Rules.

The transformer is an example of a device based on electromagnetic induction. An alternating current in the primary winding produces a continually changing magnetic field which also embraces a secondary winding. An e.m.f. is therefore developed in the secondary winding.

The electromagnetic or radio wave is based on an extension of this principle. If a changing magnetic field produces a changing electric field, then the changing electric field can itself give rise to a changing magnetic field, hence the two fields are bound together with energy being continually transferred between them.

(* Faraday's Law, Lenz's Law, Magnetic Flux, Weber, Electromotive Force, Fleming's Rules, Transformer, Electromagnetic Wave, Tesla >> Generator)

ELECTROMAGNETIC MOTOR ACTION   In 1821 the English physicist, Michael Faraday discovered that a wire carrying an electric current moved if placed within the field of a magnet. This is the principle of the electric motor and a simplified way of looking at motor action is that motion arises from forces associated with the interaction of the magnetic field due to the current in the wire with that of the surrounding field. For a better understanding of the basic principle however a few formulae are useful.

It is an experimental fact and one which can be proved theoretically that the force on a charge moving in a magnetic field varies linearly with the charge velocity, i.e.:

$$F \propto qv$$

where F is the force exerted on a charge, q and v is the charge velocity. Working next in terms of a single electron of charge, e:

$$F \propto eV.$$

The force is also proportional to the strength of the magnetic field (i.e. the magnetic flux density, B) hence:

$$F = Bev \text{ newtons}$$

124

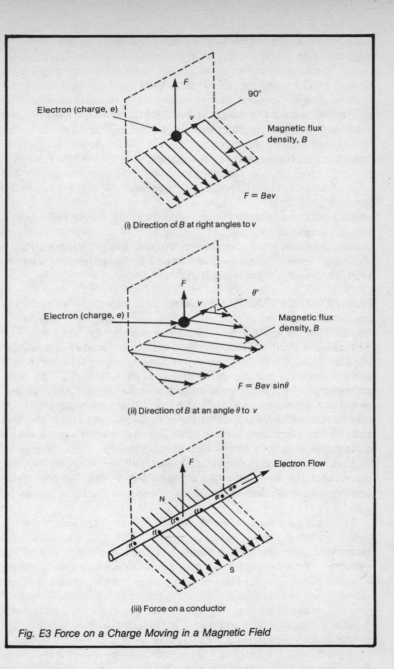

(i) Direction of B at right angles to v

$F = Bev$

(ii) Direction of B at an angle θ to v

$F = Bev \sin\theta$

(iii) Force on a conductor

Fig. E3 Force on a Charge Moving in a Magnetic Field

with B in tesla, e in coulombs and v in metres per second.

If the electron is moving at right angles to the magnetic field, then F is perpendicular to both B and v. This is illustrated in Figure E3(i). In (ii) is shown how F is reduced to $Bev \sin \theta$ when the electron cuts the lines of flux at an angle $\theta°$. Because the electrons are captive within the wire, the total force on them adds up to a much greater force on the wire itself, tending to move it in the direction of F as shown in (iii).

In terms of current rather than charge:

$$F = BIl \sin \theta \text{ newtons}$$

where I is the current flowing in a conductor of length l metres in a uniform magnetic field.

The *direction* of F can be determined using Fleming's Rules. (* Charge, Force, Magnetic Field, Magnetic Flux Density, Newton, Tesla, Coulomb $\gg$ Electromagnet)

ELECTROMAGNETIC RADIATION   For some this is one of the more difficult terms to understand yet one of the most important, especially in these days of information technology. Some of our difficulties may arise from the fact that other waves we know are more obvious, waves on water or on a string can be watched, sound waves cannot be seen but they make themselves heard. All these are vibrations of some kind within a material and they cannot progress in a vacuum. On the other hand the electromagnetic wave can, in fact the wave travels best in a vacuum. The reason for this arises from the nature of the electric field, it does not require a medium in which to act, a vacuum does just as well. Within an electric field both the strength and direction of the electric force at any point can be represented by an *electric field vector*. This represents one of the forces which vibrates in an electromagnetic wave.

By causing a charge to oscillate in an antenna, a changing electric field is set up in the space surrounding it. The fact that the charges are moving indicates that an oscillating magnetic field is also set up. Figure E4(i) demonstrates in a very simple form how the two fields (electric and magnetic) arise at a particular instant around a dipole antenna (one which is designed especially for its radiation properties). It is evident from the figure that the electric and magnetic fields are at right angles and that at a distance as (ii) shows, they can be considered as straight lines. There is a continual transfer of energy between the two fields since each field gives rise to the other. The fields are therefore inseparable, hence the description "electro-

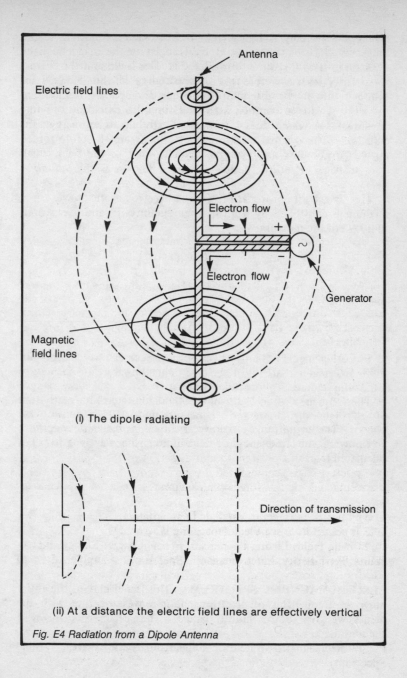

Antenna

Electric field lines

Electron flow

+

~

−

Electron flow

Generator

Magnetic
field lines

(i) The dipole radiating

Direction of transmission

(ii) At a distance the electric field lines are effectively vertical

Fig. E4 Radiation from a Dipole Antenna

magnetic". Energy is transferred from the antenna current to the fields.

A finite time is required for the fields to collapse so if the generator polarity reverses before this is completed, all of the field energies cannot return to the antenna because new and opposite fields are in the way. This is in contrast with for example, the field surrounding an inductance which does return practically all of its energy as it collapses. The original electromagnetic fields are therefore forced outwards, i.e. they are *propagated*. That part of the field which does manage to return to the antenna is known as the *induction field*.

The speed of propagation (v) of electromagetic waves in a medium is controlled by both the permeability (μ) and the permittivity (ϵ) of the medium:

$$v = \sqrt{1/(\mu\epsilon)} \ .$$

For free space, $\mu = \mu_0$ and $\epsilon = \epsilon_0$. Hence, now using c for the free space velocity:

$$c = \sqrt{1/(4\pi \times 10^{-7} \times 8.854 \times 10^{-12})} = 2.998 \times 10^8 \text{ m/s} \ .$$

For other media v is lower because both permeability and permittivity are greater than 1. In the case of air the values are so close to 1 that the velocity is almost identical with c.

The frequency of an electromagnetic radiation (f) is exactly that of the originating source and frequencies up to 10^{22} Hz or more are known. The entire range is known as the *electromagnetic spectrum*.

Knowing the frequency of a radiation, the wavelength (λ) is calculated from:

$$\lambda = c/f \text{ metres}$$

(c is in metres per second [m/s] and f is in hertz).

For *polarization* see Electromagnetic Wave.
(* Electric Field, Electromagnetism, Force, Charge, Energy, Permeability, Permittivity, Electromagnetic Spectrum >> Dipole Antenna)

ELECTROMAGNETIC SPECTRUM   This is a display of the entire range of frequencies of electromagnetic waves together with the names we give to the various bands. The spectrum is shown in Figure E5.
(* Electromagnetic Radiation, Electromagnetic Waves, Visible Spectrum)

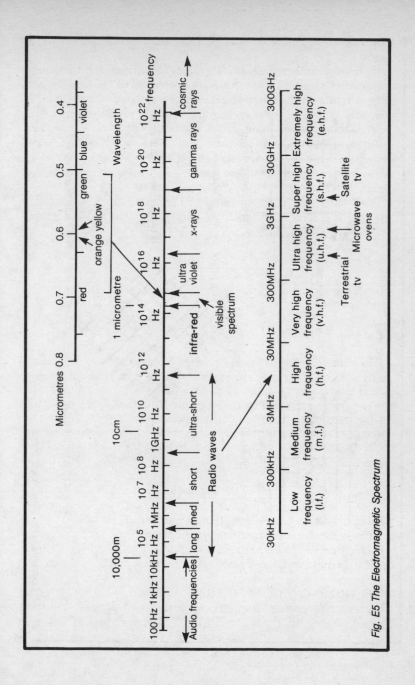

Fig. E5 The Electromagnetic Spectrum

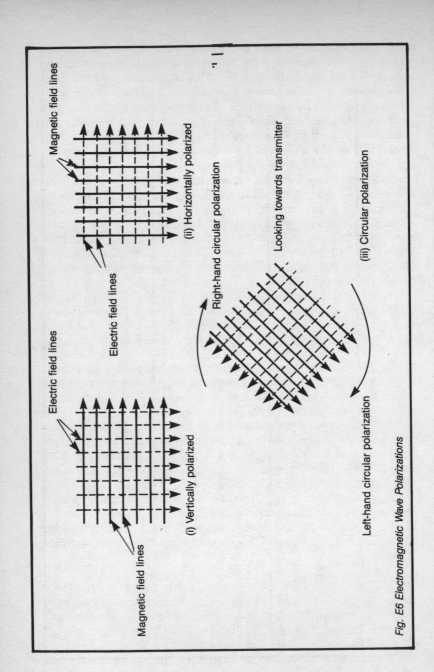

Fig. E6 Electromagnetic Wave Polarizations

ELECTROMAGNETIC WAVE   Much about the electromagnetic wave can be understood from the explanation of *electromagnetic radiation*, brief though it may be. However, when used for radio transmissions, there are some important features about the wave which should also be appreciated. Reception of an electromagnetic wave is based on the simple fact that the varying electric and magnetic fields of the wave are capable of exciting electrons within a material, usually a piece of wire specially formed for the purpose, i.e. the receiving antenna.

Once under way from the transmitting antenna, we can see from Figure E4(ii) that as the electric and magnetic field lines expand outwards, they soon appear to an observer facing them as the lines on a sheet of graph paper as depicted in Figure E6. The arrows reverse direction at each half-cycle of the wave and the fields are at right angles to each other. When, as in this case, the fields and the direction of propagation are mutually perpendicular, it is said to be a *plane wave*.

Polarization of the wave is determined by the direction of the electric field so (i) of Figure E4 shows a *vertically polarized* wave. In (ii) of Figure E6 the wave is *horizontally polarized*. For radio working a receiving antenna should have the same polarization as the wave to be received, i.e. for Figure E6(i) the receiving antenna should be vertical, if it is horizontal reception is at a minimum.

The *plane of polarization* of an electromagnetic wave is the plane which contains both the direction of the electric field and the direction of propagation (see Fig.P12).

There is a further method of wave polarization, *circular*, see (iii) of the figure. In this case the electric and magnetic fields remain at right angles to each other but now as a pair, they continually rotate. Circular polarization is used for example, in reception from satellites, for this special antennas are required.

Light arises from a very limited band of electromagnetic waves, see Electromagnetic Spectrum, Visible Spectrum.
(* Electromagnetic Radiation, Antenna, Field, Electric Field, Magnetic Field, Polarization >> Ground Wave, Ionosphere, Satellite Television)

ELECTROMAGNETISM is concerned with the magnetic force produced by electricity. It is a special force between charges in motion and it is important to keep in mind that charge is one of Nature's fundamental devices (fundamental because it does not arise from something else), but the same cannot be said for magnetism because it is a force which arises from charge. Electricity and magnetism are in fact different aspects of the same force.

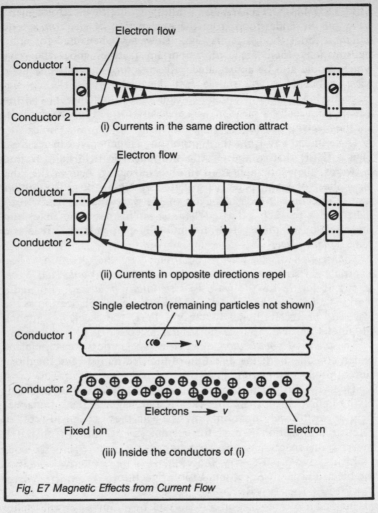

Fig. E7 Magnetic Effects from Current Flow

It is possible to obtain a hint of what goes on if we enlist the help of two famous men of science, Albert Einstein (the German-Swiss physicist) and Henricke Anton Lorentz (a Dutch physicist). From their work we find that distances are not what they seem when observers are moving relative to one another. However, first let us get to grips with the problem.

Consider the two parallel wires carrying electric currents in the same direction as shown in Figure E7(i). The wires are attracted to each other but if the currents flow in opposite directions as in (ii), there is repulsion. Charge cannot build up in a wire when current is flowing so the question is therefore, how can such forces arise when apparently neither wire exhibits a charge?

Lorentz expressed the distance problem mentioned above mathematically by what we now call the *Lorentz contraction.* For example, using electronics terms, a distance d associated with one particle (negative electron or positive ion) as seen by another particle becomes $d\sqrt{1 - (v^2/c^2)}$ where v is the relative velocity between the two particles and c is the velocity of light. The formula holds good everywhere but considering that $c^2 = 9 \times 10^{16}$ metres per second, v must be very large for the effect to show. Just to get this formula into perspective, it shows that one would need to fly over a football pitch at about 150 million kilometres per hour (some 100 million miles per hour) for the length apparently to be reduced by 1%.

Figure E7(iii) looks inside the wires of (i) but for clarity shows one electron only in conductor 1. Assume that electrons in both wires are travelling to the right with a velocity, v. Then to the electron in conductor 1:

(i)   the relative velocity of the negative charges in conductor 2 is zero (because they are travelling in the same direction at the same speed);
(ii) the relative velocity of the stationary positive charges in conductor 2 is v.

Condition (ii) is the important one for whatever the value of v, the Lorentz contraction shows that from the point of view of the electron in conductor 1, the distances between the positive charges in conductor 2 are *reduced*, hence a greater concentration of charge arises. This leads to an attractive force produced entirely from the relative motions.

If we were to repeat this reasoning for (ii) in the figure, we would find that our lone electron in conductor 1 has a relative velocity to the negative charges in conductor 2 of $2v$, but to the positive charges of v, hence overall there is repulsion.

These forces between the two wires arise only when the charges have *relative velocities* and they are the basis of *electromagnetism.*

Infinitesimally small though the distance contractions may be, we must remember that not only are atomic forces very great but so is the total number of electrons flowing (6.24×10^{18} per second for one ampere) and that the increases in charge are additive. It is clear too that the magnetic force is directly proportional to the current flowing (as is shown by the formula for magnetmotive force). (* Charge, Current, Electron, Ion, Force, Magnetomotive Force, Lorentz Contraction >> Electromagnet)

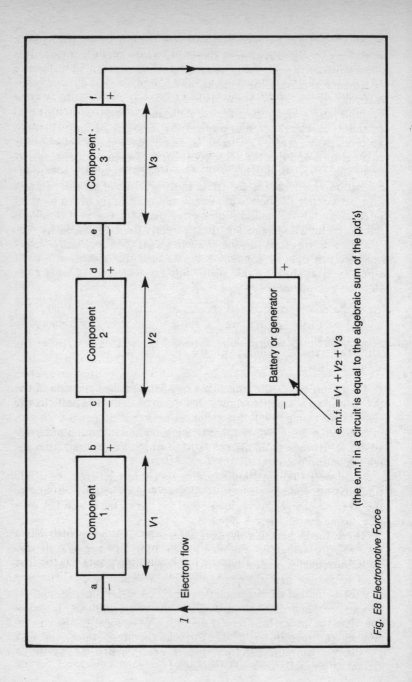

Fig. E8 Electromotive Force

(the e.m.f in a circuit is equal to the algebraic sum of the p.d's)

$$e.m.f. = V_1 + V_2 + V_3$$

ELECTROMOTIVE FORCE   This is a measure of the ability of a source of electricity to cause a current to flow round a circuit. It is the driving or generating force which sets up a potential difference (p.d.). Like p.d. it is measured in volts. The symbol is E.

Consider the electrical circuit of Figure E8. Work has to be done on an electric charge to move it round a circuit (i.e. a current flows) and the amount of work depends on the ease with which each particular part or component of the circuit enables electrons to flow through (its *conductance* or conversely if we talk in terms of the opposition it puts up, its *resistance*). An electric field is the means by which a force is made to act on a charge so causing it to move and therefore have work done on it.

Electric fields are established between two points in a circuit when there is a difference of potential (p.d.) across them, e.g. between points a and b of component 1. If R is the resistance between a and b, then the p.d. (v_1) required to provide sufficient electric field strength to get the current I through is, by Ohm's Law, $I \times R$ volts (I in amperes and R in ohms). The p.d.'s v_2 and v_3 will have such values that they too achieve the same result. The supply of these p.d.'s comes from the battery or other generator and whereas the charge moves through the components from a to f i.e. from negative to positive, the battery has the ability to move the same charge from positive to negative against the total p.d. across its terminals, viz. $(v_1 + v_2 + v_3)$. This is the electromotive force. In any electrical circuit the e.m.f. is equal to the algebraic sum of the p.d.'s and it is a measure of the work required to move a unit electric charge completely round the circuit.

Electromotive force is generated by several means, mostly by energy conversion e.g. batteries (chemical), generators (mechanical), photovoltaic cell (light), thermocouple (heat).

See also Internal Resistance.
(* Force, Work, Charge, Current, Circuit, Potential Difference, Electric Field, Volt)

ELECTRON is a minute negatively charged particle which has a normal habitat in orbit round a parent atom (see Fig.A7). It also spins as it moves. J. J. Thomson (an English physicist) was the first to prove that such particles as electrons actually existed. This was in 1897. He showed by using an apparatus not unlike the present day cathode ray tube that a stream of particles could be generated and all particles seemed to have similar mass and charge. In fact we now know that all electrons have exactly the same characteristics and therefore behave similarly. Earlier in 1884, George Johnstone Stoney (an Irish scientist) had suggested the name "electron" for the elementary particle and the name was adopted. It is derived from the Greek *elektron* for amber which had already been found to develop certain forces when suitably rubbed. Gradually the true value for the charge of an electron has emerged as $(-)$ 1.602×10^{-19} coulombs. This high-speed little packet of charge does have some mass but it is only 9.109×10^{-31} kilograms. It therefore takes about 10^{27} of them to add up to about 1 gram (about one-thirtieth of an ounce). Clearly then little of the weight of a material is due to its electrons. It is generally considered that electrons are fundamental particles and therefore not divisible (but there are some who dispute this).

The release of an electron from its parent atom occurs when sufficient energy is given to it (e.g. by an electric field, heat, light, etc.). As an example, given 13.6 electron-volts (eV) of energy), the single electron of a hydrogen atom can escape, for copper only 7.7 eV is required (an electron-volt is a measure of *energy* and is equivalent to 1.602×10^{-19} joules). Copper is a metal which gives up the single electron in each atom outermost orbit quite freely so that it is available as a charge carrier. By surrounding them with an electric field, the "free" electrons are forced to move and negative charge is transferred along the material — this is an electric current.

The electron in its orbit is a very fast mover, calculations on, for example, the hydrogen atom reveal almost unbelievable figures — the velocity is some two thousand kilometres per second!

With the most powerful modern microscope, atoms can be seen but electrons never will (they move too fast anyway). Accordingly our pictures of them as small black balls or dots are probably far from the truth, we might preferably imagine them as infinitesimal balls of cotton wool or when many are gathered together, as a cloud.

See also de Broglie Waves.

(* Atom, Ionization, Mass, Charge, Energy, Coulomb, Conductivity, Electron-volt, Spin)

ELECTRON CHARGE is that property possessed by an electron through which it exerts an attractive or repulsive force on other particles. We label the electron charge *negative* and it has a value of $(-)$ 1.60219×10^{-19} coulombs.

(* Electron, Charge, Coulomb, Negative)

ELECTRON-HOLE PAIR   When an electron is excited into the conduction band it is considered that two charge carriers are produced, the free electron and the vacated hole. Together they are known as an electron-hole pair.

(* Electron, Charge Carrier, Energy Levels, Energy Bands, Hole)

ELECTRON OPTICS is the science concerning the behaviour of electron beams especially in how they can be focused as a ray of light is focused by a lens. There are both electromagnetic and electrostatic lenses.
(>> Electron Beam Focusing, Electrostatic Deflection, Electron Gun)

ELECTRON-VOLT   In atomic considerations the joule is a comparatively large unit of energy, accordingly one referring to a single electron is frequently used. An electric field is capable of accelerating a "free" electron and the electron-volt (symbol eV) is the work done by a field or equally the energy acquired by an electron when the latter is accelerated through a potential difference of one volt. Hence:

$$\text{work done} = e \times V$$

where e is the electron charge (1.602×10^{-19} coulombs) and V is the field voltage through which it has been transported (1V).

$\therefore$ $1 \text{ eV} = 1.602 \times 10^{-19}$ coulomb-volts, i.e. joules .

(It is important to remember that although "volt" appears in the name of the unit, the electron-volt is a unit of energy, not voltage).
(* Energy, Electron, Field, Electric Field, Charge, Coulomb, Joule)

ELECTROPHORESIS is the movement of very finely divided particles in a fluid when under the influence of an electric field.
(* Particle, Electric Field)

ELECTROSCOPE   This is a laboratory instrument used for detecting electric charges. The earliest electroscopes employed a pith ball hanging by a fine silk thread, the ball being attracted to a charged rubber or glass rod. Then in the late 1700's came the gold-leaf electroscope as depicted in Figure E9. In operation, if for example, a positive charge is brought near to the top plate, electrons are attracted from the gold leaves to it, leaving the plate negatively charged but the leaves positively charged. The repulsion between the like charges on the two gold leaves causes them to move apart so indicating that a charge is present near or on the top plate. A further development of the device replaces one of the gold leaves by a metal plate.
    An example of the use of an electroscope is shown in Figure P6.
(* Positive, Negative, Charge)

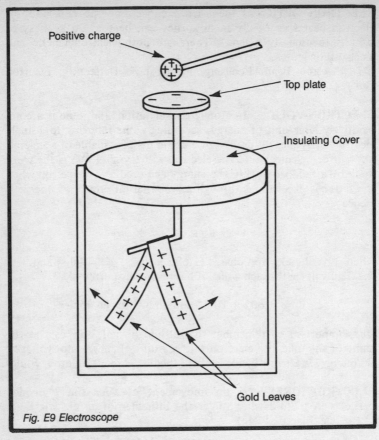

Fig. E9 Electroscope

ELECTROSTATIC BOND – see Bond

ELECTROSTATIC FIELD – the electric field arising from an electric charge at rest.
(* Charge, Electric Field)

ELECTROSTATIC INDUCTION is the rearrangement of the charges on a body when in the vicinity of another more highly charged body. The charged body has associated with it an electrostatic field, its effect is best illustrated as in Figure E10. Here we consider the charged body to be a plastic ruler which has been rubbed on a piece of flannel to accumulate a high negative charge as shown. The drawing shows that in a nearby piece of paper the electrostatic field is capable of ionizing some of the molecules and the electrons so

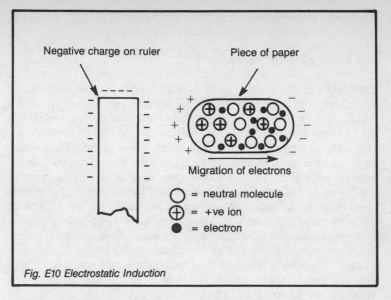

Negative charge on ruler

Piece of paper

Migration of electrons

○ = neutral molecule
⊕ = +ve ion
● = electron

Fig. E10 Electrostatic Induction

freed are repelled away from the ruler hence leaving the paper positively charged on the left and negatively on the right. This is an example of *electrostatic induction*. A positively charged body would have the opposite effect. That these charges are present is shown by the fact that the ruler can pick up the piece of paper through the attraction of its negative charge on the positive charge induced nearby in the paper.
(* Charge, Electrostatic Field, Ionization, Static Electricity, Positive, Negative)

ELECTROVALENT BOND is formed when there is a transfer of one or more electrons between two atoms so that both will have complete outermost shells — see Bond.

ELEMENT   Of all the substances encountered on earth, just over 100 are known as elements, meaning that they are pure and contain nothing else. Each of the elements is made up of its own particular atoms and these are different from those of other elements. When there are only one or two electrons in the outermost shell (the valence shell), the element is usually a good electrical conductor, e.g. copper (atomic number 29) and silver (atomic number 47) are both good conductors and have only one. When there are 4 electrons in the outermost shell, groups of atoms can form covalent bonds, essential in semiconductor technology, e.g.

139

silicon and germanium.
(* Atom, Electron, Ionization, Shell, Bond, Valency)

E.M.F. — see Electromotive Force

EMISSION is the general term used for the release of electrons or electromagnetic radiation from the surface of a solid, usually a metal. Atoms in a metal or other conductor are constrained within the lattice structure with free electrons moving between them randomly. Inevitably therefore those electrons at the surface which have a component of velocity in a direction out of the surface are able to jump clear provided that they have sufficient energy, the result can be imagined as in Figure E11. Remember that at atomic level there is no clean-cut surface as we might see on a piece of polished metal but simply a jagged line where the lattice terminates, as the figure attempts to illustrate. However those electrons which do escape from the "surface" are encouraged back by the positive charges left behind and also they themselves congregate at the surface and repel the emission of more. Hence effectively a few electrons do escape but the *space charge* they set up limits the liberation of others. It is a dynamic process, electrons with sufficient

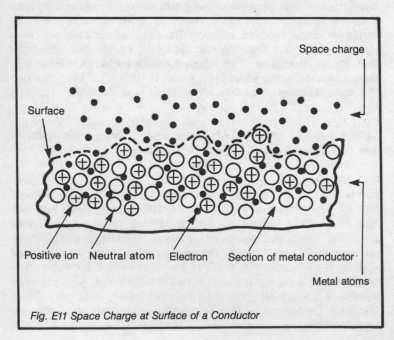

Fig. E11 Space Charge at Surface of a Conductor

140

kinetic energy continually join the escapers while others go back home. Overall an equilibrium occurs and because the space charge is so close to the material it can really be considered as part of it.

At room temperature and below, with no outside help very few electrons have enough energy to escape from the space charge. Energy must therefore be supplied for this to happen and the amount energy per electron is known as the *work function*, usually measured in electron-volts. The energy can be supplied in several different ways:

   (i)   by heat (thermionic emission)
  (ii)   by radiation, for example light (photoemission)
 (iii)   by bombardment (secondary emission)
 (iv)   from an external field (field emission).

In practical circuits for useful emission electrons are drawn off from the space charge in a vacuum. For this the metal must be connected into an electrical circuit able to replenish the electrons removed. As an example, a thermionic emission device gives the electrons extra energy by heat and removes them from the space charge by surrounding it with a positively charged electrode (the anode — see Fig.T2). A photoelectric cell gains the energy required from incident light photons and collects the electrons similarly at a positive anode.

There is also *stimulated emission* — see Laser.
(* Atom, Electron, Current, Space Charge, Work Function, Electron-Volt, Electric Image, Photon, Thermionic Emission, Photoemission, Secondary Emission, Field Emission, Thermionic Valve, Lattice Structure, Random)

EMITTER is one of the regions of a bipolar transistor. From the emitter majority charge carriers flow into the base region where they become minority carriers — see Transistor.

ENERGY is the prime mover of life. Much of the analysis we carry out on the busy life of the electron rests on the energy it possesses, hence so much electronics theory is in terms of *energy levels* and *energy bands*. A simple example of how an active unit functions according to its store of energy is given by the human being. He or she wakes up in the morning (usually) "full of energy" and hence has the power to do things for this is what energy is. The energy level is high. During the day things are done and the level goes down. With food and rest the level rises again. Thus the amount (or level) of body energy varies continuously. So it is with the electron, it has a store of energy (of infinitesimally small value)

141

which while the electron is simply in orbit does not change because none is used up in travelling through the space within an atom. Electrons however can gain energy from many different sources and they can also lose it in many different ways.

We define energy as the capacity for doing work for work can only be carried out if energy is expended. Energy is measured in *joules* (J) and because heat is a *form* of energy, it is measured in the same unit. (See also Kinetic Energy, Potential Energy).

There are several forms of energy apart from the human kind, each of which can on its own, or through some intermediate device, do work. Some are given below with a single example in each case of the work done:

chemical	explosives
electrical	drives trains
heat	expands metals
nuclear	electricity generation
radiant	moves a photometer needle
sound	moves ear drums.

Einstein, in his famous equation showed that mass and energy are related to one another and that each can be converted into the other. He expressed this by:

$$E = mc^2$$

where E is the energy, m the mass and c the speed of light.

Hence mass can be converted into energy by, for example, a nuclear reaction. Equally energy is convertible into mass and as the speed of an object increases so its kinetic energy increases, resulting in an increase in mass of E/c^2. But note that c^2 is so large (9×10^{16} m/s) that speeds approaching that of light are necessary before an appreciable change in mass takes place.

See also Potential Energy.

(* Work, Joule, Mass, Kinetic Energy)

ENERGY BANDS   In an atom each electron possesses energy, potential energy by virtue of its orbital position relative to the nucleus and kinetic energy because of its motion. The net energy is complicated and is described in detail by quantum theory. The electrons can only have certain discrete energy levels and Pauli's exclusion principle states that not more than two electrons can occupy each level (and these must have opposite spins). Accordingly the electrons occupy the lower levels first, then progressively higher levels as the lower ones become filled.

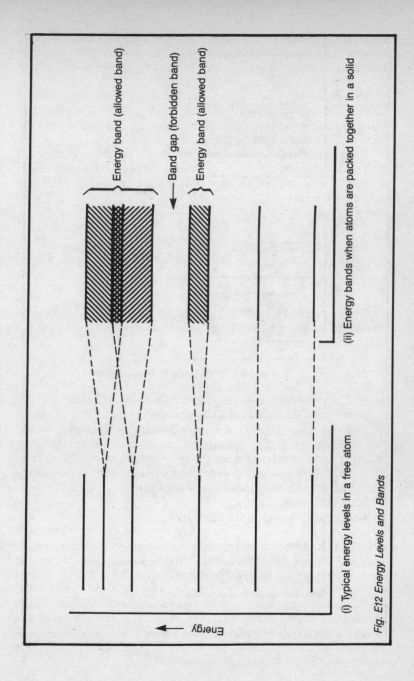

Fig. E12 Energy Levels and Bands

(i) Typical energy levels in a free atom

(ii) Energy bands when atoms are packed together in a solid

Energy band (allowed band)

Band gap (forbidden band)

Energy band (allowed band)

Energy

143

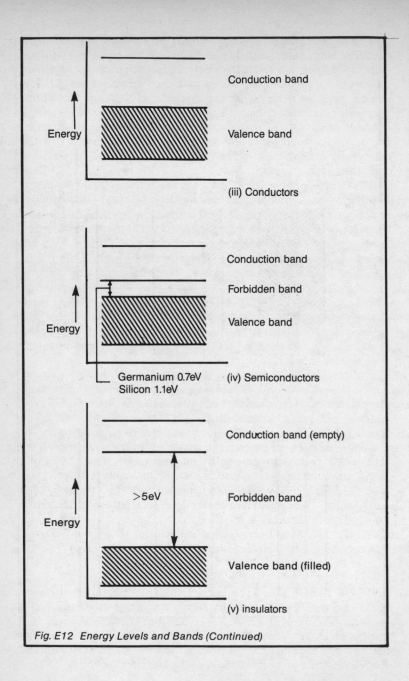

Fig. E12   Energy Levels and Bands (Continued)

144

The discrete levels of energy existing in a particular atom might therefore be pictured as in Figure E12(i). When however atoms are packed together in a solid, the electrons in the outermost shells are disturbed by neighbouring atoms and their energies change. The energy levels for these higher energy electrons therefore spread out into bands, each containing a large number of closely spaced energy levels as in (ii) of the figure. The bands may overlap as shown or there may be *band gaps*, also known as *forbidden bands*. In the solid therefore, no electron has a level of energy falling within a forbidden band.

The inner electrons of an atom are much less affected by neighbouring atoms, hence we can demonstrate practical conductivities as in Figure E12(iii), (iv) and (v) for conductors, semiconductors and insulators. In conductors the valence band (i.e. the band of energy levels possessed by the valence electrons) and conduction band are close together or even overlap. The conduction band is not full so there are some vacant energy levels. This means that any electron receiving the correct amount of energy from, for example, an electric field, can continue at this new energy level. Having filled the energy "vacancy", no other electron can do so. From the figure it is evident that little additional energy needs to be supplied to electrons in the valence band for them to break free and "enter" the conduction band.

For semiconductors there is a forbidden band, i.e. no electron within the material can function at an energy level within this band. Hence to jump from the valence to the conduction band needs the provision of around one electron-volt of energy as shown. The forbidden band widens considerably for insulators, accordingly for a valence electron to be freed to act as a charge carrier it must be accelerated greatly to gain sufficient energy to "cross the gap".

At absolute zero temperature, where energies in a solid are low, the lower energy levels are occupied and the valence band is partly filled. The maximum energy level under these conditions is known as the Fermi Level.

(* Atom, Electron, Energy, Pauli's Exclusion Principle, Valency, Fermi Level, Electric Field, Semiconductor, Absolute Zero)

ENERGY DIAGRAM   This is a graphical representation of energy levels of atomic particles and an energy diagram is especially useful in understanding what goes on deep down in semiconductors. It is energy which enables the electron to act as it does and its energy level at any time tells us much about the electron's movements at that time. The energy is usually measured in electron-volts.

The best way of getting to grips with this type of diagram is by example, such as given in Energy Bands and Doping. An example of interpretation of an energy diagram is given under the heading P-N Junction.

(* Electron, Energy, Energy Bands, Energy Levels, Electron-Volt)

ENERGY LEVELS A body in orbit possesses kinetic energy depending on its mass and velocity and generally within an atom, the larger the orbit, the greater is the electron energy. This is referred to as the electron *energy level* or *state*. The energy levels required by the various shells have certain fixed values and for an electron to be within a particular orbit it must have exactly the energy associated with that orbit. Electrons cannot orbit between shells, only within, hence gaps between shells represent unusable energy levels and within the range of energy levels this gives rise to *forbidden energy gaps*. Thus if an electron gains energy from the force due to an electric field, it can jump from one orbit to the next higher but the energy increase must be exactly that required to satisfy the new orbit, i.e. there is a discrete amount of energy required. Once within another orbit the electron continues in it until it loses that same discrete amount of energy and falls to an orbit nearer the nucleus. Such discrete amounts of energy can also be supplied or given up as heat, light or radiation. The lowest possible energy level for an atom is known as the *ground state*, anything higher is known as an *excited state*.

A practical outcome of this phenomenon is the laser in which electrons are raised to higher energy levels by pumping energy in. They are then induced en masse to fall suddenly to the original level and in so doing each releases the discrete amount of energy in the form of light. With a sufficient number of electrons in action, a very short duration but intense beam of light is produced.

(* Atom, Electron, Orbit, Shell, Mass, Electric Field, Kinetic Energy, Laser)

ENVELOPE VELOCITY is the velocity at which a group of waves as a whole is propagated through a particular medium or over a line — see Group Velocity.

EXCITATION is a term used in several different spheres of electronics. In general excitation induces activity in a device, for example:

(1)   It is the provision of sufficient energy to an atom or molecule to raise one of its orbital electrons to a higher energy state

but without detaching it completely, i.e. without ionization. When this happens the atom is said to be *excited*.

(2)   The current which flows in an electromagnet is known as the *excitation current*.

(3)   It is the application of an input signal to the base of a transsistor or grid of a thermionic valve.

(4)   It is the application of a voltage to a crystal to start it oscillating or maintain it in oscillation. Also the application of periodic pulses to a radio frequency tuned circuit to maintain oscillations (e.g. from a Class C amplifier).

(5)   An antenna is said to be excited when radio frequency power is switched to it.

(* Atom, Molecule, Energy, Energy Levels, Ionization >> Electromagnet, Class C Amplifier)

EXCITED STATE refers to the energy possessed by an atom or molecule. The *ground state* is the lowest possible energy level, at any higher level the atom or molecule is said to be in an *excited state* − see Energy Levels.

EXTRINSIC SEMICONDUCTOR is one which has greater conductivity by virtue of the addition of an impurity − see Semiconductor, also Intrinsic Semiconductor.

FARAD is the S.I. unit of capacitance, symbol F, named after Michael Faraday (the English chemist and physicist). It is the capacitance of a capacitor between the plates of which there appears a difference of potential of one volt when it is charged by a quantity of electricity equal to one coulomb. It happens to be an inconveniently large unit so in practice the sub-multiples, microfarad (10^{-6} F), nanofarad (10^{-9} F) and picofarad (10^{-12} F) are more likely to be used.

(* S.I., Capacitance, Coulomb, Volt)

FARADAY CONSTANT has the symbol F and a value of 96 487 coulombs per mole (C/mol). It is the amount of charge required to deposit or liberate one mole of a univalent ion in electrolytic action. The constant is calculated from the fact that there are 6.023×10^{23} molecules per mole (Avogadro's constant) so with this number releasing one electron each and therefore themselves becoming positive charges of 1.602×10^{-19} coulombs, we have $(6.023 \times 10^{23}) \times (1.602 \times 10^{-19}) = 9.649 \times 10^4$ C/mol.
(* Electrolyte, Electron, Charge, Ion, Coulomb, Mole, Valency, Atomic Mass Unit)

FARADAY LAW OF ELECTROLYSIS states that in electrolytic action the mass of a substance deposited at one electrode or equally liberated from the other electrode varies (i) directly as the quantity of electricity, (ii) directly as the atomic weight of the substance deposited and (iii) inversely as its chemical valence. The Faraday electrolytic constant (Faraday constant) is the amount of charge required to liberate one mole of any univalent element and it is equal to 96 487 coulombs per mole.
(* Electrode, Electrolyte, Electrochemical Equivalent, Coulomb, Faraday Constant, Mole, Valency)

FARADAY'S LAW (after Michael Faraday, the English chemist and physicist). This is concerned with electromagnetic induction. It states that:

> "when the magnetic flux through a circuit is changing, an induced electromotive force (e.m.f.) is set up, the magnitude of which is proportional to the rate of change of flux."

Society owes much to Faraday for following his discovery in 1831, (i) generators which change the flux in a coil by rotating electromagnets past them and (ii) transformers which change the flux in a coil by varying the current in an adjacent coil, were developed. They still are the backbone of our electricity power systems.
(* Electromotive Force, Electromagnetism, Electromagnetic Induction, Magnetic Flux, Transformer >> Generator, Electromagnet)

FEEDBACK This refers to a system in which a fraction of the output voltage or current of a circuit (usually an amplifier) is returned to the input, just as an echo is a fraction of the voice returned to a talker. In the case of an amplifier the feedback may be applied back over the same or a preceding stage.

148

Feedback is used or exists in many electronics systems and in the case of amplifiers their performance in terms of gain stability, frequency response, distortion and noise can be greatly improved with it. However, feedback is not always applied to a circuit by a designer, it has a habit of turning up where it is not wanted due to stray reactances and efforts must then be made to reduce it.

There are two classes of feedback: *positive* in which the energy fed back augments the input signal and *negative* in which the feedback diminishes the input signal. Any feedback system can be represented as in Figure F1(i). The amplifier output voltage is connected to a feedback network which inserts a fraction of it in series with the input circuit. This fraction is normally designated by β. From the figure, $v_o = A \times v_i$ and v_o acting at terminals 1 and 2 of the β network results in a voltage βv_o at terminals 3 and 4. This in the circuit shown is added in series with the generator voltage v_s so that v_i now becomes $v_s + \beta v_o$. Hence now that feedback has been added:

$$v_o = A(v_s + \beta v_o)$$

from which,

$$A v_s = v_o - A\beta v_o = v_o(1 - A\beta)$$

so the modified amplifier gain is equal to:

$$\frac{v_o}{v_s} = \frac{A}{1 - \beta A} .$$

To maintain v_o at its original level (no feedback), v_s must therefore be increased.

This however is not the full story because it is possible that there will be phase shift through the amplifier varying with frequency. The feedback network may also contain reactive components, in fact sometimes deliberately introduced so that the gain/frequency characteristic of the amplifier is modified. Under these conditions the gain of the amplifier is quoted as $A \angle \theta$ meaning that its output is A times the input and the two differ in phase by the angle θ. Similarly the feedback network is described by $B \angle \phi$. Going through the same procedure as above:

$$\text{gain with feedback} = \frac{v_o}{v_s} = \frac{A \angle \theta}{1 - \beta A \angle (\theta + \phi)}$$

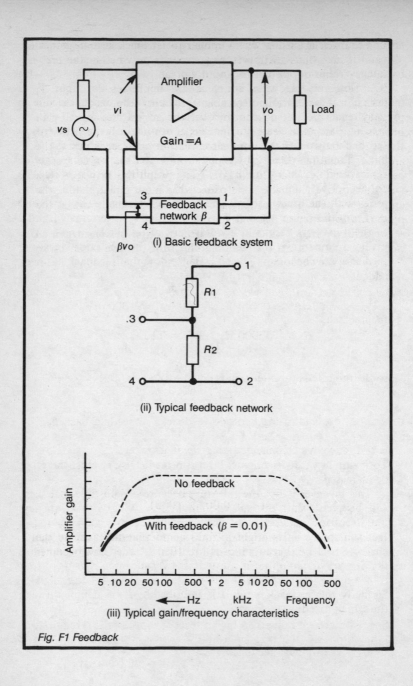

(i) Basic feedback system

(ii) Typical feedback network

(iii) Typical gain/frequency characteristics

Fig. F1 Feedback

an important relationship whcih applies to feedback systems generally and it is obvious that everything depends on whether the feedback voltage aids or opposes the input voltage.

Positive Feedback: when the feedback reinforces the input, v_i increases, v_o therefore increases and so does the feedback and provided that there is no control over the action, the overall gain increases. From the general equations above it can be seen that if the second term in the denominator reaches or exceeds unity, the amplifier gain theoretically becomes infinite and the whole system becomes unstable. Many oscillators function on this principle, in a way the positive feedback takes over as the input signal, that is, the amplifier supplies its own input and can therefore keep going at the particular frequency of instability.

Negative Feedback: it may be instructive first to consider practical values in a typical system employing non-reactive feedback so that we do not get lost in complex algebra. Let the feedback network be as shown in Figure F1(ii). Then let:

$$v_s = 10\,\text{mV}, \; A = 100 \; \text{so that} \; v_o = 1000\,\text{mV}$$

$$R_1 = 56000\,\Omega, \quad R_2 = 110\,\Omega$$

$$\therefore \quad \beta = -\frac{R_2}{R_1 + R_2} = -\frac{110}{56110} \simeq -0.002 \,,$$

the minus sign indicating *negative* feedback, so feeding back βv_o, i.e. $-0.002 \times 1000 = -2\,\text{mV}$.

With the feedback connected, the overall gain:

$$A_f = \frac{A}{1 - \beta A} = \frac{100}{1 - (-0.002 \times 1000)} = 83.3 \,.$$

To maintain v_o at its original value, v_s must be increased by the amount fed back so that v_i is restored to $10\,\text{mV}$, i.e. v_s now becomes $12\,\text{mV}$ and again:

$$A_f = v_o/v_s = 1000/12 = 83.3 \,.$$

So what have we gained? A higher level of input signal is required and the output signal is no greater but:

151

(i) *gain stability* – if βA is very much greater than 1, i.e. when A is high and β not too low, then the general equation reduces to $-1/\beta$, i.e. the gain is constant whatever happens inside the amplifier (e.g. change of transistor parameters with temperature). Clearly the greater the feedback, the greater the gain stability;

(ii) *reduction of non-linearity distortion and noise* – because a fraction of any distortion occurring within the amplifier is fed back, then after amplification it appears at the amplifier output in antiphase to the inherent distortion, thus tending to cancel it. It can be shown that the distortion component in the output is reduced by the factor $1/(1 - \beta A)$, hence if $\beta A \gg 1$ it is reduced approximately to $-1/\beta$. Internally generated amplifier noise is similarly affected;

(iii) *improved frequency response* – many amplifiers suffer from amplitude/frequency distortion with which the gain falls usually at the lower and upper ends of its frequency range as shown in Figure F1(iii). When feedback is applied, because it is proportional to the gain, there is less reduction of overall gain at the low and high frequencies, resulting typically in a "flatter" characteristic as also shown in the figure.

There are four methods of applying negative feedback to an amplifying system. The one shown in (i) of the figure is classed as *voltage output – series input*. The term is self-explanatory, the feedback network input terminals sense the amplifier output voltage and the network applies the desired fraction in series with the input. Alternatively a series input may be controlled by sensing the current in the output circuit. Similarly there is shunt input controlled by either the output voltage or current. In many types of transistor circuit, negative feedback is present although because it is not recognizable in the form of Figure F1(i), it is sometimes difficult to understand which of the four types it is.

In what is intended to be a negative feedback system it is possible for the feedback to become positive at certain frequencies with the attendant loss of stability. There are several techniques through which the degree of stability can be determined, particularly as developed by Nyquist and Bode.

The operational amplifier is one which has a very high gain and in use a large amount of feedback is applied to reduce this gain to that required. The amplifier is almost invariably an integrated circuit and the feedback network is connected externally.

(* Amplifier, Phase Angle, Phase Shift, Oscillator, Operational Amplifier, Nyquist Diagram, Bode Diagram >> Current Feedback, Regeneration, Acoustic Feedback)

FELICI MUTUAL INDUCTANCE BALANCE is a form of alternating current bridge used for measurement of mutual inductance. Its accuracy is mainly at the lower frequencies (e.g. audio) where winding capacitances are small. The basic circuit is shown in Figure F2 where M_x is the mutual inductance of the windings under test and M_s is the variable mutual inductance of a standard transformer.

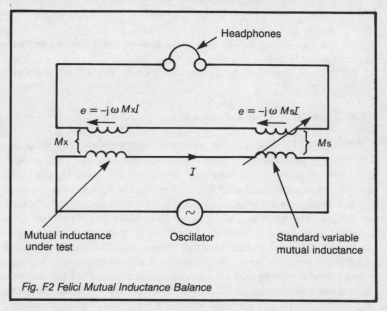

Fig. F2 Felici Mutual Inductance Balance

At balance the voltages developed in the headphones (or other suitable indicating instrument) are equal and produce a null. These two voltages for a current I in the oscillator circuit are $-j\omega M_x I$ and $-j\omega M_s I$ so for their sum to be zero,

$$M_x = -M_s .$$

See also Hartshorn Bridge.
(* Inductance, Bridge, Complex Notation)

FERMI – a length, 10^{-15} metres. Named in honour of the 20th century physicist, Enrico Fermi for his statistical analysis of atomic particles.

FERMI-DIRAC DISTRIBUTION   This is a statistical formula developed by Enrico Fermi and Paul Dirac during their work on quantum theory. They used a "free electron model" in an effort to explain the function of energy in electron movements. From the main form of the distribution it is possible to express the probability of a given energy level, E being occupied by an electron as:

$$f(E) = \frac{1}{\exp(E - \mu)^{kT} + 1}$$

where μ is a constant, k is Boltzmann's constant and T is the temperature in degrees Kelvin.
(* Electron, Energy Levels, Boltzmann's Constant, Thermodynamic Temperature)

FERMI ENERGY — see Fermi Level.

FERMI LEVEL De Broglie, in introducing his wave theory, showed that only certain electron orbits are possible and that to remain in any particular orbit an electron must possess exactly the right amount of energy for that orbit. From this it follows that because a wave motion is associated with each electron, the wave properties of the *free* electrons in a metal limit the values which their energies may take. Moreover, when electrons are in close proximity as they are within a metal, nearby atoms modify their behaviour in such a way that their energies change and what was previously a single energy level is spread out into a range of levels. Then Pauli stepped in and with his Exclusion Principle showed that only two electrons are permitted to occupy each of the energy states allowable. The result is therefore a cloud or gas of free electrons with energies spread over a range of levels and only two electrons at each level.

Enrico Fermi (an Italian-US physicist) first developed the statistics of free electrons and was able to show that the electrons occupy the lowest energy levels possible but since each level can only take two electrons, progressively higher levels must be occupied until all electrons are accommodated. The highest energy level which an electron can have at a temperature of absolute zero is known as the *Fermi energy* or *Fermi level*, E_F of the metal. From Fermi's work, E_F can be calculated:

$$E_F = \frac{h^2 (3N/8\pi)^{2/3}}{2m_e}$$

where N is the number of valence electrons per m^3, h is Planck's constant (6.626×10^{-34} J s), m_e is the electron mass (9.109×10^{-31} kg) and as an example, taking N for copper as 8.5×10^{28}, E_F works out to 1.13×10^{-18} J, i.e. 7.05 eV.

So far we have considered the Fermi level for a metal at a temperature of absolute zero. At higher temperatures the value is obtained from the *Fermi-Dirac distribution* which has temperature as one of its variables. It is the energy at which this distribution has a value of ½. Put in other words, at a given temperature, it is the energy of the state which has 50% probability of being occupied.

The theory indicates that those electrons which have energies approaching the Fermi level are the ones which effectively contribute to the conductivity of a metal. The concept of Fermi levels is very useful in conductivity calculations, especially with semiconductors.

(* de Broglie Waves, Pauli Exclusion Principle, Joule, Electron-Volt, Fermi-Dirac Distribution, Valency, Absolute Zero)

FERRIMAGNETISM is a magnetic effect found mainly in ferrites. The effect undergoes a fundamental change at a certain critical temperature known as the *Néel temperature, T_N*. In an *antiferromagnetic* material the magnetic moments of the ions are equal and with equal numbers aligned in opposite directions, they cancel out. However, if the magnetic moments are not all equal then pairs in opposition may exhibit some magnetisation, put more technically, there will be unpaired electron spins. In such a case the material is said to be *ferrimagnetic* and this is what occurs at temperatures below T_N. The material behaves similarly to a *ferromagnetic* material but with weaker magnetisation.

At temperatures above T_N thermal agitation breaks up the pairing and the magnetic moments are then aligned at random, consequently the material is magnetically weak i.e. *paramagnetic*.

Generally ferrimagnetic materials have high resistivity up to some 10^9 Ω m. This makes them suitable for transformer cores in which eddy current losses must be very small.

(* Ion, Antiferromagnetism, Ferromagnetism, Magnetisation, Mangetic Moment, Ferrite, Paramagnetism, Resistivity, Spin, Transformer, Eddy Current)

FERROELECTRICITY Polarization is normally created in a dielectric material when an electric field is applied (see Figs. D3 and D7). However, some materials exhibit polarization even when no electric field is present, explained in simple terms as being due to the alignment of the dipoles by an *internal* field. It so happens that the dielectric polarization mirrors some of the features of ferromagnetic materials especially in that the curve of displacement v electric field strength shows hysteresis (see Fig.M3), hence the term *ferroelectrics*. The phenomenon of spontaneous polarization disappears in all ferroelectrics when heated above a certain critical temperature.

Rochelle salt is an organic ferroelectric material, other inorganic ones include potassium dihydrogen phosphate (KDP) and barium titanate. Ferroelectric materials may be used in heat sensors because the polarization varies with temperature and in miniature variable capacitors, by making use of their high permittivities which vary with applied electric field. They also exhibit piezoelectric properties. (* Electric Field, Electric Polarization, Ferromagnetism, Displacement, Permittivity, Dipole, Hysteresis, Capacitor, Piezoelectric Effect, Piezoelectric Crystal >> Ceramic)

FERROMAGNETISM occurs usually in metals and for these the relative permeability is greater than 1, up to many thousands. The relative permeability, μ_r can be used as a guide to the effect of a magnetizing field on a material. (We have to be careful in this particular case however with the simple idea of using μ_r as a guide because it varies with the field applied). In ferromagnetic materials the magnetization is in such a direction as to aid the applied field and a typical use of such a material is in the core of an electromagnetic relay where the iron or other metal core enables a magnetic flux to be set up very much greater than that which would be obtained with an air core. The maximum relative permeabilities for some typical materials are, pure iron and silicon iron, 7–8000, cast iron, 90, cobalt and nickel, 50–60.

If the temperature of the material is raised sufficiently, an abrupt change occurs in the characteristics of the material, it no longer is ferromagnetic but changes to *paramagnetic*, i.e. μ_r falls to just over 1. The temperature is known as the *Curie Point*. As an example, for iron the Curie point is about 870°C.

It is considered that in ferromagnetic materials the electron spin axes are aligned parallel to each other and that the material is formed of microscopic *magnetic domains*, each of which has a net overall magnetization. Normally the domains lie randomly hence the material itself is not magnetic. However, when a magnetic field is applied, the domains easily line up with the field so resulting in high magnetization.

Ferromagnetic materials are classed as either *hard* or *soft*, generally hard material have high coercivity (the magnetism is not easily removed), high remanence (remaining magnetism) and relatively low permeability (magnetisation for a given applied field strength). They are especially useful for the manufacture of permanent magnets. In such materials magnetic domain rotation into alignment with the applied field is relatively difficult. There is some relationship between magnetic and mechanical hardness e.g. in chromium steel and carbon steel. Many other special alloys have hard magnetic properties, usually containing mixtures of one or more of iron, chromium, aluminium, nickel or cobalt. *Ferrites* are also used, these are prepared by sintering and firing iron, barium, or other oxide powders which at the same time are pressed into the shape required. Again the technique aims at producing magnetic domains which cannot easily revert to the random state.

Soft ferromagnetic materials have low coercivity, fairly low remanence and high permeability, i.e. they are easily magnetised and demagnetised and have low hysteresis loss. These characteristics make such materials suitable for applications involving alternating magnetic flux, e.g. in generators, transformers, electric motors. The ease of magnetisation and demagnetisation implies that the magnetic domains are readily brought into alignment with an applied magnetic field and that the alignment is easily destroyed, i.e. little energy is required to turn them. Materials used are iron and certain iron alloys (especially with silicon, nickel and cobalt).

See also Paramagnetism, Diamagnetism.

(* Magnetism, Magnetisation, Magnetic Field, Permeability, Coercivity, Remanence, Domain, Antiferromagnetism, Core, Magnetic Hysteresis, Spin >> Relay, Generator, Electric Motor)

F.E.T.   Abbreviation of Field-Effect Transistor — see this term.

FIELD   A field can be described in various ways, for example, as a sphere of influence or as something in space which has the potential to create some sort of a force. The one we all know so well is the *field of gravity* and it may be difficult to appreciate what power lurks in the air around us, but jump up and that force immediately pulls us back down again. Other equally invisible, intangible fields are those of radio transmissions, the force they are capable of exerting, although infinitely smaller than that of gravity, can vibrate electrons in an antenna (aerial) as a radio or tv set will prove. Each type of field affects certain objects only, e.g. gravity produces a force on anything which has mass (which is just about everything), a magnetic field acts on certain metals but an electric field affects other electric charges only, nothing else.

We know so little about what a field is but we do understand what it can do.

(* Force, Charge, Magnetic Field, Electrostatic Field >> Free Field)

FIELD-EFFECT TRANSISTOR (F.E.T.) The word "transistor" on its own usually implies a bipolar device (both positive and negative carriers). The f.e.t. operates on a somewhat different principle, it is based on both p-type and n-type semiconductors but the current path is wholly through one type. It is therefore classed as *unipolar*. N-type material is more commonly used for the current path because the mobility of its carriers (electrons) is higher than that for p-type (holes). This type is known as *n-channel* and the reason for the term "channel" will be seen from Figure F3(i) which shows a typical cross section of the device. Electrons flow from *source* to *drain* (somewhat analogous to emitter and collector in the bipolar transistor) along the bar of lightly doped n-type material under the influence of the V_{ds} battery. On the upper and lower surfaces of the bar are diffused high density p-type layers which produce p-n junctions with their attendant depletion layers. These are connected in parallel and form the *gate* electrode. As the figure shows, the depletion layers spread well into the bar leaving only a narrow *channel* of unaffected n-type material through the centre. This type is correctly known as a *junction f.e.t.* (j.f.e.t.) or *junction gate f.e.t.* (j.u.g.f.e.t.).

The potential V_{gs} connected between source and gate reverse biases the p-n junctions and the magnitude of this potential clearly affects the depth of penetration of the depletion layers, hence the width of the unaffected channel. Since the d.c. potential rises positively from source to drain, the depletion layers are not of constant width but increase on the drain side because the potential between p and n is greater there. We can therefore imagine the shape of the depletion layer to be as shown in the figure.

As V_{gs} becomes more negative, the effective width of the channel decreases, the channel resistance increases and electron flow, i.e. the drain current I_d, falls. Overall therefore a relatively large current is dominated by a small voltage. Here is the important difference compared with the bipolar transistor, the f.e.t. control is by application of an electric field, set up by an extremely small current. Accordingly the gate resistance is very high (in the megohm range), a desirable property for applications where the device must absorb practically no power from its input circuit.

V_{gs} can be increased to the extent that the depletion layers expand sufficiently to meet whereupon the channel is constricted almost to closure. I_d is then extremely small and very nearly independent of drain-source voltage. The value of V_{gs} at which this occurs is known as the *pinch-off* voltage.

P-channel f.e.t.'s are based on similar principles and the f.e.t. can therefore be summed up as being a unipolar device with output

158

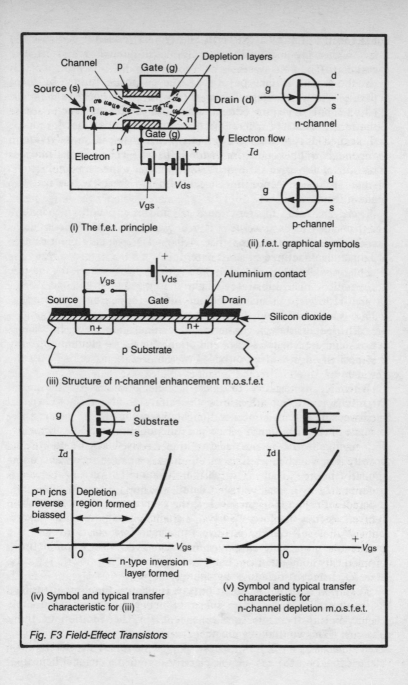

(i) The f.e.t. principle

(ii) f.e.t. graphical symbols

(iii) Structure of n-channel enhancement m.o.s.f.e.t

(iv) Symbol and typical transfer characteristic for (iii)

(v) Symbol and typical transfer characteristic for n-channel depletion m.o.s.f.e.t.

Fig. F3 Field-Effect Transistors

characteristics similar to those of the bipolar transistor but with a much higher input impedance. Graphical symbols are given in Figure F3(ii).

In the second main type of f.e.t. the channel is formed by the action of the gate voltage. It is known as an *insulated gate* f.e.t. (i.g.f.e.t.) but there are several other names also in general use. Because the structure consists of successive layers of metal, oxide and semiconductor (m.o.s.), an alternative name is *metal-oxide-semiconductor field-effect transistor* or *m.o.s.f.e.t.*, for short m.o.s. transistor is also used or even m.o.s.t. Usually the semiconductor material is silicon hence m.o.s. can also be interpreted as metal-oxide-silicon.

There are four different kinds of m.o.s.f.e.t., both n-channel and p-channel in *enhancement* and *depletion* modes. We consider n-channel only on the basis that p-channel are equally practicable although manufactured to a less extent.

Enhancement-type m.o.s.f.e.t.: Figure F3(iii) shows the basic construction. The substrate is lightly doped p-type and therefore of high resistivity. A silicon dioxide film is formed on the surface, windows are etched and through these two heavily doped n regions are diffused as shown. Aluminium contacts are made to these regions and are labelled source and drain. Finally an aluminium film is deposited on the silicon dioxide between source and drain to form the gate.

When V_{gs} is negative the electric field generated by the gate attracts holes from within the p substrate to the surface, hence increases the p-type concentration between the two n^+ layers (n^+ indicates heavy n doping). Two p-n junctions are therefore formed, V_{gs} maintains the left-hand one in a reverse-biassed condition, equally V_{ds} which is positive at the drain keeps the right-hand one similarly biased. There is virtually no channel between source and drain and $I_d = 0$. On the other hand, when V_{gs} is slightly positive, a depletion region is formed below the gate because the holes in the p-type substrate are forced away. A channel is not created however until V_{gs} is sufficiently positive to attract free electrons to the interface and so create an n-type *inversion layer*. Now a conducting channel exists and drain current flows. Figure F3(iv) shows a typical transfer characteristic and the graphic symbol.

Depletion-type m.o.s.f.e.t.: this type is manufactured by diffusing an n-type channel into the substrate between source and drain. Figure F3(iii) therefore applies except for the addition of this channel. This continuous channel therefore allows current to flow even when $V_{gs} = 0$. If however V_{gs} is increased negatively the electric field on the gate repels electrons from the channel beneath it, so inducing a positive charge and in effect converting the channel to p-type whereupon the two p-n junctions move into reverse bias. With V_{gs} sufficiently negative, the drain current is cut off as shown in (v) of the figure.

It is mentioned above that n-channel devices are generally preferable to p-channel. A major factor in this is that the mobility of electrons is more than double that of holes. From this it follows that any n-channel device needs less than half the area of an equivalent p-channel for the same drain current. In integrated circuits therefore the packing density of n-channel is higher.

(* Electric Field, Semiconductor, Transistor, Doping, Mobility, Bias, P-N Junction, Inversion Layer >> Planar Process, Integrated Circuit, MOS Integrated Circuit, Common-Gate . . . Source . . . Drain Connections, y-Parameters)

FIELD EMISSION   If in a high vacuum tube an electric field of sufficient magnitude is maintained between a cathode an anode up to 10^9 to 10^{10} volts per metre (V/m), then the potential barrier at the surface of the cathode due to the space charge will be reduced. When the barrier becomes thin enough (around 10^{-8} m), electrons are able to escape by tunnelling through. This is known as *field emission* and the current depends on field strength rather than on temperature.   The emitted current density (J) conforms approximately to:

$$J = CE^2 \exp(-D/E)$$

(the Fowler-Nordheim equation) where E is the electric field strength and C and D are constants for the particular material (D is determined mainly by the work function). Emission currents are of the order of microamperes.

Because the very strong electric fields exist mainly at points on the cathode surface, field emission must be taken into account in the design of very high voltage apparatus. On the other hand the effect is found useful in the *field emission microscope* in which electrons from field emission from the tip of a single crystal are projected onto a screen. The various intensities in the image are an indication of the work functions at different areas on the crystal tip.

(* Electric Field, Electric Field Strength, Emission, Anode, Cathode, Space Charge, Schottky Effect, Tunnel Effect, Work Function)

FILTER   This is an electrical network which when presented at the input with a range of frequencies, attenuates certain ones but not others. The range of frequencies passed by a filter is known as

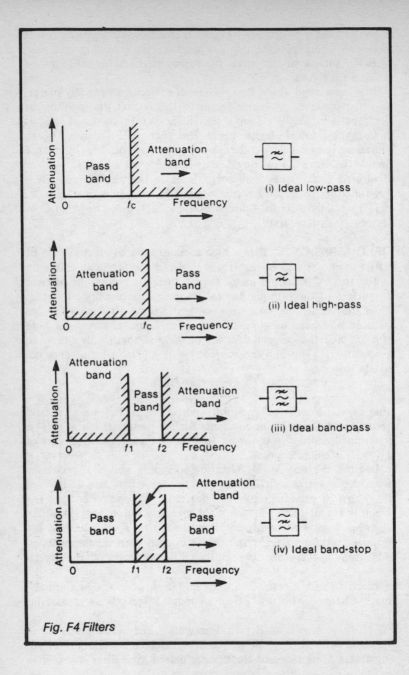

Fig. F4 Filters

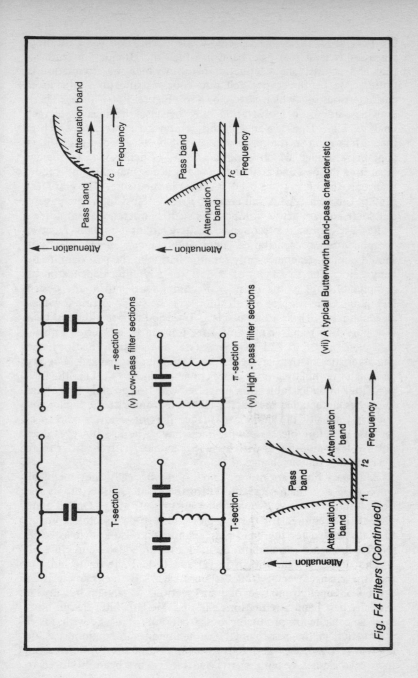

(v) Low-pass filter sections

π-section

T-section

(vi) High-pass filter sections

π-section

T-section

Attenuation band

Pass band

f_c Frequency

Pass band

Attenuation band

f_c Frequency

(vii) A typical Butterworth band-pass characteristic

Attenuation band

Pass band

Attenuation band

f_1 f_2 Frequency

Fig. F4 Filters (Continued)

the *pass band*, the range rejected is the *attenuation band*. A filter possesses at least one pass band in which the attenuation tends to zero and at least one attenuation band in which the attenuation is finite. Most filter types fall into four classifications, the *ideal* characteristics of which are shown in Figure F4(i)–(iv). These drawings are for demonstration only because the ideal is in fact unattainable. One reason for this is easy to appreciate which is that attenuation in the pass band cannot be zero because all filters contain resistance which creates a loss. Generally the frequency separating the pass and attenuation bands is designated f_c but if more than one, then f_1, f_2 are used as shown in the figure. The graphical symbol for each type is shown to the right. Most filters are passive but some contain active components such as operational amplifiers.

Because a filter is a frequency sensitive circuit it contains reactive components, i.e. capacitance and/or inductance. In fact ideally it should contain reactance only for attenuation in the pass band to be truly zero. The sharpness of cut-off for any filter depends on its complexity both in the number of components and in the design technique. The simplest of all filters are the single-section low-pass and high-pass. These are available as T-section or π-section as shown in Figure F4(v) and (vi). Any T-section can be converted into its equivalent π-section and vice versa (star-delta transformation), the characteristics of the particular filter remaining unchanged. For any design the terminating impedances must be known. Taking the low-pass filter as an example, in a simplified way it is possible to see that the series inductance presents a higher reactance at the higher frequencies, equally the shunt capacitance presents a lower reactance, the loss therefore increases with frequency. The loss however does not increase smoothly as with a single reactance, with the filter there is a relatively sudden change at f_c.

Band-pass filters are more complicated. Basically they might be considered as a high-pass filter cutting off at f_1 [see (iii) of the figure] followed by a low-pass filter cutting off at f_2. Only 3 components are required for the low-pass and high-pass sections but up to 6 are needed for the band-pass. Band-stop (also known as *band-reject*) filters are less commonly used and are equally complicated.

The simple designs shown in (v) and (vi) of the figure indicate that the change-over at f_c is far from ideal. Better characteristics can be obtained from two or more sections in tandem but in this case the pass band attenuations add up. Modern filter design however is capable of producing a sharper cut-off at f_c with lower attenuation in the pass band. Two techniques in common use are known as *Chebyshev* and *Butterworth*. From the formulae from these two design systems charts and tables have been produced to ease the mass of calculations required in design. Typically a Butterworth band-pass filter would have a response as shown in Figure F4(vii). The sharpness of cut-off is clearly superior to that of the single sections shown in (v) and (vi).

(* Frequency, Attenuation, Reactance, Star-Delta Transformation, Cut-Off Frequency, Coupled Circuits >> Constant-k Filter, m-Derived Filter, Crystal Filter, Operational Amplifier)

FIRST IONIZATION POTENTIAL is the minimum energy required to remove one electron only from the outermost shell of an atom or a molecule (theoretically to infinity) — see Ionization Potential.

FLEMING'S RULES   In the electrical workshop there is occasionally the need to determine for example, the direction of motion of an electric motor or the direction of current in a generator. John Ambrose Fleming (an English electrical engineer and physicist) developed a set of rules which provide us with a handy way of linking current, magnetic flux and motion. Fortunately these are mutually at right angles. The rules assume conventional current flow (positive to negative) and as shown in Figure F5, the thumb

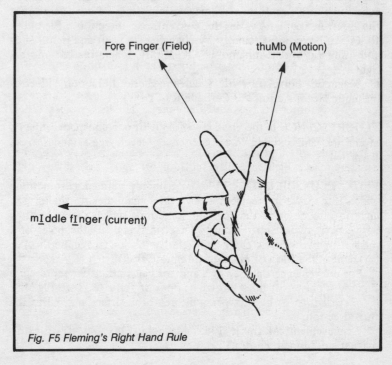

Fore Finger (Field)   thuMb (Motion)

mIddle fInger (current)

Fig. F5 Fleming's Right Hand Rule

and first two fingers of the hand are used and these are extended mutually at right angles to suit. A right hand is shown in the figure but the left hand is also used in the same manner. The remaining two fingers of the hand are not used.

The right hand is used to determine the direction of the induced e.m.f. or current in a generator as shown. If the forefinger is placed in the direction of the magnetic field and the thumb in the direction of motion of the conductor, then the middle finger indicates the direction of current in the conductor. Thus given the directions of any two of these, the direction of the third is indicated.

The left hand is for motors and the indications for each finger are the same so for example, knowing the current and field directions, the direction of motion of the conductor is given.

It is especially important to remember that current direction is "conventional" and field direction is that in which a "free" N-pole would move. A suitable mnemonic is the word GRuMbLe, generators right, motors left.

However we may wish to be more up-to-date and work on the basis that current flow is usually by electrons and therefore from negative to positive. A good example arises from the cathode-ray tube for by no stretch of the imagination can it be considered that the electron beam flows in the conventional direction. Fleming's Rules can be modified simply by changing over left and right hands and using a different mnemonic, GLaMouR, generators left, motors right.

(* Magnetic Flux, Current, Electromagnetic Induction, Electromagnetic Motor Action >> Cathode-Ray Tube)

FLUORESCENCE is the emission of light from a phosphor while its atoms are being excited to a higher energy level —see Luminescence, Persistence.

FLUX, FLUX DENSITY   Flux is generally defined as something which flows. We in electronics have three main uses for the term in an effort to describe that certain something which seems to flow between (i) two electric charges (electric flux), (ii) the poles of a magnet or two electric charges in relative motion (magnetic flux) or (iii) light in the form of photons (luminous flux).

For convenience on drawings and for calculations we represent a flux by a cluster of lines known as *lines of force* (e.g. see Fig.M2).

Flux density is the flux per unit area of a surface normal to the flux direction.

(* Displacement, Magnetic Flux, Magnetic Flux Density, Electromagnetism, Lumen, Photon)

FM (f.m.)   Abbreviation of Frequency Modulation — see this term.

FORBIDDEN BAND is a band of energy levels on an energy level diagram which electrons are not permitted to have. Figure E12 is such a diagram and in (ii), (iv) and (v) the forbidden bands are indicated. Generally forbidden bands lie in between the valence and conduction bands. Electrons with energy levels appropriate to the valence band can only be excited to the conduction band if sufficient energy is supplied for them to be able to jump the forbidden band energy-wise. In (v) of Figure E12 for example, a valence band electron needs more than 5 eV of energy for it to be freed for conduction, i.e. to have an energy level appropriate to the conduction band. In this particular case supplies of energy of less than 5 eV are not acceptable. See also Allowed Band.
(* Energy, Energy Bands, Energy Levels, Electron-Volt, Valency)

FORCE is Nature's tool for moving things around. It can be explained not by what it is but by what it does and is defined as "that which changes the state of rest or of motion of a body". Changing velocity implies acceleration which obviously depends on the force applied, hence:

$$\text{acceleration } (a) \propto \text{force } (F)$$

However, the greater the mass of a body, the greater is its inertia (the opposition it puts up to having its velocity changed), hence:

$$\text{acceleration} \propto 1/\text{mass} .$$

Sir Isaac Newton, the English physicist and mathematician put this together in his "Second Law of Motion", saying that: "Force is equal to mass multiplied by acceleration", so

$$F = m \times a \text{ newtons}$$

where m is the mass in kilograms and a, the acceleration in metres per second per second (m/s^2).

Although force would appear to be more proper to the study of mechanics, it is also of major importance in electronics. This is because it is the force provided by an electric field which increases the acceleration and hence the energy of an electron. Energy is the vital component in our use of the electron as electricity.
(* Mass, Newton, Field, Energy)

FORCED OSCILLATION   When an electrical or mechanical system which is capable of oscillation or vibration is given the chance to do so by the input of a short duration burst of energy, the oscillation dies away because of energy losses. This is *free oscillation* and for the electrical circuit it runs at its *natural frequency:*

$$f_r = \frac{1}{2\pi \sqrt{LC}} \quad \text{Hz}$$

where L is the inductance in henries and C, the capacitance in farads.

The circuit or system can be made to vibrate however at a frequency other than the natural frequency by coupling it to an oscillator, this is then *forced oscillation* which occurs at the oscillator frequency although within the circuit there is a small natural frequency component. When forced and natural frequencies are the same, the current is maximum.

(* Oscillation, Free Oscillation, Resonance Frequency, Damping, Oscillator >> Shock Excitation)

FORM FACTOR is a feature of an alternating waveform. It gives the relationship between the root mean square (r.m.s.) value and the mean value of a positive or negative half cycle and is helpful in describing the shape of a waveform, especially when used in conjunction with the *peak factor*. For a sinusoidal waveform the r.m.s. value is $V_{max}/\sqrt{2}$ where V_{max} is the maximum voltage of the wave. The mean value, $V_{av} = 2V_{max}/\pi$, hence:

$$\text{form factor} = \frac{\text{r.m.s. value}}{\text{mean value}} = \frac{\pi}{2\sqrt{2}} = 1.11 \ .$$

For a square waveform both the r.m.s. value and the mean value are equal to V_{max}, the form factor is therefore 1.0.

See also Peak Factor.

(* Alternating Current, Waveform, Sine Wave, Square Wave, Root Mean Square)

FORWARD DIRECTION applies to electronic devices and is the direction in which the device has a lower resistance compared with the opposite direction. A voltage applied so that the device operates in the forward direction is known as a *forward bias* and the current it produces is the *forward current*. These terms are especially used with diodes [see Fig.P10(iii) and (iv)].

See also Reverse Direction.

(* Diode)

FORWARD TRANSFER ADMITTANCE – see Mutual Conductance

FOURIER ANALYSIS (HARMONIC ANALYSIS) deals with complex waveforms which are periodic, i.e. they recur regularly and therefore have a fundamental frequency. There is a multiplicity of such waves but by considering only a few of the regular and well known ones it is possible to understand the basic idea of waveform analysis. The technique arises from a theorem published by Jean Baptiste Joseph Fourier (a French mathematician and physicist) regarding "continuous periodic functions", meaning continuous waves with all cycles the same (we could hardly analyse a wave which varies from cycle to cycle).

Basically Fourier's theorem states that such waveforms can be expressed as the sum of a number of *sine* waves, each with different amplitude and frequency. It is perhaps difficult for use to appreciate that the square wave which is so angular consists of nothing more than smooth sine waves but this is easily proved both mathematically and graphically. Fourier of course used more advanced mathematics than we have at our disposal, hence this excursion into his techniques must be limited mainly to stating his results rather than deriving them.

In essence, Fourier's theorem states that any continuous periodic function can be expressed as the sum of a number of sine waves of differing frequency, amplitude and relative phase. For example, in voltage terms:

$$e = c + E_1 \sin(\omega t + \phi_1) + E_2 \sin(2\omega t + \phi_2) +$$

$$+ E_3 \sin(3\omega t + \phi_3) + \ldots$$

where c is a constant which can be shown to be the mean value of the wave over one cycle, E_1, E_2 etc. are the maximum values of the various components and ϕ_1, ϕ_2 etc. are the phase angles.

This can be reduced to a general expression:

$$e = c + a_1 \sin \omega t + a_2 \sin 2\omega t + a_3 \sin 3\omega t + \ldots$$

$$+ b_1 \cos \omega t + b_2 \cos 2\omega t + b_3 \cos 3\omega t + \ldots$$

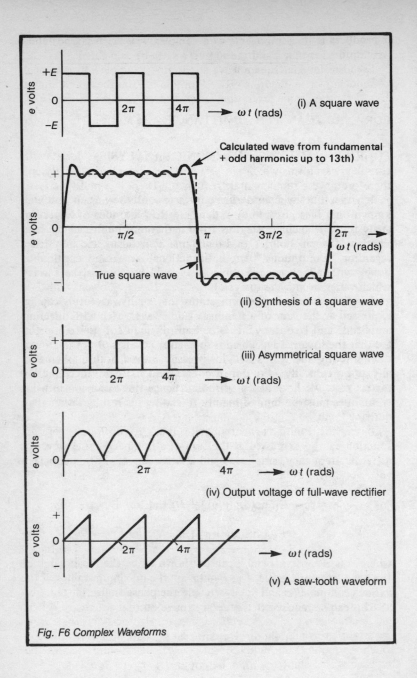

Fig. F6 Complex Waveforms

and with this the components of a complex waveform can be determined provided that c and the a's and b's can be calculated.

Take the familiar square wave as the first example. Its graphical form is shown in Figure F6(i). For this $c = 0$ (the graph shows that the mean value over one cycle is zero). Also $a_1 = 4E/\pi$, $a_2 = 0$, $a_3 = 4E/3\pi$, $a_4 = 0$, $a_5 = 4E/5\pi$ . . . with all b terms = 0. Hence:

$$e = \frac{4E}{\pi}\left(\sin \omega t + \frac{1}{3}\sin 3\omega t + \frac{1}{5}\sin 5\omega t + \ldots\right) \text{ volts}$$

from which it is evident that a square wave consists of a fundamental wave of the same frequency plus all the odd harmonics to infinity with amplitude decreasing as the harmonic number increases. Graphically this can be checked by first calculating the amplitude of each of these waves then adding them together over half or a complete cycle. Figure F6(ii) shows the result when the fundamental plus all odd harmonics up to the 13th are involved. This is a rewarding pictorial representation for it clearly shows how the square wave is forming. Obviously adding the 15th and onwards harmonics will complete the job. Fourier analysis is therefore not just a mathematical concept but is proved in practice.

This is for a square wave symmetrical about the time axis. For an asymmetrical wave as shown in (iii) of the figure, the change is simply that c is now equal to $E/2$. The coefficients a and b have the same values as for the symmetrical wave.

For a full-wave rectifier output as in (iv), $c = 2E/\pi$ and:

$$e = \frac{2E}{\pi} - \frac{4E}{\pi}\left[\frac{\cos 2\omega t}{3} + \frac{\cos 4\omega t}{15} + \frac{\cos 6\omega t}{35} + \ldots\right] \text{ volts.}$$

For a saw-tooth waveform as in (v), $c = 0$ and:

$$e = \frac{2E}{\pi}\left[\sin \omega t - \frac{\sin 2\omega t}{2} - \frac{\sin 3\omega t}{3} - \frac{\sin 4\omega t}{4} - \ldots\right] \text{ volts.}$$

Unquestionably such analysis is extremely useful in practice especially the conclusion that any distortion of a sine wave generates harmonics. More at home perhaps is the fact that it is important in the design of electronic music generators for knowing which harmonics are required for a particular sound enables the required waveform shape to be determined.

171

(* Sine Wave, Square Wave, Periodic, Fundamental Frequency, Harmonic)

FREE ELECTRON is one which is not bound to an atom or molecule and is therefore available for conduction. Its energy is entirely kinetic.
(* Electron, Atom, Molecule, Kinetic Energy)

FREE OSCILLATION occurs when an electrical resonant circuit or mechanical system receives a short-duration input of energy and is then left to oscillate on its own. A mechanical example is given by a weight suspended on a coiled spring. If the weight is pulled down and then released it bobs up and down, in other words the system

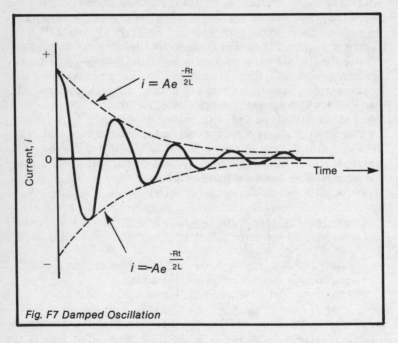

Fig. F7 *Damped Oscillation*

of springs plus weight oscillates at its natural frequency. If for example, in a resonant circuit the capacitor is first charged and then allowed to discharge through the inductance, the circuit oscillates at its own natural frequency. In all such free oscillations, damping by, for example friction in mechanical systems or resistance in electrical circuits, progressively reduces the amplitude of the vibration. An example is shown in Figure F7. It so happens that the actual frequency of oscillation is affected slightly by the degree of damping but provided that the resistance is not too large compared with the inductance ($R^2/4L^2$ should be low), we can use the general formula for the frequency of resonance:

$$f_r = \frac{1}{2\pi\sqrt{LC}} \text{ Hz}$$

where L is the inductance in henries and C the capacitance in farads.

The decay of free oscillations follows a curve given by:

$$i = Ae^{-(Rt/2L)}$$

where A is a constant for the particular circuit conditions and i is the current at time, t.

Such a curve is shown in Figure F7 from which it is evident that the rate of decay for a given oscillatory circuit is controlled solely by the resistance, R.

(* Oscillation, Resonance, Resonant Circuit, Damping, Damping Factor, Logarithmic Decrement)

FREE SPACE means just that, a vacuum free not only of air but everything else. This implies that no gravitational or electromagnetic fields can be present hence truly free space is not attainable. We use it as an absolute standard in many theoretical calculations and it can be shown to possess an electric constant (ϵ_0, the *permittivity* of free space) and a magnetic constant (μ_0, the *permeability* of free space). From these two constants the intrinsic impedance of free space, Z_0 is derived as follows:

$$Z_0 = \sqrt{\mu_0/\epsilon_0} = 120\pi = 377 \ \Omega \text{ (non reactive).}$$

(* Field, Permittivity, Permeability, Intrinsic Impedance)

FREQUENCY is the number of complete cycles of a periodically varying quantity occurring in a specified time. The unit is the *hertz* (after Heinrich Hertz, a German physicist) which is equal to one cycle in one second. A wave having a frequency of f hertz therefore completes f cycles in each second.

"Frequency" is often the term employed to denote a particular wave, i.e. instead of quoting "a wave of frequency f", the expression used is "a frequency of f".

(* Cycle, Harmonic, Period)

173

FREQUENCY BAND is simply the range of frequencies between any pair of specified limits. There is also an internationally agreed classification of frequency bands as shown below. The *band number* is the exponent of 10 used in converting the range 0.3 − 3 Hz to that required, e.g. band number n covers the range 0.3×10^n to 3×10^n Hz (these band numbers should not be confused with those used for television). The upper limit is included in each band, the lower limit is excluded.

Band No.	Frequency Range	Description	Letter Designation	Metric Subdivision (Waves)
4	3–30 kHz	Very Low Frequency	VLF	Myriametric
5	30–300 kHz	Low Frequency	LF	Kilometric
6	300 kHz – 3 MHz	Medium Frequency	MF	Hectometric
7	3–30 MHz	High Frequency	HF	Decametric
8	30–300 MHz	Very High Frequency	VHF	Metric
9	300 MHz – 3 GHz	Ultra High Frequency	UHF	Decimetric
10	3–30 GHz	Super High Frequency	SHF	Centimetric
11	30–300 GHz	Extremely High Frequency	EHF	Millimetric

(* Frequency, Wavelength)

FREQUENCY DEVIATION   A term used in frequency modulation techniques. It is the maximum variation in frequency for a particular system — see Frequency Modulation.

FREQUENCY CHANGING is the process by which a circuit changes the carrier frequency of a modulated wave without change to the modulation. Most frequency changing is to a lower carrier frequency because lower frequencies are easier to handle. In superheterodyne receivers the frequency changer transfers the modulation of all incoming signals to a lower intermediate frequency. In a broadcasting satellite it is essential that the signals arriving from the ground station do not interfere with those going back down, accordingly a frequency changer is employed to make the change but with the modulation still intact.

Such a device relies on the fact that if a signal frequency f_s is mixed with a higher oscillator frequency f_o in a non-linear device then two additional frequencies are produced, $(f_o + f_s)$ and $(f_o − f_s)$, the sum and difference. One of these is rejected by a filter, say, $(f_o + f_s)$. This leaves $(f_o − f_s)$ which is the required difference frequency. We can go one stage further by considering

174

that f_s is really a carrier frequency, f_c with its sidebands $(f_c \pm f_m)$ where f_m represents a *band* of modulating frequencies. On mixing there will be sum and difference frequencies of f_c, $(f_c + f_m)$ and $(f_c - f_m)$ so when these terms are included in the basic equation for a non-linear element and this equation is expanded (see Mixer), it all gets rather complicated. Ultimately however, after filtering we can be left with:

$$f_{nc}, \ (f_{nc} + f_m), \ (f_{nc} - f_m)$$

and with the reminder that f_m represents a band of modulating frequencies, this indicates a modulated wave centred on f_{nc} where f_{nc} is the new carrier frequency. As an example, an incoming radio frequency, $904 - 914$ kHz centred on 909 kHz (i.e. 909 ± 5 kHz) can be converted to $465 - 475$ kHz centred on 470 kHz by mixing with an oscillator frequency of 1379 kHz and selecting only the lower sideband. 470 kHz would be the intermediate frequency of a superheterodyne receiver and the original modulation will have passed through the process unchanged.

(* Superheterodyne Reception, Modulation, Filter, Intermediate Frequency, Oscillator >> Mixer, Radio Receiver)

FREQUENCY DISTORTION – see Attenuation/Frequency Distortion.

FREQUENCY MODULATION (F.M.) is a modulation technique in which the frequency of a carrier wave is varied according to the amplitude of the modulating wave and at its frequency. An f.m. wave therefore has constant amplitude but varying frequency. In radio and line systems interference voltages produce amplitude modulated waves so f.m., being insensitive to amplitude changes has the great advantage over amplitude modulation that it is unaffected by these. On the other hand, f.m. requires a greater bandwidth.

The constant amplitude and variation in frequency can be seen from Figure F8(i) which is drawn as an illustrative but hardly practical example. Here the carrier wave has an unmodulated frequency of 250 kHz with a plus or minus 100 kHz *frequency deviation* (Δf – also called the *frequency swing*) as the modulating frequency varies between its positive and negative maximum levels. The maximum frequency deviation (Δf_{max}) is chosen by the system designer so because this is related to the maximum modulating frequency amplitude, the frequency *deviation* at any instant is equal to $\Delta f_{max} \sin \omega_m t$ where the modulating wave is expressed mathematically as in the figure. Accordingly at any instant the frequency

175

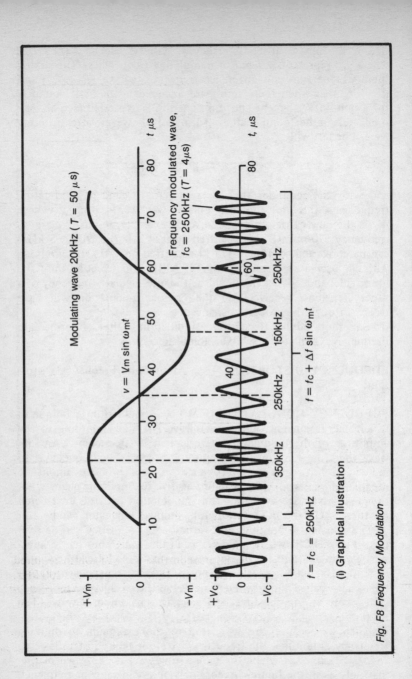

Fig. F8 Frequency Modulation

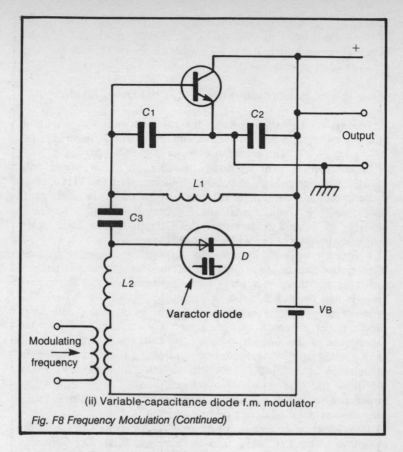

(ii) Variable-capacitance diode f.m. modulator

Fig. F8 Frequency Modulation (Continued)

of the modulated wave is given by:

$$f = f_c + \Delta f_{max} \sin \omega_m t \text{ Hz}$$

where f_c is the carrier frequency.

The figure may give the impression that the bandwidth required for the particular waves shown is from $150 - 350$ kHz, i.e. 200 kHz. However, this ignores the fact that when a sine wave is changing in frequency, the individual cycles become stretched out or cramped, i.e. they are no longer sine waves. As Fourier shows us, harmonics are therefore generated. Some of the higher ones can be left out and so we arrive at a general formula:

$$\text{approx. system bandwidth} = 2(\Delta f_{max} + f_{m(max)})$$

where $f_{m(max)}$ is the highest modulating frequency.

We can see what this means by considering practical f.m. radio broadcasting in which $f_{m(max)}$ might be some 15 kHz for high quality audio. In this case Δf_{max} is about 75 kHz, hence:

approx. system bandwidth $= 2(75 + 15) = 180$ kHz.

The system *deviation ratio* is the ratio between the maximum frequency deviation and the maximum modulation frequency, i.e. $\Delta f_{max}/f_{m(max)}$. The *modulation index* is given by $\Delta f/f_m$.

In comparison with amplitude modulation which would only need 30 kHz bandwidth, the above requirement of 180 kHz appears to be exorbitant but this is the price which has to be paid for its advantages. In radio broadcasting where a particular service is available on both a.m. and f.m., the latter is usually on a higher frequency because of the wider bandwidth required.

Frequency modulation is usually achieved by means of an oscillator embodying an LC tuned circuit in which the capacitance is varied by the signal voltage. The undisturbed value of the capacitance is that which holds the frequency to that of the carrier. This is most easily understood from a typical modulator circuit as in Figure F8(ii). Here L_1 with C_1 and C_2 in series and with the capacitance of the diode in parallel, form the tuned circuit, normally oscillating at f_c. An incoming modulating frequency varies the capacitance of the diode, hence the oscillator frequency, V_B biases the diode and L_2 is a radio frequency choke which presents a high impedance to f_c but not to f_m so minimizing interaction between the resonant and modulating frequency circuits.

Demodulation is accomplished by various methods but basically all convert the f.m. wave into an a.m. one first, i.e. frequency deviations are translated into amplitude variations. Interference picked up on the way can be removed by *amplitude limiting*, i.e. reducing the f.m. wave so that all cycles have the same amplitude. None of the information is lost but the interference is. Following the limiting is a *discriminator*, frequently based on an LC circuit which when the carrier is applied is purely resistive but at frequencies below f_c the circuit develops a positive angle, equally at frequencies above f_c there is a negative angle. These phase changes control the period of time collector current flows in a transistor and charges a capacitor. Summing up, the frequency deviation of the f.m. wave is first expressed as a phase shift, then as an amplitude variation. It is now perhaps evident why f.m. is one of the methods classed under *angle modulation*.

The names of two American engineers, Foster and Seeley, are linked with this type of discriminator but since their original work, integrated circuits have become available embodying more complex arrangements and in fact a single radio receiver integrated circuit can contain not only the discriminator but intermediate and audio frequency amplifiers as well.

See also Amplitude Modulation.

(* Modulation, Carrier Wave, Fourier Analysis, Oscillator, Tuned Circuit >> Varactor, Choke, Limiter, Frequency Discriminator, Radio Receiver)

FULL-WAVE RECTIFICATION is the term used when both positive and negative half-cycles of a single-phase a.c. input supply power to the load – see Rectification and/or Figure R3.

FUNDAMENTAL FREQUENCY (frequently shortened to "fundametal"). A composite or complex wave is one which includes one or more others. It can be shown to consist of a fundamental (lowest frequency wave) together with harmonics. Each harmonic has a definite relationship with the fundamental and in nearly all cases is of a higher frequency. An example can be seen in Figure P3 where at (i) the complex waveform is seen to consist of a fundamental frequency together with a 2nd harmonic. The complex waveform always has the same frequency as the fundamental. We might sum this up by saying that the fundamental frequency is the lowest frequency in a complex wave and it has the same frequency as the wave.

(* Sine Wave, Waveform, Harmonic, Fourier Analysis)

G

GAIN is a general term used as a measure of the extent to which a device increases the amplitude of a signal relative to another known condition. For amplifiers the gain is simply the ratio of the output power, current or voltage relative to that at the input. For antennas the gain is expressed as the antenna output relative to that of a standard antenna operating under the same electrical and spatial conditions.

Gain is frequently quoted in decibels, e.g. an amplifier which has an output of 10 watts for an input of 1 milliwatt has a gain of $10/0.001 = 10\,000$. Expressed in decibels this gain is $10 \log 10\,000 = 40$ dB.

(* Amplifier, Antenna, Antenna Gain, Decibel)

GALLIUM ARSENIDE (GaAs) is a grey brittle material important in the semiconductor world. It has a large energy band gap (about 1.5 eV) which gives it high resistivity and it also has high electron mobility (about 0.85 m^2/Vs) which makes it suitable for high speed applications. Gallium arsenide has the comparatively rare property that its electrons can exist in either of two separate energy bands about 0.36 eV apart. It is used mainly for Schottky diodes, Gunn diodes, light-emitting diodes and semiconductor lasers.

(* Energy Bands, Drift Velocity, Electron-Volt, Semiconductor)

GALVANOMETER is an instrument used for detecting and measuring small currents and is named after Luigi Galvani (an Italian physiologist). Early galvanometers were based on the discovery that current flowing through a wire deflected the needle of a magnetic compass, subsequently it was found that a magnetized needle could be used to replace the compass.

Modern galvanometers consist of a coil of fine wire suspended in a magnetic field so that when a current flows through the coil, it tends to rotate. The movement is amplified by use of a mirror attached to the coil or its suspension. A pencil beam of light falling on the mirror is reflected onto a scale at some distance away, hence tiny movements of the coil are indicated by amplified movements of the light beam. Figure G1 shows how a mirror galvanometer might be constructed and in fact it is easily recognized as the forerunner of the moving-coil instrument. The suspension is of springy material so that it provides torsional control and restores the coil to its "zero" position when the current is removed. The magnetic flux density is high, hence the earth's magnetic field has little effect. The pole pieces of the magnet are shaped so that, together with the iron core a magnetic circuit is created with the magnetic flux radial. The flux "lines" are therefore always at right angles to the coil wires whatever the position of the coil. Accordingly the deflection is always proportional to the product of the magnetic field strength and the current flowing. The magnetic field strength is constant, hence the deflection is proportional to the current, so resulting in a linear scale.

There are many different types of galvanometer. One worthy of mention because of its high sensitivity is the *astatic galvanometer.*

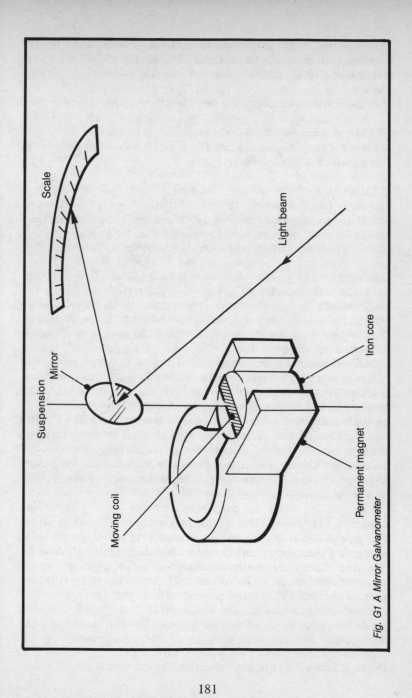

Fig. G1 A Mirror Galvanometer

This has two magnetized needles mounted in opposition on the same suspension so that the effect of the earth's and other extraneous magnetic fields cancel. The coils are wound round the needles but are so connected that the torques they produce, add.

Galvanometers generally are capable of measuring currents down to $0.1\,\mu A$ but laboratory models go even lower to around $10\,nA$. (* Current, Electromagnetic Motor Action, Magnetic Field Strength, Magnetic Flux, Magnetic Flux Density, Core, Moving-Coil Meter >> Differential Galvanometer)

GAMMA RAYS are an electromagnetic radiation of very high frequency (between about 10^{19} and 10^{22} Hz – see Fig.E5). Changes within the nucleus of certain radioactive elements result in spontaneous emission of gamma rays. They are produced in nuclear reactions when an atomic nucleus emits excess energy in the form of a high energy photon. The process is akin to that of an excited atom returning to the ground state by the emission of electromagnetic radiation. The spacing of nuclear energy levels is not just a few electron-volts but of the order of millions. Accordingly, when a photon is emitted by a nucleus it has a very high energy indeed. This energy is up to thousands of times the energy of a photon emitted from the atom itself. We can see this for ourselves from Planck's formula, $E = hf$ where E is the energy, f, the frequency of radiation and h is the Planck constant. In the visible region radiation frequencies are around $10^{14} - 10^{15}$ Hz whereas gamma rays are some 10^{20} Hz, hence their energies are at least 10^5 greater.

Such photons are known as *gamma rays* and it follows that a single gamma particle passing through a material or gas can ionize a considerable number of atoms or accelerate many electrons. It follows that nuclear radiation is definitely not good for our health. (* Atom, Photon, Energy Level, Planck Constant, Radioactivity, Visible Spectrum)

GAS BREAKDOWN This is a special type of breakdown occurring in a gas-filled tube leading to a *gas discharge*. The voltage across the electrodes needs to be sufficient for the electric field to raise the velocities of electrons and ions so that their high energies are capable of releasing more through collisions. Newly released particles are then accelerated sufficiently to create more by collision.

Overall a chain reaction takes place throughout the gas, known as *gas breakdown*. At this point the multiplicity of free electrons and ions greatly reduces the resistance of the path through the gas between the electrodes.
(* Gas Discharge, Ionization, Breakdown)

GAS DISCHARGE   This is the passage of an electric current between two electrodes in an ionized gas-filled tube. Let us approach this by considering a vessel or tube containing two electrodes across which is a voltage, calling the electrode which is positive the *anode*, and the negative one the *cathode*. Around the cathode is the normal space charge and electrons may be drawn from it depending on the strength of the electric field between the electrodes. How much current flows is dependent not only on the electric field strength but also on the gas and its pressure within the tube.

Consideration of the electron mean free paths under various gas pressures is a good way of sorting out what goes on. If, for example, the tube is filled with say, air at normal air pressure, then it can be shown that the mean free path is extremely short, indicating that any electron escaping the space charge will travel only a very short distance (tiny fraction of a millimetre) before colliding with a gas atom (both oxygen and nitrogen molecules comprise two atoms). Because the gas molecules are densely packed and the mean free path length is very short, the electric field has no time in which to accelerate the electrons appreciably.   On collision therefore each electron loses some of the little energy it has, doing no more than *excite* any atom with which it collides.   The number of electrons which complete the journey from cathode to anode is therefore minimal.   On the other hand, if the tube is evacuated to a very low pressure, few gas molecules get in the way so the mean free path is very long, indicating that most electrons have an unimpeded passage across. The current is then determined mainly by the voltage across the electrodes.

It is when a gas such as neon or xenon is introduced into the tube at moderately low pressure (say, around $1.5\,N/m^2$) that usable gas discharges take place. The gas molecules are widely separated so that the mean free path is of such a length (several cm) that electrons escaping from the cathode are sufficiently accelerated to ionize atoms with which they collide. The positive and negative ions produced make their way under the influence of the electric field to the appropriate electrodes. Again, because of the moderately long mean free path these too are sufficiently accelerated to cause further ionization on collision resulting in a chain reaction in which the whole of the gas rapidly becomes ionized. With free electrons and ions around the ionized gas is a good conductor and while current flows through the gas, it remains ionized because although recombinations continually take place, atoms are quickly re-ionized by further collisions.   Clearly a sufficiently high voltage must exist across the electrodes for the chain reaction to start, this is known as

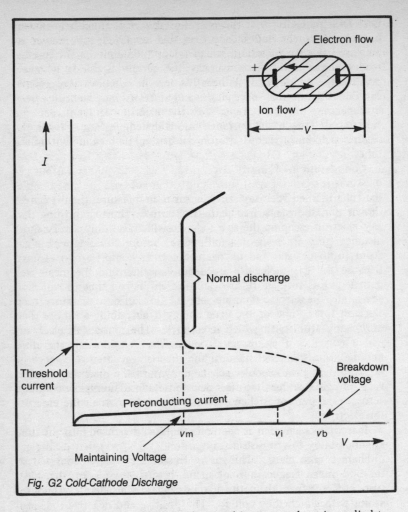

Fig. G2 Cold-Cathode Discharge

the *breakdown voltage*. Note that in this case no heat is applied to the cathode, hence the description, *cold-cathode*.

The complete process is illustrated best by a current/voltage graph as in Figure G2. At low voltages a few electrons travel to the anode and a few ions to the cathode, the current is therefore small (the *preconducting current*). At v_i the electron velocities are sufficient to cause ionization and on further increase to v_b the ionization spreads throughout the gas and *breakdown* occurs. The tube resistance thereupon falls, the current increases and ionization continues. The curve then reverses back to v_m, the dashed line in

184

the figure indicating that this is an unstable region, neither voltage nor current can be held steady over this range. At v_m, known as the *maintaining voltage* and which is approximately at the ionization potential of the particular gas, the current is able to increase considerably as shown. Within this region, when excited atoms revert to the ground state, photons are emitted so giving the characteristic glow of the gas, typified by the neon tube or lamp.

(* Electrode, Space Charge, Electric Field Strength, Mean Free Path, Excitation, Ionization, Impact Ionization, Ionization Potential, Collision, Energy, Energy Levels, Plasma, Paschen's Law >> Discharge Lighting, Arc Lamp)

GAS NOISE   The ionization of gas molecules in a gas discharge tube is a random process hence the current flowing through the tube when it is conducting has a minute fluctuation imposed on it. This fluctuation has constant power per unit bandwidth and theoretically extends over all frequencies. It is therefore classed as *white noise.* Such noise voltages when amplified may be employed in a noise generator.

(* Ionization, Gas Discharge, Noise, White Noise, Noise Generator)

GAUSS'S THEOREM refers to electric fields.   It follows from Coulomb's Law of electrostatics and it shows mathematically that the amount of electric flux passing through any closed surface is proportional to the amount of charge contained within the surface. From this it is evident that the electric field inside a hollow conductor in which there are no charges is zero irrespective of the electric field outside.

A second conclusion is that excess static charge on a conductor remains wholly on the outside.

There is a magnetic analogue of this theorem which shows that the amount of magnetic flux passing through any closed surface is zero, i.e. as many magnetic flux lines leave the closed surface as enter it.

The theorem shows how the technique of *screening* is possible, i.e. being able to shield apparatus from the effects of electric or magnetic fields.

(* Electric Field, Charge, Coulomb's Law, Magnetic Field, Magnetic Flux >> Screening)

GERMANIUM (Ge), is a grey brittle element of atomic number 32 with four electrons in its outermost shell. It is a semiconductor and is the material in which transistor action was first observed. It held sway until silicon came along. Unlike silicon, the oxide of

germanium is not stable which precludes its use in planar technology. Germanium has an energy band gap of 0.67 eV.
(* Shell, Semiconductor, Silicon, Energy Bands, Electron-Volt >> Planar Process)

GOLD-LEAF ELECTROSCOPE – see Electroscope.

GRID is an electrode consisting of a mesh of fine wires surrounding the cathode of a thermionic valve. The cathode to anode electron stream passes through the interstices of the grid. Potentials on the grid exercise control over the electron stream. This is the *control grid*. There may be others in a thermionic valve, e.g. *screen grid, suppressor grid* – see Thermionic Valve and/or Figure T3(iii).

GRID BIAS is the steady potential applied to the grid electrode of a thermionic valve to ensure that the valve operates over the desired portion of its output characteristic. For Class A the bias can be determined for a particular load by the *load line* which is drawn on the output characteristics. The actual bias to be provided depends on the class of operation of the valve.
(* Thermionic Valve, Characteristic >> Load Line, Class A Amplifier)

GROUND STATE is the condition in which an atom or molecule is said to be when its energy level is lowest – see Energy Levels.

GROUP DELAY   In any system (such as a transmission line), an input frequency of $A_1 \sin 2\pi ft$ results in an output of $A_2 \sin(2\pi ft - \phi)$, i.e. the output lags on the input by a phase angle, ϕ. The group delay is the time taken for a particular point on the input waveform to pass through the system or to a given point along a transmission line. It is computed at any frequency as:

$$\text{group delay} = (1/2\pi) \frac{d\phi}{df} \text{ seconds.}$$

Group delay is also known as *envelope delay* since it is the envelope of the waveform we are concerned with rather than any particular frequency component.
(* Transmission Line, Phase, Phase Angle, Group Velocity, Delay Distortion)

GROUP VELOCITY   If a composite wave, i.e. one which is a group or packet of constituent waves of different wavelengths, is transmitted over a channel in which the propagation coefficient is constant over the frequency band required, then the whole group arrives at its destination with its form unchanged. Alternatively, if the propagation coefficient is not constant with frequency then the velocity of each component will vary according to its frequency. This is generally known as *dispersion* and the overall wave shape will change as the wave travels.

It is evident that we cannot use the standard formula, $v = f \times \lambda$ where v is the velocity, f, the frequency and λ, the wavelength, because for a group of waves there is no single value for f or λ. In fact, for a wave comprising only two components (f_1, λ_1 and f_2, λ_2) where f_1 is approximately equal to f_2 as is most frequently the case, and remembering that the relationship between f_1 and λ_1 is not the same as that between f_2 and λ_2:

$$\text{group velocity, } v_g = \frac{\lambda_1 \lambda_2 (f_1 - f_2)}{\lambda_2 - \lambda_1}$$

v_g is the rate at which the group as a whole or the wave envelope is propagated, hence the term *envelope velocity* is also used. It is also possible to visualize group velocity as the rate at which the *energy* of the wave is propagated.

See also Phase Velocity.

(* Frequency, Wavelength, Transmission Line, Propagation Coefficient, Group Delay)

GUNN EFFECT was first reported in 1963 by J. B. Gunn. He found that microwave oscillations were generated in a sample of gallium arsenide when a steady strong electric field was set up in it. The electric field strength needed was at least 300 kV/m, the current through the sample then flowing in pulses at a frequency in the gigahertz region. This has led to the development of a simple microwave oscillator requiring a reasonably low voltage for its operation (e.g. if the sample is of length 0.1 mm, the electric field needed is only 30 V for an electric field strength of 300 kV/m).

The effect arises from the fact that gallium arsenide is a semiconductor which has two conduction bands and the explanation is usually in terms of the relationship between the electron energy, its momentum (mass × velocity) and its mobility. In the lower energy band it can be shown that the electron mobility is high at around 0.5 m^2/Vs because of a low effective mass whereas when the electric

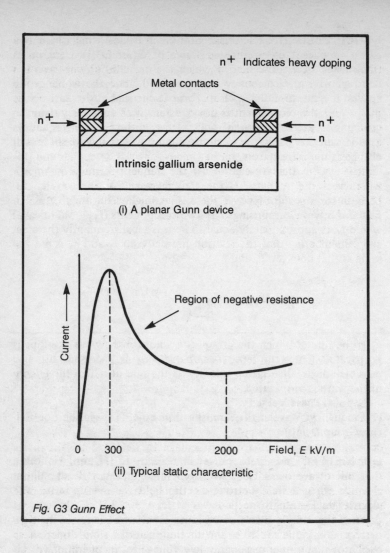

n+ Indicates heavy doping

Metal contacts

n+

n+

n

Intrinsic gallium arsenide

(i) A planar Gunn device

Region of negative resistance

Current

0   300   2000   Field, E kV/m

(ii) Typical static characteristic

Fig. G3 Gunn Effect

field is sufficiently high, the electrons transfer to the higher energy band where the effective mass increases and mobility therefore decreases to as little as 0.02 m^2/Vs. Summing this up, when the applied field is low most electrons are in the lower conduction band. As the field is increased electrons gain energy and transfer to the upper conduction band and when the field is sufficiently high, all electrons are transferred. This is the basis of a *Gunn device*, also known as a *transferred electron device*.

A typical static characteristic of a Gunn device which is simply a tiny slice of gallium arsenide as shown in Figure G3(i), is shown in (ii). When the electric field, E, reaches about 300 kV/m, there is a rapid transfer of electrons to the upper conduction band, hence the current begins to fall because of the lower mobility. Just above 300 kV/m the characteristic shows a region of negative resistance, changing to positive again at much higher levels of E. This is always a good sign that oscillations can be produced. For a device of length say, 0.1 mm the electron transit time is some 10^{-9} seconds and this determines the oscillation period, hence frequencies are in the microwave region.

(* Gallium Arsenide, Electric Field, Electric Field Strength, Energy Bands, Drift Velocity, Negative Resistance, Oscillation, Microwave)

H

HALF-WAVE RECTIFICATION is the term used when only alternate half-cycles of a single phase alternating current input supply power to the load — see Rectification and/or Figure R3(ii).

HALL EFFECT was discovered by the American physicist Edwin Herbert Hall. It is a potential difference which appears across a current carrying conductor when a magnetic field acts at right angles to the current. The effect is due to the ability of the field to deflect the path of a moving electric charge, remembering that a spinning electron for example behaves as though it were a microscopic magnet (see Fig.M5).

In Figure H1 a block of conducting material is shown with a current flowing through it. With the magnetic field direction as also shown, by Fleming's rules we find that an electron will be forced towards the top surface while holes move downwards. There is therefore a potential difference between top and bottom of the block, known as the *Hall voltage* or *Hall potential*.

For calculations a *Hall coefficient*, R_H is used such that when unit current density flows at right angles to unit magnetic flux density, a potential R_H is developed across the conductor, i.e. the electric field $E = -R_H BJ$ where B is the flux density and J is the current density (the — sign is for electron movement). It can further

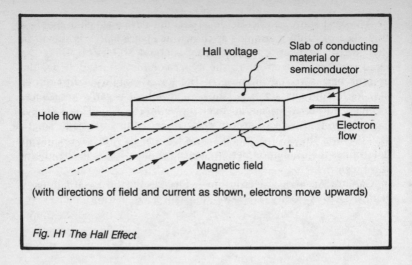

Hall voltage

Slab of conducting material or semiconductor

Hole flow

Electron flow

Magnetic field

(with directions of field and current as shown, electrons move upwards)

Fig. H1 The Hall Effect

be shown that $R_H = 1/ne$ where n is the carrier density (electrons per m^3) and e is the current carrier charge (coulombs). R_H therefore increases as charge density decreases. Also from the Hall coefficient the *Hall mobility* of the carriers, μ_H can be determined since the conductivity:

$$\sigma = ne\mu_H \quad \therefore \quad \mu_H = \sigma R_H$$

hence by measurement of the conductivity and R_H the carrier mobility is found. This also shows that materials with very high electron mobility (e.g. indium arsenide or indium antimonide) are preferable for devices which rely on the Hall effect.

For some materials the direction of the Hall voltage is reversed, implying that the current is carried mainly by holes, hence the Hall effect can be used to distinguish whether currents in semiconductors are electron or hole. Hall effect devices are also used for measuring magnetic fields.

(* Potential Difference, Electron, Magnetism, Magnetic Field, Magnetic Flux Density, Hole, Fleming's Rules, Charge, Mobility, Conductivity, Current Density, Coulomb, Spin >> Fluxmeter)

HALOGEN is any one of a group of non-metallic elements, all in the group having 7 electrons in the outer shell. The elements in the group are fluorine (9 electrons), chlorine (17), bromine (35), iodine (53) and astatine (85). Many atoms prefer to have a complete outer shell and so each of these readily picks up an electron from another

atom and therefore becomes a negative ion. The halogens also form molecules by ionic bonding, i.e. by sharing electrons.
(* Element, Atom, Molecule, Shell, Bond, Ion)

HARMONIC is one of the frequencies of a complex wave which is an integral multiple of the fundamental frequency (this is also the frequency of the complex wave). Harmonics are numbered according to the ratio between their frequencies and that of the fundamental. Of course, the fundamental has a ratio of 1 and therefore according to this is the "1st harmonic". However, this description is not used, "fundamental" is preferred. The 2nd harmonic has a frequency twice that of the fundamental, the 13th harmonic has a frequency 13 times that of the fundamental etc.

Harmonics are classed as *odd* or *even* according to their denomination, e.g. the 4th harmonic is even, the 5th is odd. Where in musical instruments for example, a "harmonic" frequency is not an integral multiple of the fundamental frequency, the term "overtone" is preferred. In fact it is the presence of harmonics and overtones which make music so delightful.

Any *periodic* wave, whatever its shape, is made up of a fundamental wave at the same frequency plus a series of harmonics. The exception is the pure sine wave which is a fundamental only and contains no harmonics.
(* Frequency, Wave, Sine Wave, Fourier Analysis)

HARMONIC ANALYSIS – see Fourier Analysis.

HARTSHORN BRIDGE is an alternating current (a.c.) bridge used for the measurement of mutual inductance. It is capable of greater accuracy compared with the Felici mutual inductance balance which is generally limited to the lower frequencies. The main problem is due to the self and mutual coil capacitances through which unwanted voltages are produced in the coils in addition to the desired voltages via the mutual inductance. The basic circuit is shown in Figure H2 in which the resistor R balances these unwanted components out. Zero indication on the a.c. voltmeter is therefore obtained by adjustment of the standard mutual inductance in conjunction with resistor R. For zero reading, $M_x = M_s$.

See also Felici Mutual Inductance Balance.
(* Frequency, Bridge, Inductance, Capacitance)

HAY BRIDGE is an a.c. bridge network suitable for measuring inductances with high Q-factors. The circuit is shown in Figure H3. The Hay bridge is similar to the Maxwell bridge except that the

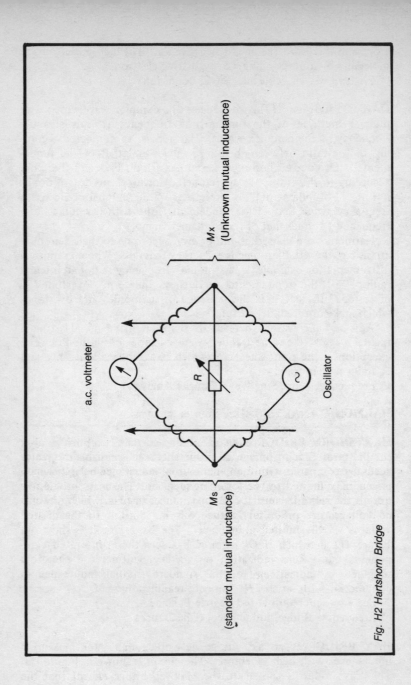

Fig. H2 Hartshorn Bridge

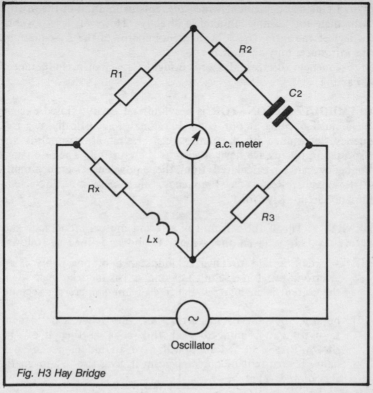

R2
R1
C2
a.c. meter
Rx
R3
Lx
~
Oscillator

Fig. H3 Hay Bridge

resistance-capacitance arm has a series arrangement instead of a parallel one. The advantage of this is that smaller resistance values are possible. In the figure, L_x and R_x represent the inductor being measured and Q_x its Q-factor. Let $\omega = 2\pi \times f$ where f is the frequency at which balance is obtained. At balance (i.e. when there is no deflection on the meter), then:

$$Q_x = 1/(\omega R_2 C_2)$$

and

$$L_x = \frac{R_1 R_3 C_2}{1 + \omega^2 R_2{}^2 C_2{}^2} \quad \text{or} \quad \frac{R_1 R_3 C_2}{(1 + 1/Q_x{}^2)}$$

$$R_x = \frac{R_1 R_3}{R_2 (Q_x{}^2 + 1)}$$

Q_x is frequency dependent which prevents calibration of the instrument dials for reading inductance directly. However, it is possible to neglect the term $1/Q_x^2$ in the denominator of the L_x equation, this introduces only a minimal error.
(* Frequency, Bridge, Maxwell Bridge, Capacitance, Inductance, Q-Factor)

HELMHOLTZ RESONATOR is a cylindrical cavity, closed except for a small opening at one end. It resonates acoustically at a frequency determined by the dimensions. Helmholtz resonators are also used in microwave devices such as the klystron. The resonance frequency can be calculated from the equivalent electric circuit.
(* Resonance, Resonance Frequency, Microwave >> Equivalent Electric Circuit, Klystron)

HENRY   This is the S.I. unit of self and mutual inductance and permeance. It is given the symbol H and is defined as follows:

(i)   a circuit is said to have an inductance of one henry if an electromotive force (e.m.f.) of one volt is induced in it when the current is changing at the rate of one ampere per second; or

(ii)   because the unit of magnetic flux, the weber is defined in terms of e.m.f. induced when flux changes, then it can be shown that a closed loop will have an inductance of one henry if a current of one ampere in it gives rise to a magnetic flux of one weber.

See also Inductance.
(* Volt, Current, Ampere, Magnetic Flux, Electromotive Force, Weber)

HERTZ is the S.I. unit of frequency with the symbol Hz. It is the number of cycles through which a wave or vibrating body moves per second. The unit is named after Heinrich Hertz, the German physicist. The time required to complete one cycle is known as the period or periodic time, T, hence:

$$\text{frequency}, f = 1/T \text{ Hz}$$

where T is in seconds.
(* S.I., Frequency, Cycle, Period)

HETERODYNE is the process of combining two signals of slightly different frequencies so that the envelope of the resulting oscillation varies in amplitude at a frequency equal to the difference between the two. The new frequency is known as the *beat frequency* and it swings through an amplitude range equal to the maximum amplitude of the smaller of the two signals. Graphically the process can be illustrated as in Figure B1. This is not modulation which requires the two signals to be mixed non-linearly but simply the effect that one wave has on the other. The two sine waves to be added are shown at the top of the drawing and if at regular small time intervals they are added, then the result is as shown at the bottom. This indicates that a new double sine wave has appeared which can be shown to be equivalent to a single frequency equal to the difference between the two. In this example the two input frequencies have the same amplitude but should the amplitudes be different, the amplitude range is reduced as mentioned above. Generally the process is described as one frequency *beating* or *heterodyning* with the other.

Now we must be careful not to be misled for no difference frequency signal is actually present as a separate entity after the addition. Each rise above the time axis is cancelled out by an equal fall below. However, rectification can come to our aid so that the difference signal can be extracted.

When the beat frequency is above the audio range we use the term *supersonic heterodyne*, happily shortened to *superheterodyne*, even to *superhet.*

(* Frequency, Beat Frequency, Sine Wave, Rectification, Superheterodyne Reception, Audio Frequency)

HIGH-PASS FILTER passes frequencies above a certain design value only – see Filter and/or Figure F4.

H-NETWORK is a 4-terminal network containing 5 elements. It is more generally known as a *balanced-T network* as shown in Figure N2 – see Network.

HOLE   In semiconductor parlance this is not just "an empty place in a solid body" but something more for we ascribe to it a positive charge. When an atom loses, for example one electron, it effectively becomes a positive charge and its *vacancy* for the electron is known as a *hole*. In a solid material the position of the atom is fixed but because it now exerts an attractive force on all electrons passing by, its vacancy or hole can soon be filled whereupon the atom reverts to its neutral state. While there is plenty of energy around, e.g. from an electric field or heat, electrons continually escape and are recaptured, the process being known as *recombination*.

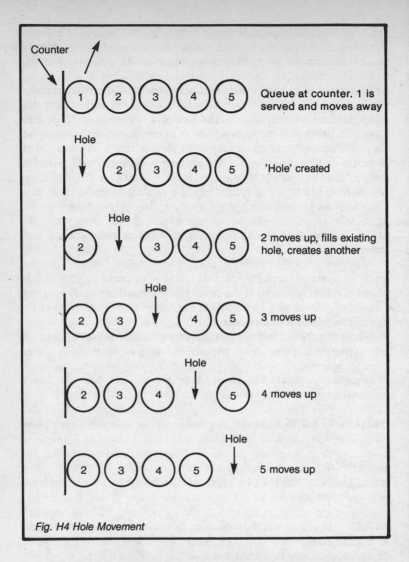

Counter

① ② ③ ④ ⑤	Queue at counter. 1 is served and moves away

Hole

② ③ ④ ⑤	'Hole' created

Hole

② ③ ④ ⑤	2 moves up, fills existing hole, creates another

Hole

② ③ ④ ⑤	3 moves up

Hole

② ③ ④ ⑤	4 moves up

Hole

② ③ ④ ⑤	5 moves up

Fig. H4 Hole Movement

Oddly enough, holes can be considered as mobile and just to get this rather obscure way of looking at things into perspective, consider Figure H4 which illustrates a queue of people at a counter. It follows that by continually filling each hole and thereby creating another, people move forwards towards the counter and a hole is actually moving backwards. A similar process takes place within a conductor under the influence of an electric field so that as Figure

196

H4 indicates, electron movement in one direction is equivalent to hole movement in the opposite direction. So we find that holes can wander about and if they do so more in one direction than any other, this can be considered as positive or *hole current*.

It is important to remember that holes are merely vacancies moving about, the only particles which move are the electrons. Nevertheless the vacancies are conveniently looked upon as positive charges. Being able to consider holes as current carriers is important in semiconductor technology in which for example, certain materials are deliberately manufactured with holes outnumbering electrons (p-type semiconductors).
(* Atom, Electron, Current, Electric Field, Electron-Hole Pair, Recombination, Positive)

HOLE CONDUCTION is said to occur when an electric field compels holes to move through a crystal lattice — see Hole and/or Figure H4.

HOLE CURRENT — see Hole.

HYSTERESIS is the term used when the effect of a varying quantity lags behind the quantity itself (from Greek, coming after). In electronics the term is most frequently used with materials undergoing magnetisation. This lags behind the magnetic field strength producing it — see Magnetic Hysteresis.

HYSTERESIS LOOP   If a curve is plotted of magnetisation or magnetic flux density (B) against magnetic field strength (H) over a complete cycle, it takes the form of a loop, known as a hysteresis loop as shown typically in Figure M3 — see Magnetic Hysteresis.

HYSTERESIS LOSS, ELECTRIC   This loss occurs in a dielectric material owing to strains set up when the material is subjected to a varying stress arising from an alternating electric field. Strains in a material generate heat from friction, hence power is absorbed from the electric field.
(* Dielectric, Electric Field, Power)

HYSTERESIS LOSS, MAGNETIC   When a coil or winding carrying an alternating current is placed round a core of ferromagnetic material, the magnetisation of the material is continually reversed. For each reversal the magnetic domains in the material change from alignment in one direction to that in the opposite direction. Work has to be done on them therefore, hence the electrical circuit must supply energy to the material, i.e. there is an electrical power loss which reappears in the form of heat in the material. The heat might be looked upon as the result of friction as the domains move. From this it is evident that the hysteresis loss varies with the number of magnetic reversals per second, i.e. with the coil current frequency. It also varies with the maximum flux density and the volume of the material.

See also Magnetic Hysteresis.
(* Ferromagnetism, Energy, Work, Power, Domain, Magnetic Flux Density, Core)

I

IF   Abbreviation of Intermediate Frequency — see Superheterodyne Reception.

IGFET   Abbreviation of Insulated Gate Field-Effect Transistor — see Field-Effect Transistor.

IMAGE ATTENUATION COEFFICIENT (or CONSTANT)   Part of the complex quantity relating to an asymmetrical 4-terminal network terminated in its image impedances — see Image Transfer Coefficient.

IMAGE IMPEDANCE   The image impedances of a 4-terminal network are those impedances such that when one of them (say, Z_1) is connected to one pair of terminals of the network, the other (Z_2) is presented by the other pair of terminals, as illustrated in Figure I1(i). Here with Z_2 connected to terminals 3 and 4, the impedance looking into terminals 1 and 2 is Z_1. Also with Z_1 connected to 1 and 2, the impedance looking into terminals 3 and 4 is Z_2. When Z_1 and Z_2 are not equal, the network is asymmetrical. Alternatively if the network is symmetrical, then $Z_1 = Z_2$ which is also known as the *characteristic impedance* of the network.

Networks designed for two different image impedances may be used for matching purposes and a single example is developed below for matching, say a 70 Ω coaxial cable to a 40 Ω amplifier (i.e.

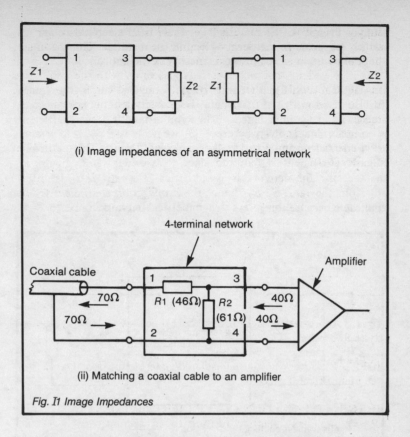

(i) Image impedances of an asymmetrical network

4-terminal network

Coaxial cable

Amplifier

70Ω

R_1 (46Ω)

R_2

(61Ω)

40Ω

40Ω

70Ω

(ii) Matching a coaxial cable to an amplifier

Fig. I1 Image Impedances

$Z_1 = 70 \ \Omega, Z_2 = 40 \ \Omega)$ as shown in Figure I1(ii). Here we must accept that the matching is for reasons other than for maximum power transfer because the network itself creates a loss.

This calls for an L-network (L-pad) and it can be shown by straightforward algebra that:

$$R_1 = \sqrt{Z_1(Z_1 - Z_2)} \qquad R_2 = Z_1 Z_2 / R_1$$

giving values, $R_1 = 46 \ \Omega, R_2 = 61 \ \Omega$. It will be seen from the figure that the image impedances of this network are 70 Ω and 40 Ω and connected as shown, both cable and amplifier are correctly matched.

See also Iterative Impedance.

(* Network, Impedance, Attenuator, Characteristic Impedance, Maximum Power Transfer Theorem >> Matching)

IMAGE PHASE COEFFICIENT Part of the complex quantity relating to an asymmetrical 4-terminal network terminated in its image impedances – see Image Transfer Coefficient.

IMAGE TRANSFER COEFFICIENT (also known as the Image Transfer Constant) is a parameter of a 4-terminal network terminated in its image impedances. The symbol used is θ, the coefficient is complex and is given by $(\alpha + j\beta)$ where α is the *image attenuation coefficient* and β the *image phase coefficient*. This particular transfer coefficient is required since it is evident from Figure I2 that because the network is asymmetrical, the ratio I_1/I_2 is different from the ratio E_1/E_2, hence the *propagation coefficient* is not applicable because this refers to symmetrical networks only.

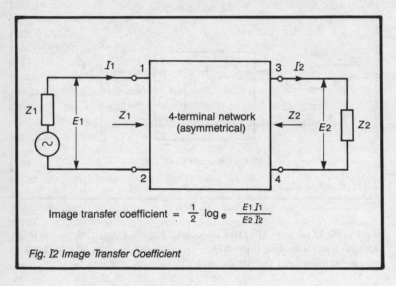

Image transfer coefficient $= \dfrac{1}{2} \log_e \dfrac{E_1 I_1}{E_2 I_2}$

Fig. I2 Image Transfer Coefficient

The image transfer coefficient θ, is such that:

$$e^{\theta} = \sqrt{(E_1 I_1)/(E_2 I_2)}$$

from which:

$$\theta = \tfrac{1}{2} \log_e \frac{(E_1 I_1)}{(E_2 I_2)}$$

or in words it is defined as half the natural logarithm of the complex ratio of the steady-state volt-amperes entering and leaving the network when the latter is terminated in its image impedances.

When two or more asymmetrical networks are connected in tandem on an image impedance basis, it can be shown that the overall image attenuation coefficient is equal to the sum of the image attenuation coefficients of the individual networks, similarly for the image phase coefficients. From these overall coefficients the overall image transfer coefficient can be calculated.

(* Network, Impedance, Image Impedance, Complex Notation, Volt-Ampere, Propagation Coefficient)

IMAGINARY COMPONENT – see Complex Notation.

IMPACT IONIZATION   This is the term used for the ionization of atoms or molecules arising from the liberation of orbital electrons following collision or impact with free electrons of high energy. An electron moving at high speed has high kinetic energy (k.e. $\propto v^2$). If therefore one collides with another locked in orbit, the speed and therefore the k.e. of the first electron must fall. The energy is given up to the orbiting electron and if this should exceed the first ionization potential, this electron is freed from orbit and the atom becomes a positive ion. In a semiconductor the same process is said to generate electron-hole pairs.

(* Atom, Electron, Molecule, Ion, Ionization Potential, Energy, Kinetic Energy, Collision, Electron-Hole Pair, Positive)

IMPEDANCE   This in an alternating current circuit expresses the degree of opposition the circuit presents to the passage of an electric current. It is denoted by the symbol Z, with the unit, the ohm (Ω). When there is a phase difference between current and voltage in a circuit, the impedance is complex (i.e. has real and imaginary components). The real component is the circuit resistance, (R) and the imaginary component is the reactance, (X), then:

$$Z = R + jX .$$

The modulus of the impedance is given by:

$$|Z| = E_{max}/I_{max} \quad \text{or} \quad E_{rms}/I_{rms} = \sqrt{R^2 + X^2}$$

as shown in Figure I3(i).

The argument (i.e. the phase angle, ϕ) is given by $\tan^{-1} X/R$. X represents the total reactance of the circuit, bearing in mind that inductive reactance is considered to be positive, capacitive reactance as negative. When ϕ is positive, then the circuit current lags on the

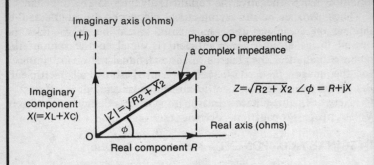

(i) Circuit containing resistance and reactance

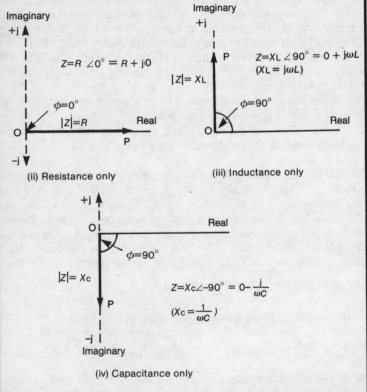

(ii) Resistance only

(iii) Inductance only

(iv) Capacitance only

Fig. I3   Impedance Phasors

202

voltage, when ϕ is negative the current leads the voltage.

The impedance of any circuit can be calculated provided that the impedance of each of the fundamental quantities R, L and C is known. Impedance diagrams showing (i) the general condition and (ii) to (iv) the mainly theoretical conditions of one quantity only, are illustrated in Figure I3. The impedance is shown as a phasor OP and is also expressed in polar and rectangular forms. In (i), if X_C exceeds X_L then the impedance phasor OP falls below the real axis and ϕ is negative. In (i) the impedance is complex, in (ii) wholly resistive and in (iii) and (iv) wholly imaginary.

Impedance is the reciprocal of *admittance*, i.e. $Z = 1/Y$.

(* Complex Notation, Phase, Phase Angle, Admittance, Reactance, Polar Coordinate, Cartesian Coordinate)

IMPURITY   One of the dictionary definitions of *impure* is "mixed with foreign matter" and this is the one which applies in electronics. In semiconductor parlance an impurity atom is an atom in a material which is foreign to that material. Foreign atoms always exist although usually few in number. Alternatively they are deliberately introduced in small controlled quantities into a semiconductor element to produce p-type or n-type conductivity — see Doping.

IMPURITY SEMICONDUCTOR — see Doping.

INCREMENTAL PERMEABILITY is used to indicate the permeability of a material subjected to a steady magnetising force (e.g. an iron cored inductor with steady direct current flowing in the winding). It is the ratio between the change in magnetic flux density to the small change in magnetising force which gives rise to it — see Permeability.

INDIRECT-GAP SEMICONDUCTOR   A semiconductor such as germanium or silicon in which for an electron to make a transition from the conduction energy band to the valence band, it must first reduce its momentum by creation of a phonon — see Direct-Gap Semiconductor.

INDUCED CURRENT is one which flows as a result of an electromotive force being generated within a conductor by a changing magnetic flux intersecting with the conductor. The conductor must of course be part of a closed circuit otherwise no current can flow — see Electromagnetic Induction.

INDUCED E.M.F. is an abbreviation of *induced electromotive force*. It is the e.m.f. which is generated (induced) in a conductor by a changing magnetic flux intersecting with the conductor — see Electromagnetic Induction.

INDUCTANCE   Current flowing in a conductor has associated with it a magnetic field, the strength of which is proportional to the current.   Accordingly if the current increases, the magnetic field increases.   This field surrounds the conductor and itself while changing, induces an electromotive force (e.m.f.) in the conductor. The direction of the induced e.m.f. is, as stated by Lenz's Law, such that it produces a current which opposes the change of magnetic flux. Similar conditions apply if the original current decreases, the induced e.m.f. acts to oppose the decrease. Hence, with any conductor or coil of wire, there is a self-induced e.m.f. which always acts to oppose the passage of an alternating current. Such opposition is known as *self-inductance*, but usually known more simply as *inductance* (symbol L). This is defined in terms of the current as:

A circuit has a self-inductance of one henry (H) if an e.m.f. of one volt is induced in it when the current is changing at the rate of one ampere per second, i.e.:

$$e = -L \times \mathrm{d}i/\mathrm{d}t \text{ volts}$$

where $\mathrm{d}i/\mathrm{d}t$ represents the rate of change of current with time, the minus sign indicating that the induced e.m.f. opposes the applied e.m.f. The induced e.m.f. is also known as the *back. e.m.f.*

A second definition in terms of the actual magnetic flux is:

A circuit has a self-inductance of one henry if it is associated with a total flux of one weber due to a current of one ampere flowing.

Inductances may be connected in series or parallel arrangements, but the need of such networks does not often arise, especially since modern circuit design tends to avoid inductances when possible owing to their cost and bulk. The appropriate formulae, however, happen to be of identical form to those for resistances, i.e.:

series $\qquad\qquad L_S = L_1 + L_2 + L_3 + \ldots$

where L_S is the combined inductance of the individual inductances, L_1, L_2, etc.

parallel $1/L_P = 1/L_1 + 1/L_2 + 1/L_3 + \dots$

where L_P is the combined inductance.

The formulae are only valid provided that there is no mutual coupling, i.e. the magnetic flux of one inductor does not affect another (see below).

Mutual Inductance (*M*) relates to the effect a changing current in one circuit has on another nearby circuit when they are linked magnetically (i.e. no direct connection between them). In this case:

$$e = -M \times di/dt$$

The two definitions now become:

(i)   two circuits magnetically coupled have a mutual inductance of one henry if an e.m.f. of one volt is induced in one circuit when the current in the other is changing at the rate of one ampere per second;

(ii) two circuits magnetically coupled have a mutual inductance of one henry when a magnetic flux of one weber is set up in one circuit by a current of one ampere flowing in the second circuit.

The inductance of a wire can be increased by coiling it in order to increase the linkages with the magnetic field. It is also increased by introduction of a magnetic core, the effect of which is to reduce the reluctance of the magnetic circuit.

(* Current, Magnetic Field, Magnetic Flux, Lenz's Law, Weber, Reluctance, Felici Mutual Inductance Balance, Back E.M.F., Core)

INDUCTION FIELD – see Electromagnetic Radiation.

INDUCTIVE REACTANCE   This is a means of expressing in Ohm's Law terms the opposition offered by an inductance to the passage of an alternating current. The unit is therefore the ohm. The reactance is denoted by the symbol X_L. Hence by Ohm's Law, $I = E/X_L$ where I and E are current through and voltage across an inductance (L).

The induced e.m.f. $e = L di/dt$ where di/dt is the rate of change of current.

The rate of change of current of a sine wave is given by $2\pi f I$, hence $E = L \times 2\pi f I$ and so that inductive reactance can fit into Ohm's Law calculations, inductive reactance, $X_L = E/I = 2\pi f L$ or ωL ohms (where $\omega = 2\pi f$, E is in volts and I in amperes).

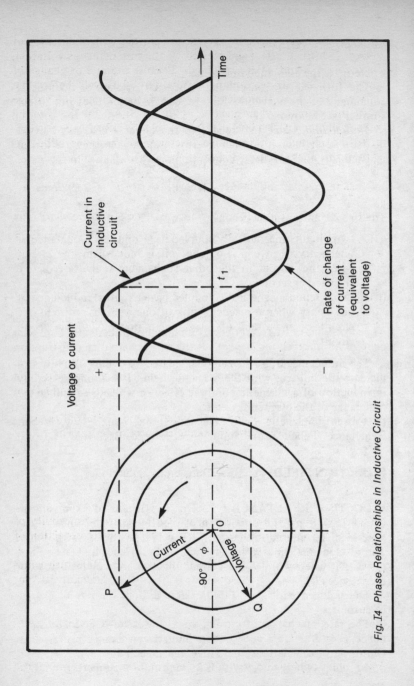

Fig. I4 Phase Relationships in Inductive Circuit

Next, if instantaneous currents are plotted with their rates of change (which in effect are related to the instantaneous voltages), curves as in Figure 14 are obtained. Because the rate of change of current reaches its maximum one quarter of a cycle before the current itself does, then clearly in an inductive circuit the voltage leads the current by an angle $\phi = 90°$ as shown by the rotating voltage phasor OQ leading the current phasor OP. Hence to complete the formula for inductive reactance a j must be added to express this phase difference, i.e.:

reactance of an inductance L henries $= j2\pi fL = j\omega L$ ohms.

By convention, inductive reactance is given a positive sign. The above considerations assume that no resistance is present. If this is not the case then ϕ is no longer 90° but something less.
(* Inductance, Sine Wave, Ohm's Law, Complex Notation, Phasor, Phase Angle, Phase Difference)

INDUCTOR   A component having the property of inductance, i.e. there is a self-induced e.m.f. accompanying any change in current. Inductors almost invariably consist of a coil of insulated or bare wire wound on a *former* or *bobbin*. If the wire is bare then construction is such that adjacent turns cannot come into contact with each other. The inductance depends mainly on (i) the coil geometry and whether or not there is a core with magnetic properties and (ii) on the square of the number of turns.

The simplest form of inductor is the air-cored solenoid (a cylindrical coil of wire). For this the inductance is theoretically:

$$L = \frac{4\pi N^2 \mu_r a}{10^7 \, l} \text{ henries}$$

where N is the number of turns, μ_r is the relative permeability of the magnetic path (μ_r for air = 1), a is the area of cross-section of the winding and l its length.

As an instructive example, the inductance of a 1000 turn winding which has a cross-sectional area 20 cm² and length 10 cm:

$$L = \frac{4\pi \times 10^6 \times 20 \times 10^{-4}}{10^7 \times 10^{-1}} = 0.025 \text{ H} = 25 \text{ mH}$$

For a practical coil this can only be approximate because not all the flux is fully effective with all the turns. Moreover, determination of the effective cross-sectional area is beset with difficulties.

The inductance of a coil increases considerably when a magnetic core is introduced and the above formula allows for this with the factor μ_r. However, it becomes even less reliable for calculating inductance because μ_r falls as flux density increases so it is hardly possible to determine a single value for it. Then again, iron cores are often laminated which brings in the problem of minute air-gaps at the joints. These greatly increase the magnetic path reluctance. Overall it is better perhaps to consider the formula as useful for our understanding of the basic principles, but admit that design relies as much on measurement as on calculation.

Inductors come in all shapes and sizes from those with laminated iron cores with inductances of say, 10 H for a small low frequency "choke", to small air-cored ones in the micro or millihenry range for radio frequencies as typically shown in Figure I5(i). This particular one also includes a tuning *slug*, a solid iron-dust plug which when screwed into the centre of the coil raises the inductance by

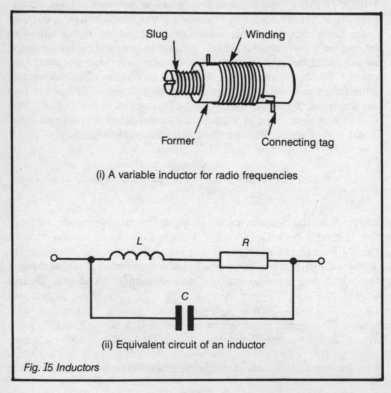

(i) A variable inductor for radio frequencies

(ii) Equivalent circuit of an inductor

Fig. I5 Inductors

decreasing the reluctance of the magnetic circuit. This is also known as *permeability tuning*.

Inductors cannot provide pure inductance because:

(i)   it is impossible to avoid resistance which exists in the winding;
(ii) there is also capacitance in the winding because each pair of adjacent turns constitutes a minute capacitor. The total capacitance is distributed in a complex manner throughout the winding but it is easily measured;
(iii) for iron-cored inductors there are also energy losses in the core, these can be considered as a series resistance.

The equivalent circuit of a practical inductor may therefore be developed as in Figure 15(ii). *R* includes winding losses (plus core losses if appropriate), *L* is the pure inductance and *C* is the *lumped capacitance*.

(* Inductance, Magnetic Field, Magnetic Flux, Permeability, Reluctance, Core, Capacitance >> Solenoid, Lamination)

INFORMATION THEORY is the quantitative study of the transmission of information by signals in communication systems. In 1948, C. E. Shannon (an American mathematician) published his now universally accepted work on the theory which can broadly be described as an attempt to analyse and quantify *information*, a word which in everyday use has a rather imprecise meaning. From this work it is possible to calculate *information flow* for any waveform such as that of speech, music, television or data. The complete theory is more than a little complicated but it is possible to get a feeling for it if we first consider the elementary piece of information known as a *bit* (not quite the bit of *binary digit*). With a binary signal for example, the probability, *P* of a 0 or 1 arriving at the distant end of a channel is 0.5 and the theory shows that:

$$\text{Information content of a signal}, I = \log_2 P^{-1} \text{ bits,}$$

hence for a binary signal, $I = 1$, meaning that 1 *bit* of information is required to distinguish between 2 equiprobable signals. The binary digit is the most elementary signal, other more complex signals produce information at very different rates. Measured in *bits per second* (b/s), for example, high quality speech requires around 40 000 b/s, music, 90 000 b/s and teleivison, 50–100 million b/s (these figures are very approximate and continuously vary with the signal itself). The figures, however, at least allow us to get information rates into some sort of perspective. As far as a practical channel is concerned therefore, what matters is just how many bits of information can be transmitted over it per second. It is not simply a question of the bandwidth of a channel for its signal-to-noise ratio (s/n) also has an effect.

The general formula from Shannon is:

$$C = B \log_2 (1 + s/n) \text{ b/s}$$

where C is the channel capacity, B is the channel bandwidth and s/n is the channel signal-to-noise ratio and evidently it is not so much the noise level which matters but the degree to which the signal exceeds it. An elementary example helps to make the use and value of the theory clear. Suppose a channel has a bandwidth of 200 kHz with a s/n ratio of 20 dB (100), then:

$$\text{Channel capacity}, C = 2 \times 10^5 \times \log_2 (1 + 100)$$

$$= 2 \times 10^5 \times \frac{\log_{10} 101}{\log_{10} 2} = 1.33 \text{ Mb/s}$$

Next suppose that the signal-to-noise ratio worsens to 10 dB (10), then for the same channel capacity:

$$B = \frac{C}{\log_2 (1 + 10)} = 385 \text{ kHz} .$$

The exchange of signal-to-noise ratio for bandwidth is evident. Worsening of this particular s/n ratio by 10 dB requires an increase in bandwidth from 200 to 387 kHz for an equally efficient transmission of information.

(* Binary, Probability, Bandwidth, Signal-to-Noise Ratio, Decibel)

INFRA-RED is the label given to electromagnetic waves having wavelengths just beyond the red end of the visible spectrum and extending to the microwave region (see Fig.E5). Infra-red radiation is emitted by a hot body at between about 100 and 200° C, the effect can be felt as radiant heat. Infra-red heating has many uses in industry, e.g. for drying paint and it has uses in medical treatment since the rays penetrate body tissues.

(* Electromagnetic Radiation, Electromagnetic Spectrum, Visible Spectrum, Wavelength)

IN-PHASE COMPONENT   This applies to either current or voltage in an alternating current circuit. When for example an alternating voltage is applied to a circuit containing reactance, i.e. it is expressed mathematically by $R + jX$, then the current and the voltage are not in phase. This can be shown on a phasor diagram as in Figure I6.

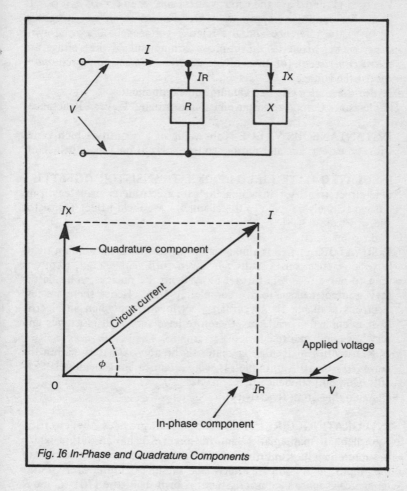

Fig. I6 In-Phase and Quadrature Components

OV represents the applied voltage and OI the current. In the figure the current leads the voltage by an angle ϕ, it could equally lag on the voltage, depending on the sign of the reactance.

Any phasor can be resolved into two *components* at right angles, in this case OI_R and OI_X. The current phasor OI_R is in phase with

211

the voltage and is known by various names such as *in-phase compon-ent, active component, active current* or *power component.*

The terms "active" and "power" arise in the alternative descrip-tions because it is the component which produces power. This follows from the fact that power in an a.c. circuit is calculated from $VI \cos \phi$ (V and I are the r.m.s. values) and when $\phi = 0°$, $\cos \phi = 1$.

Similar conditions apply when the current in an a.c. current is taken as the reference and the relative voltage phasors are drawn. Other names given to the in-phase component of the voltage are *active component* (of the voltage), *active voltage, power compon-ent* (of the voltage).

For the phasor OI_X see Quadrature Component.
(* Phasor, Complex Notation, Phase Angle, Power, Reactance)

INSTANTANEOUS VALUE is the value of a quantity which varies with time (e.g. an alternating voltage or current) at any instant.

INSULATED GATE FIELD-EFFECT TRANSISTOR (IGFET) is a field-effect transistor in which the gate electrode is insulated from, but capacitively coupled to the channel — see Field-Effect Transistor and/or Figure F3(iii).

INSULATOR This is a material in which the atoms hold on tight-ly to their electrons. Although, given sufficient energy, electrons tend to move to orbits further away from the nucleus, in insulators they seldom manage to get completely free. Hence there are few electrons available to act as an electric current when an electric field is applied. Insulators therefore have very high resistance and very low conductance.

Resistivities of insulating materials lie approximately within the range 10^7 to 10^{23} ohm-metres, e.g. ceramics are generally $10^{10} - 10^{12}$ Ωm, polyethylene 10^{16} Ωm, glass 10^{11} Ωm.
(* Atom, Electron, Resistivity)

INTEGRATING CIRCUIT is one which provides the electrical equivalent of mathematical integration, i.e. it has an output which is approximately proportional to the integral with respect to time of the input. A simple integrating circuit or *integrator* is the resistance—capacitance arrangement shown in Figure I7(i). C and R are such that their time constant CR is large compared with the periodic time (T) of the input voltage. The reason for this is that only the reasonably straight part of the exponential curve of the capacitor will have been used by the time the input voltage reverses. It can be shown that under this condition, $v_c \ll v_r$ and:

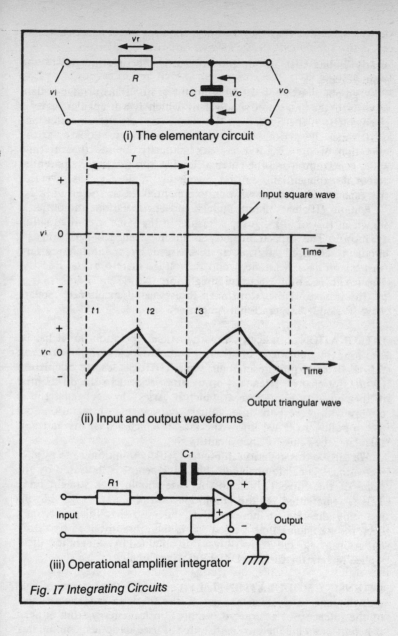

(i) The elementary circuit

Input square wave

Time

Output triangular wave

(ii) Input and output waveforms

Input

Output

(iii) Operational amplifier integrator

Fig. I7 Integrating Circuits

$$v_o \simeq 1/CR \int v_i \, dt$$

clearly stating that the output voltage is the time integral of the input voltage.

A graphical example of how an integrator transforms a square wave into the integrated equivalent which is a triangular wave is given in (ii) of the figure. In this particular case the time constant is 10 times the periodic time of the square wave. Looking at the operation of the circuit non-mathematically we see that at time t_1, v_i is maximum and the current flowing into C raises the potential across it exponentially until t_2 whereupon, since v_i has reversed, the capacitor discharges with an exponential fall as shown until t_3.

A more efficient circuit built round an operational amplifier is shown in (iii) of the figure, it results in the same overall equation as above. The capacitance, C_1 is in the feedback path and the circuit is arranged so that it is charged by a constant current (instead of via a resistance) and its voltage therefore rises linearly. This results in a more accurate integration.

(* Integration, Time Constant, Resistance, Capacitance, Square Wave, Period >> Operational Amplifier)

INTEGRATION is basically a mathematical operation but it has its electronic resemblance. Firstly it is better to look at *differentiation*; this is related to infinitesimal differences so it can lead to calculation of *rates* of change. Hence if a quantity varies then the differential of that quantity is the rate at which it varies. In electronics this is usually with respect to time, voltage, current, etc. Integration does the opposite, so if we know the rate at which a quantity varies, it calculates the values of that quantity.

We can see this in action in Figure I7(ii). From time t_1 to t_2 v_o is increasing. The rate at which this is happening is indicated by the *slope* of the curve (which in this case should be a straight line). This is represented by the amplitude of v_i from t_1 to t_2, showing not only the rate of increase of v_o but also that this is constant over the particular time period. v_i is therefore obtained by differentiation of v_o and conversely v_o is obtained by integration of v_i.

See Integrating Circuit, Differentiating Circuit.

INTENSITY MODULATION (I.M.) is applied both to beams of light radiation and to electron beams. In the first case it is the variation of the intensity of a directed beam of optical energy from either a coherent or an incoherent light source as used in optical communications. Note that whatever the type of modulation, the output power of a light emitter must always be positive.

214

Intensity modulation also varies the intensity of an electron beam in accordance with a modulating signal. As an example, i.m. is used to vary the brightness of the spot on the screen of a t.v. receiver through control of the electron beam intensity by the luminance signal.

(* Modulation, Coherence, Visible Spectrum >> Television Signal, Television Receiver)

INTERFERENCE In optics (but also with any wave motion) interference is a natural phenomenon which arises when light waves from one source are mixed with waves from another source. The two wave trains are said to *interfere*. For two or more waves of the same nature travelling past a point at the same time, the net amplitude is equal to the sum of the instantaneous amplitudes of the individual waves. There are two types of interference, *constructive* and *destructive*. In the first case the waves are in phase and therefore reinforce; in the second the waves are out of phase resulting in partial or full cancellation as demonstrated in Figure I8. A third condition arises when two waves of differing wavelengths pass through the same point, they sometimes reinforce, sometimes cancel, the net amplitude varies rhythmically resulting in *beating* (particularly noticeable with sound waves).

(* Electromagnetic Wave, Optoelectronics, Visible Spectrum, Phase Angle, Beating >> Interference)

INTERMEDIATE FREQUENCY is in a superheterodyne receiver. A frequency-changer shifts the carrier wave of the required incoming transmission together with its sidebands to a certain lower, fixed frequency. This latter frequency, known as the intermediate frequency (i.f.) is then amplified by the i.f. amplifier stages with greater selectivity and less risk of instability — see Superheterodyne Reception.

INTERNAL RESISTANCE is the inherent resistance of a device, usually one which supplies electrical energy such as a generator, primary or secondary cell. It is generally given the symbol r and the unit is the ohm. It is the internal resistance which accounts for the voltage drop when a generator or cell is put on load, i.e.:

$$r = \frac{(e - V)}{I} \text{ ohms}$$

where e is the e.m.f. generated within the device (volts), I is the

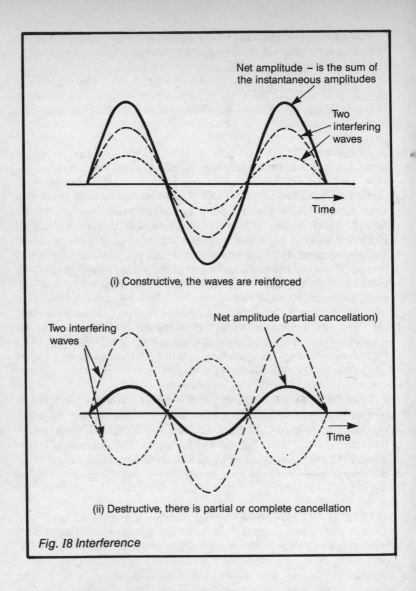

Net amplitude – is the sum of the instantaneous amplitudes

Two interfering waves

Time

(i) Constructive, the waves are reinforced

Two interfering waves

Net amplitude (partial cancellation)

Time

(ii) Destructive, there is partial or complete cancellation

Fig. I8 Interference

current drawn by the load in amperes and V is the device terminal voltage. Hence V falls as I is increased since $V = e - Ir$. For a practical example, see Figure O1.
(* Resistance, Electromotive Force, Ohm's Law, Cell, Primary Cell >> Generator)

INTRINSIC CONDUCTIVITY is that of a "pure" semiconductor, i.e. one to which no impurities have been added — see Intrinsic Semiconductor.

INTRINSIC IMPEDANCE is the impedance inherent in a medium, i.e. it belongs naturally to it. It has many similarities to the characteristic impedance of a line. The medium which crops up most frequently is *free space* and the formula for its intrinsic impedance is given under that term.
(* Impedance, Characteristic Impedance, Free Space)

INTRINSIC SEMICONDUCTOR   The term *intrinsic* is used to distinguish a semiconductor from one which relies on the presence of impurities for its special semiconducting properties. In other words, it refers to the pure semiconducting material. At absolute zero of temperature the uppermost energy band is the valence band for there is an energy gap [the forbidden band — see Fig.E12(iv)] between the valence and the conduction band which no electron has the energy to jump. Accordingly the conduction band is empty and the semiconductor is in fact an insulator. As temperature rises however, some electrons in the valence band gain energy and are excited across the energy gap into the conduction band, so leaving an equal number of holes in the valence band as suggested in Figure I9. The semiconductor therefore exhibits a positive temperature-dependent conductivity, this is the intrinsic conductivity.

The temperature dependency of available charge carriers is indicated by the equation for the density of conduction electrons, n_e:

$$n_e = K_e \exp\left(-E_g/2kT\right)$$

where E_g is the energy gap, k is Boltzmann's constant and T is the absolute temperature. K_e depends on the particular material and itself is temperature dependent but this dependency is small compared with the exponential term.

The number of holes is determined by a similar equation. Going one step further it can be shown that the conductivity, σ is given by:

$$\sigma = A \exp\left(-E_g/2kT\right)$$

where A is another constant for the particular material. It is from this relationship that the value of E_g for a semiconductor can be determined.

At low temperatures, when a semiconductor has an impurity added, the conductivity depends mainly on the impurity concentration and

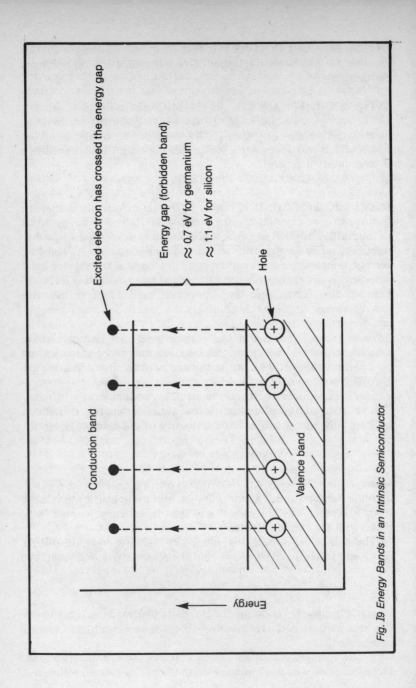

Fig. 19 Energy Bands in an Intrinsic Semiconductor

little on the charge carriers available from the intrinsic material. However, as shown above the intrinsic conductivity increases with temperature, hence at some higher temperature the intrinsic carrier concentration becomes sufficiently great that the intrinsic conductivity exceeds the extrinsic conductivity (i.e. that due to the impurity). At sufficiently high temperatures therefore the material although doped, has mainly intrinsic conductivity. The temperature range over which this occurs is known as the *intrinsic temperature range*.

(* Semiconductor, Impurity, Doping, Energy, Energy Bands, Valency, Charge Carrier, Hole, Boltzmann's Constant, Absolute Zero)

INTRINSIC TEMPERATURE RANGE refers to a semiconductor and is the range of temperature over which the number of electrons excited from the valence energy band to the conduction band by heat is such that the conductivity is mainly intrinsic irrespective of the fact that impurity atoms have been added — see Intrinsic Semiconductor.

INVERSION LAYER is a layer of opposite polarity induced within a semiconductor by an electric field. The principle is employed in an insulated-gate field-effect transistor to link drain and source regions by a channel of the same polarity.

The layer is produced at the surface of a semiconductor when it is in contact with an insulating material (e.g. silicon dioxide). Consider for example, a p-type substrate with a silicon dioxide layer and a gate electrode as in Figure F3(iii). Because the gate and substrate constitute a capacitor, any charge on the gate electrode must result in an equal and opposite charge on the substrate below it. For a negative gate voltage therefore, holes from the p-type are attracted to the area below the gate. On the other hand, a positive gate voltage repels holes and results in a depletion region there. However, at a certain positive *threshold voltage* the depletion region is so devoid of majority carriers that any further increase in the (positive) gate voltage results in the attraction of free electrons (the minority carriers) up through the depletion region to the interface. This is the inversion layer.

See also Field-Effect Transistor.

(* Semiconductor, Depletion Layer, P-N Junction, Charge, Charge Carrier, Capacitance, Hole, Majority Carrier, Minority Carrier)

ION This is the particle which remains when a neutral atom gains or loses one or more electrons, i.e. an atom without a complement of electrons equal to the atomic number. An atom gaining one or more electrons becomes a negatively charged ion (*anion*), losing one or more electrons it goes positive (*cation*). Exhibiting charge therefore, the ions, if free to move, are available as charge carriers, they move in the direction positive to negative but compared with electrons, much more slowly because of their greater mass.

Ions are also formed when certain substances are dissolved in water for example, a 2-element molecule such as that of common salt (sodium chloride) splits up into ions of sodium and chlorine, one electron having been transferred from the sodium atom to the chlorine atom. Neither particle is now a normal atom hence the use of the term ion (from Greek, *go* or *wander*). Of the two separate ions, the sodium is positively charged because it has lost an electron, the chlorine is negatively charged because it has gained one. The ions are available as charge carriers within the solution (the electrolyte), hence this is now a conductor of electricity.

(* Atom, Electron, Charge, Charge Carrier, Molecule, Electrolyte, Positive, Negative)

IONIC BOND   The type of bond between atoms created by the attraction between positive and negative ions — see Bond.

ION IMPLANTATION is a method of doping a semiconductor with an impurity. It relies on the fact that when ions are accelerated by energies up to some 200 keV, they are able to penetrate the surface of the semiconductor to a depth of a few micrometers. Since the accelerating potential, the total ion current and time of exposure can be accurately monitored, there is precise control of both the amount and depth of the dose of dopant.

We can be excused some initial doubt as to how impurity ions can be used in this way. Take Figure D9(ii) as an example. In this an arsenic atom with 5 valence electrons locks into the normal silicon lattice and leaves one electron spare. However, an arsenic ion has only 4 valence electrons so from where do we get the spare one? Actually the semiconductor being doped is connected to the extreme negative end of the accelerating potential, hence there are plenty of electrons around. When positive ions enter the material, each picks up one electron and accordingly reverts to the neutral atom. As such it then settles down within the lattice as one would expect.

In the ion source high speed electrons bombard a quantity of the particular impurity (e.g. boron or phosphorus), dislodging valence electrons and so creating a large quantity of various ions.

So that the dopant is very pure those required for implantation are selected by a mass analyzer (the various ions have different masses and so can be separated into different ion streams). A high potential accelerates the required ions and they are focussed into a narrow beam which is scanned across the wafer. Given sufficient energy therefore, the ions of the dopant force their way into the semiconductor lattice. This tends to distort the material so implantation is usually followed by an annealing process.

(* Atom, Semiconductor, Electron, Electron-Volt, Doping, Ion, Energy, Collision, Valency, Lattice Structure)

IONIZATION is the process of producing a positive or negative charge on an electrically neutral atom by removal or addition of electron(s). It arises in solid materials and gases when charged particles collide with or pass atoms at a sufficiently high velocity (and therefore kinetic energy) to separate one of the valence (outer) electrons from them. This results in ion pairs, each of which consists of one positive ion (the atom minus one electron) and a negative free electron (see also Impact Ionization). In atomic research it is also possible for uncharged particles (e.g. neutrons) to produce ion pairs by collision with atomic nuclei. As an example of ionization, ultraviolet radiation from the Sun ionizes the air in the upper atmosphere.

In an electrolyte the ions formed when certain compounds are dissolved in liquids are charged carriers and mobile and are therefore capable of transporting electricity.

(* Atom, Electron, Ion, Collision, Electrolyte, Charge, Positive, Negative >> Ionization Pressure Gauge)

IONIZATION POTENTIAL   This is a measure of the energy required to remove an electron from a given atom or molecule (theoretically to infinity so that it is completely away from the influence of the nucleus). It is also defined as the minimum potential difference through which the electrons must fall to be able to ionize a particular material.

The electrons on the outside peripheral shell of an atom are unique in that, because they are shielded from the positive charge of the nucleus by the electron charges in the shells in between, they are the most loosely bound and therefore the most easily removed. The energy required to do this for one electron only is known as the *first ionization potential* (I_1). The formula for calculation of I_1 is given in the Bohr Theory as:

$$I_1 = \frac{e}{8\pi\epsilon_0 r} \text{ eV}$$

where e is the electron charge, ϵ_0 is the permittivity of free space and r is the radius of the orbit.

The theory also gives us r for the hydrogen atom as 5.292×10^{-11} m, hence, I_1 for the hydrogen atom is equal to:

$$\frac{1.602 \times 10^{-19}}{8\pi \times (8.854 \times 10^{-12}) \times (5.292 \times 10^{-11})} = 13.6 \text{ eV} .$$

Thus for a hydrogen atom in the ground state (electron in orbit nearest to the nucleus), given 13.6 eV or more energy, the electron is released.

The first ionization potential of other atoms varies in a complex way according to the radius of the outer orbit and the total number of electrons. Copper, for example, has a first ionization potential of 7.72 eV, silicon 8.15 eV, neon is high at 21.6 eV.

In some cases, more than one electron can be removed from an atom. To do this greater ionization potentials are required, these are termed second, third ionization potentials respectively (I_2, I_3, etc.). (* Atom, Electron, Shell, Ion, Ionization, Bohr Theory, Energy, Potential Difference, Permittivity)

ISOTOPE   Nuclei of certain elements do not necessarily have the same number of neutrons. For any particular element the number of protons is of course equal to the atomic number, Z, but the number of neutrons varies, it is never less than Z and is usually more. An isotope is one of two or more forms of an element differing only in the number of neutrons in the nucleus, hence differing also in atomic weight. The chemical properties of the isotopes of an element are all the same since the nucleus takes no part in chemical reactions, physical properties may however differ. The word "isotope" is derived from Greek, meaning *equal place* (i.e. in the periodic table of elements).

As an example, chlorine is an element of atomic number 17. It has two isotopes, one with 18 neutrons, the other with 20. (* Atom, Nucleus, Neutron)

ITERATIVE IMPEDANCE is a characteristic of a 4-terminal network and it is the input impedance measured at one pair of terminals when an infinite number of such networks are connected in tandem.

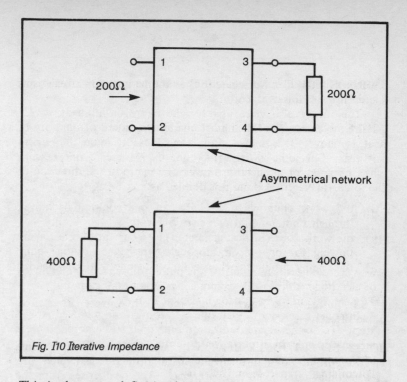

Fig. I10 Iterative Impedance

This is the exact definition but in practice it becomes the value of the impedance measured at one pair of terminals of the network when the other pair of terminals is terminated with an impedance of the same value. This is illustrated in Figure I10 which shows a 4-terminal network having iterative impedances of 200 and 400 Ω. In this case the network is asymmetrical, accordingly it has two iterative impedances, one for each pair of terminals (hence the description "iterative" from *iterate* = to repeat). When the network is symmetrical the two iterative impedances are equal and are then known as the *characteristic impedance.*

See also Image Impedance.
(* Network, Impedance, Characteristic Impedance, Propagation Coefficient)

J

JOHNSON NOISE   Noise due to the thermal agitation of electrons — see Thermal Noise.

JOULE   This is the S.I. unit of energy, work and of quantity of heat, symbol J. It is named after James Prescott Joule, the English scientist. One joule is the work done by a force of one newton when its point of application moves one metre in the direction of the force. In electrical terms it is defined as:

(i)   the work done when a charge of one coulomb is moved through a potential difference of one volt;

(ii)   the work done (or heat generated) by a current of one ampere flowing for one second through a resistance of one ohm;

(iii)   the energy produced when a power of one watt is expended for one second.

(* S.I., Force, Work, Newton, Coulomb, Volt, Ampere, Resistance, Joule Effect)

JOULE EFFECT/JOULE HEATING   When a steady or alternating electric current flows through any material, heat is generated, this is sometimes referred to as *Joule heat*. The heat arises from the resistance of the material to the flow of current. The energy lost from the electric circuit is equal to the amount of heat produced and Joule's Law states that the rate of heat generation is proportional to the square of the current.

The rate of loss of energy from a circuit is equal to I^2R where I is the current in amperes and R is the resistance in ohms. This energy is released as a quantity of heat, Q, then:

$$Q = I^2Rt \text{ joules (J)}$$

where t is the time during which the current is flowing.
(* Ohm's Law, Energy, Current, Joule, Power)

JUNCTION   This term arises frequently especially with semiconductors and in this case refers to the region of joining of two different types of conductivity. Thus we have such descriptions as *p-n junction, junction diode, junction transistor*.

The term is also used for the point or area of contact between two different conducting materials, for example as in metal

rectifiers and thermocouples.
(* Semiconductor, Conductivity, P-N Junction, Diode, Transistor
>> Selenium Rectifier, Thermocouple)

JUNCTION-GATE FIELD-EFFECT TRANSISTOR (JUGFET)
Taking an n-channel type as an example, this is one in which a
region of p-type material is inserted between source and drain leaving a narrow n-type channel. The p-type is connected to the gate
terminal and potentials on this terminal determine the width and
therefore the conductivity of the channel — see Field-Effect
Transistor.

JUNCTION TRANSISTOR is a transistor which embodies a p-n
junction. The term usually refers to a bipolar transistor rather
than a field-effect type — see Transistor.

K

KELVIN This is the basic S.I. unit of thermodynamic temperature
(named after Lord Kelvin, the Scottish physicist and mathematician).
It is denoted by the symbol K and it is defined as the fraction
1/273.16 of the thermodynamic temperature of the triple point of
water. The thermodynamic temperature scale starts at absolute
zero ($-273.16\,^{\circ}C$).
    When used as a unit of temperature difference, the kelvin is equal
to the degree Celsius.
    See Thermodynamic Temperature.

KELVIN BRIDGE (KELVIN DOUBLE BRIDGE) is used for the
precise measurement of low value resistances in the range $1\,\mu\Omega$ to
about $10\,\Omega$. Its development arose because its forerunner, the
Wheatstone Bridge is unreliable over this range because of switch
and terminal contact resistances. In the Kelvin bridge arrangements
are made to balance these out. The bridge is named after Lord
Kelvin. Because it has six resistive arms, the usual circuit may not
be immediately recognized as a bridge so here in Figure K1 it is
modified so that the essential difference from the Wheatstone bridge

225

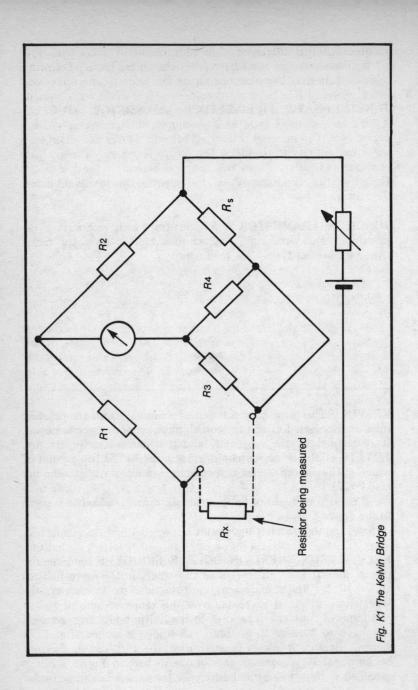

Fig. K1 The Kelvin Bridge

can be seen. This difference is the addition of two extra arms, R_3 and R_4. Nevertheless the bridge functions on the same basic principles of balancing then calculation of the value of the unknown resistance via the balance relationships. R_s is usually a standard (precision) resistor having a value of the same order as R_x.

For balance:

$$R_1/R_2 = R_3/R_4 = R_x/R_s$$

and if the two ratios R_1/R_2 and R_3/R_4 are made equal, then:

$$R_x = R_s \times \frac{R_1}{R_2}$$

(* Resistance, Bridge, Wheatstone Bridge)

KELVIN COEFFICIENT – see Thermoelectric Effect.

KERR EFFECT   The optical properties of certain transparent materials can be changed by application of a strong electric or magnetic field. Usually an electric field is used and this rotates the plane of polarization of the light. Because these materials are able to control light propagating through them they are therefore suitable for use as electrical to optical transducers, for example, for modulating a light beam in optical fibre transmission. When a voltage is applied transversely to the direction of the beam of light the rotation of the plane of polarization is known as the *Kerr effect*. A suitable material is the liquid nitrobenzene and such a device is known as a *Kerr cell.* With this type of cell polarized light can be "switched off" when a sufficiently strong electric field is applied. If the field is applied intermittently as a square wave, the system can act as a high speed light shutter.

If on the other hand electrodes are applied to a piezoelectric material such as potassium dihydrogen phosphate (KDP) so that the field is parallel to the direction of the light beam, this produces a *Pockel cell.* In this the electro-optical effect is linearly related to the applied electric field strength and is known as *Pockel's effect.* (* Electric Field, Electric Field Strength, Electromagnetic Wave, Light, Visible Spectrum, Polarization, Piezoelectric Effect, Square Wave >> Fibre Optic Transmission)

KILOGRAM is a unit of mass or weight in the metric system, adopted as the S.I. unit of mass, symbol kg. It is equal to the mass of the international prototype kept at Sèvres, near Paris. (* S.I., Mass, Arbitrary Unit)

KINETIC ENERGY   This is the energy of motion (from Greek, *kinetikos* = motion). It is very important in our understanding of electron behaviour because the electron is always moving – fast. The symbol used is E_K and the unit is the joule. The kinetic energy of a moving body depends only on its mass and velocity:

$$E_K = \tfrac{1}{2}mv^2 \text{ joules (J)}$$

where m is in kilograms and v is in metres per second. From this:

$$v = \sqrt{(2E_K)/m} \; .$$

Take for example an electron with a kinetic energy of 10 eV. This energy is equivalent to 1.602×10^{-18} J. Its mass is 9.109×10^{-31} kg so it must be moving at a speed:

$$v = \sqrt{(2 \times 1.602 \times 10^{-18})/(9.109 \times 10^{-31})} = 1.88 \times 10^6 \text{ m/s}$$

i.e. approaching two thousand kilometres *per second*. (Note that at high particle velocities an adjustment may be required because the mass of a particle increases with its velocity –see Relativistic Effect.)

Work is also measured in joules and if a body slows from v_f to v_s, it can do an amount of work equal to $\tfrac{1}{2}m(v_f{}^2 - v_s{}^2)$. Equally if energy is added to a moving object (i.e. work is done on it), then since its mass is constant, its speed must increase.

A special case arises when the velocity falls to zero. The object has stopped and all its kinetic energy has been lost. If it has a velocity, v, at the moment of stopping then it is capable of doing an amount of work equal to $\tfrac{1}{2}mv^2$. This is how electrons illuminate a cathode-ray tube screen. They are projected towards the screen at a very high speed and on hitting the screen each electron gives up its kinetic energy. This is transformed into heat and the screen glows.

The *law of conservation of energy* states that the total energy of an isolated system or group of objects is constant. An isolated system is one which neither receives nor gives energy to objects outside. For example, ignoring friction, two billiard balls colliding form an isolated system. Whatever total kinetic energy they have on collision remains intact afterwards, it is merely shared out in a different way. The same happens with electrons.

(* Work, Mass, Energy, Joule, Electron-Volt, Relativistic Effect >> Electron Gun, Cathode-Ray Tube.

KIRCHHOFF'S LAWS These are an aid in network analysis and were given to us by Gustav Robert Kirchhoff, a German physicist. By use of his two laws in conjunction with Ohm's Law a set of simultaneous equations can be derived for calculating the values of currents in a network.

Law 1 — the algebraic sum of the currents meeting at a point in a network is zero. Put in another way, this states that the current entering a point is equal to that leaving it.

Law 2 — in any closed path (or "mesh") the algebraic sum of the e.m.f.'s is equal to the algebraic sum of the products of the resistances and the respective currents in the separate parts.

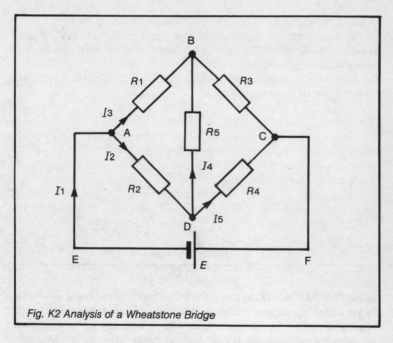

Fig. K2 Analysis of a Wheatstone Bridge

For a better understanding of what this all means, let us take as an example the resistive Wheatstone bridge as shown in Figure K2. Considering point A:

$$I_1 = I_2 + I_3$$

so that for I_3 we can write $(I_1 - I_2)$, already eliminating one unknown quantity.

Next, if I_2 flows into point D and I_4 and I_5 flow away from it, then:

$$I_5 = I_2 - I_4 \quad \text{or} \quad I_4 = I_2 - I_5 .$$

Law 2 is illustrated by consideration of any closed path, e.g. EADCFE (battery, R_2 and R_4). Then:

$$E = I_2 R_2 + I_5 R_4 .$$

Similarly for the closed path ADBA:

$$0 = I_2 R_2 + I_4 R_5 - I_3 R_1$$

(note that the p.d. $I_3 R_1$ is in opposition to the other two).

Equations for the other closed paths, e.g. DBCD, DABCD, etc. are similarly developed as required. From these the currents in every branch can be calculated.

(* Current, Electromotive Force, Potential Difference, Network, Ohm's Law, Wheatstone Bridge)

L

LADDER NETWORK is a recurrent network comprising alternating series and shunt elements as shown in Figure L1(i) for the unbalanced type and in (ii) for the balanced. Both unbalanced and balanced ladder networks can be considered as being built up of a number of basic L, T or π sections as shown in (iii) for the unbalanced type. Transmission line theory considers a line as a balanced ladder network made up of sections each representing a short length of the line. The impedance Z_1 accounts for the series resistance and inductance of the line and Z_2 is the shunt capacitance and shunt conductance.

(* Network, Transmission Line, Impedance, Resistance, Capacitance, Inductance)

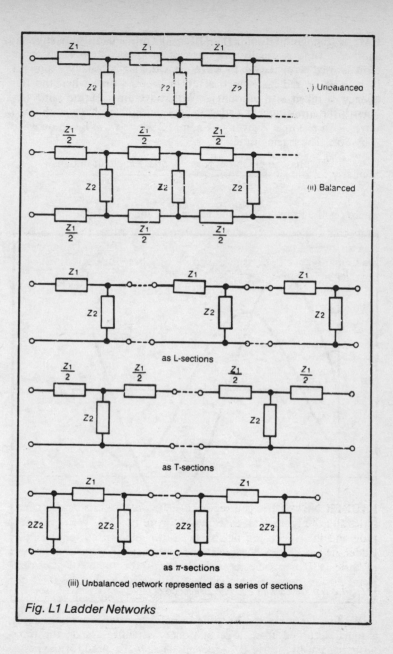

(i) Unbalanced

(ii) Balanced

as L-sections

as T-sections

as π-sections

(iii) Unbalanced network represented as a series of sections

Fig. L1 Ladder Networks

231

LAG is the amount of retardation of one quantity relative to another. Time is usually the basis of measurement but when the term is used with regard to waveforms the lag is usually expressed in degrees or radians (which after all become time when the frequency is taken into account). With waveforms of the same frequency the measurement of lag is between similar phases in the two waves. An example is given in Figure L2 where wave B lags on wave A by 60°. The lagging time:

$$t = \frac{\text{phase angle in degrees}}{360 \times f} = \frac{\text{phase angle in radians}}{\omega}$$

where f is the frequency of the two waves and $\omega = 2\pi f$.

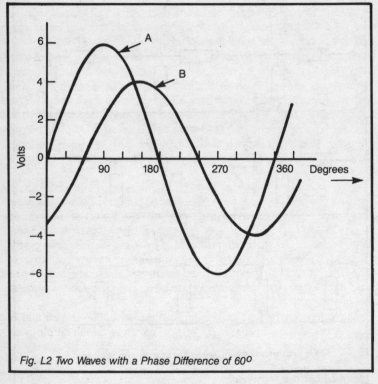

Fig. L2 Two Waves with a Phase Difference of 60°

We find lag measured by time in radio transmission for example, a signal returned from a geostationary satellite lags on the transmitted signal by nearly 0.24 seconds. Lag is also used for the persistence of the image in a camera tube.

232

See also Lead.

(* Frequency, Waveform, Radian, Phase Angle, Phase Difference, Electromagnetic Wave >> Satellite, Satellite Television, Camera Tube)

LASER is a device capable of producing a very narrow, extremely intense beam of essentially monochromatic light (one colour or wavelength only). Basically it functions by exciting atoms to a high energy level, then compelling them to drop back to the ground state en masse, emitting light as they do so. "Laser" stands for "Light Amplification by the Stimulated Emission of Radiation", an acronym which describes the basic action well. The idea behind the development arose long ago with Einstein who was then involved with Planck's radiation equation but it was not until 1960 that Theodore Harold Maiman (an American physicist) was able to develop a working model. There are gas, liquid and solid lasers, it is the latter which are in more general use.

Generally undisturbed atoms rest in the ground state, having least energy. They can be excited to higher energy levels but normally revert to the ground state within about 10^{-8} seconds with a photon emitted at each energy transition. However, with some there is also a *metastable* state, i.e. stable unless unduly disturbed. With little interference atoms remain in this state for some 10^{-3} seconds before reverting, hence remain excited for about 100 000 times as long. There are therefore three energy levels, E_1 to E_3 as shown in Figure L3(i).

An atom can be raised to an excited state (e.g. E_3) by absorbing a photon of exactly the right frequency, this is known as *induced absorption*. In *spontaneous emission* the atom emits a photon of energy and reverts to the ground state (E_1). Because there are many more atoms at E_1 than there are at E_3, absorption of energy by atoms at E_1 predominates over the emission of energy by those at E_3. What is needed therefore is an arrangement by which there are more excited atoms than ground state ones, the term used is *population inversion*.

The ruby laser is one of the earlier ones to be developed and it achieves population inversion by *optical pumping* which employs an external light source containing photons of the right frequency to raise the atoms to E_3 which then decay to E_2. Ruby crystals are made artificially and need to contain a tiny percentage of chromium ions which provide the metastable state. The chromium ions are raised in the pumping process to the energy level E_3 from which they decay to E_2 by losing energy to adjacent atoms in the crystal. A comparatively small number spontaneously fall to E_1 but the

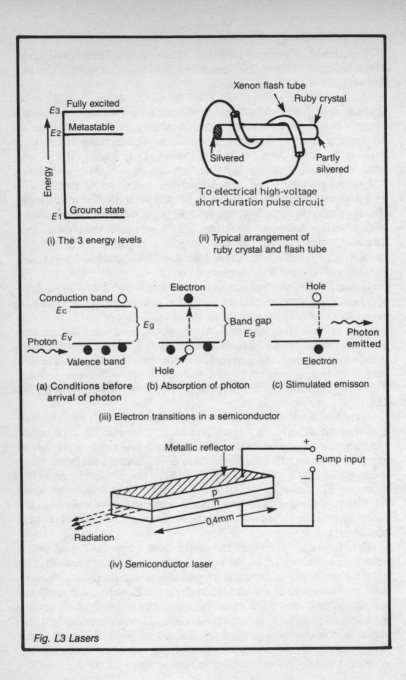

(i) The 3 energy levels

Energy

E_3 Fully excited
E_2 Metastable

E_1 Ground state

(ii) Typical arrangement of ruby crystal and flash tube

Xenon flash tube
Ruby crystal
Silvered
Partly silvered
To electrical high-voltage short-duration pulse circuit

(iii) Electron transitions in a semiconductor

Conduction band E_c
Photon E_v
Valence band
E_g
(a) Conditions before arrival of photon

Electron
Hole
Band gap E_g
(b) Absorption of photon

Hole
Photon emitted
Electron
(c) Stimulated emisson

(iv) Semiconductor laser

Metallic reflector
Pump input
p
n
0.4mm
Radiation

Fig. L3 Lasers

234

presence of light of exactly the right frequency stimulates the rest to radiate. This results in an avalanche process so producing the intense beam of light of frequency conforming to $(E_2 - E_1)/h$ where h is the Planck constant.

The elements of a ruby laser are shown in Figure L3(ii). The characteristic colour of xenon gas is green at a frequency of 5.44×10^{14} Hz, giving a photon energy of 2.25 eV, hence this is the energy level at E_3. The energy level at E_2 is 1.8 eV and this is the energy released as radiation by each chromium ion in the avalanche. An intense pulse of light is therefore emitted from the partly silvered end of the rod.

Semiconductor lasers as with all other types, also rely on population inversion. This is achieved by carrier injection across a forward biased p-n junction. Figure L3(iii) shows at (a) the valence and conduction band energy levels E_v and E_c for a semiconductor. For an electron to move from one band to the other involves the absorption or emission of a photon of energy equal to or larger than the bandgap. Hence as shown at (b) an electron absorbing a photon with energy $E > E_g$ then becomes capable of rising into the conduction band. The electron leaves behind a vacancy (hole) in the valence band. Thus photon absorption creates electron-hole pairs. Stimulated emission occurs when an incoming photon reacts with an electron in the conduction band causing the electron to fall back into the valence band and occupy a hole there as shown at (c). In doing so a photon is emitted by the electron of energy close to E_g. When a sufficiently large number of electrons is excited to the conduction band, this is population inversion and stimulated emission is possible.

A sketch of a semiconductor laser is given in (iv) of the figure. Such a device is likely to operate most efficiently between about 0.6 and 1.0 μm (see Fig.E5). Contacts are formed on the upper and lower surfaces of the block. The laser is pumped by a heavy supply of electrons to the n material so that they are driven across the junction (forward bias). This is the simplest of semiconductor lasers based on gallium arsenide. Others have several n and p layers of more complex gallium arsenide compounds.

Excitation of gas lsers is by an electrical discharge through the gas. Several gases are available which have metastable energy levels, e.g. helium, neon, argon, carbon dioxide. Population inversion arises through atom collisions which result in the transfer of energy. In the laser the discharge tube is mounted between two mirrors, one fully reflecting, the other partially reflecting and through which the laser beam is projected.

See also Maser.

(* Energy, Energy Levels, Light, Visible Spectrum, Avalanche, Planck Constant, Photon, Collision, Electron-Hole Pair, Semiconductor, P-N Junction)

LATTICE NETWORK is a 4-terminal network usually of balanced configuration comprising two series elements and two shunt elements, the latter crossing between the input and output terminals as shown in Figure L4(i). It is in fact a form of bridge network as shown in (ii) — see Bridge (Bridge Network).

LATTICE STRUCTURE   The regular arrangement of atoms or molecules within a crystal.
(* Atom, Molecule, Crystal)

L-C CIRCUIT is a combination of inductance and capacitance forming a tuned circuit. Since the frequency of resonance is inversely proportional to $\sqrt{LC}$ it is evident that the product LC is constant for any given frequency. Theoretically any combination of L and C can therefore be used for a given resonance frequency provided that their product is as required. In practice however there are disadvantages in making either L or C very large or very small. For a high Q factor the ratio L/C itself should be high.
(* Inductance, Capacitance, Tuned Circuit, Resonance Frequency, Q Factor)

LEAD is the amount of time or number of electrical degrees or radians by which one waveform is ahead of another. The measurement is between similar phases in the two waves and is illustrated by Figure L2 where wave A is said to lead wave B by 60°. The lead in degrees can be converted into time, t:

$$t = \frac{\text{phase angle in degrees}}{360 \times f} = \frac{\text{phase angle in radians}}{\omega}$$

where f is the frequency of the two waves and $\omega = 2\pi f$.
    See also Lag.
(* Frequency, Waveform, Radian, Phase Angle, Phase Difference)

LEADING CURRENT   With an alternating current it is a current which has a leading phase angle with respect to the electromotive force which produces it.
(* Alternating Current, Lead, Phase Angle)

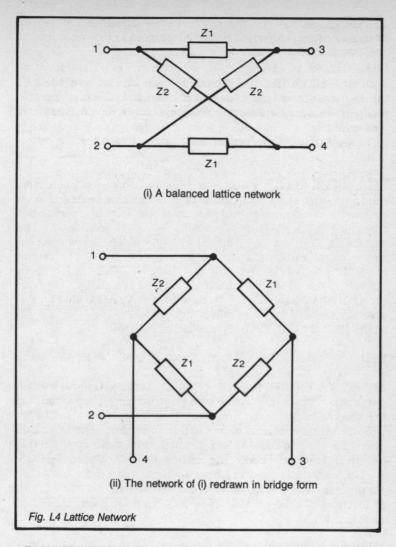

(i) A balanced lattice network

(ii) The network of (i) redrawn in bridge form

Fig. L4 Lattice Network

LEAKAGE CURRENT is another name for the reverse saturation current of a p-n junction — see Reverse Saturation Current.

LEAKAGE FLUX is that flux in a magnetic circuit which is lost. As an example, some of the flux of a transformer completes its path via the air outside of the windings and hence does not link with them. The induced voltage in the secondary winding is therefore less than

with no leakage.
(* Magnetic Flux, Magnetic Circuit, Transformer)

LEAKAGE REACTANCE   If, for example, in a transformer or alternator leakage flux cuts one coil but not another coupled to it, this increases the self-inductance of the first coil. Such an increase results in an added inductive reactance which is not required and creates losses.
(* Leakage Flux, Transformer, Inductance, Reactance >> Alternator)

LECLANCHÉ CELL   Patented in 1868 by Georges Leclanché, this cell in its original form consisted of a rod of zinc immersed in an electrolyte of ammonium chloride in which is also a porous pot containing a carbon rod surrounded by a "depolarizer". The depolarizer absorbs unwanted bubbles of gas which otherwise would adhere to the carbon rod and reduce its active area. The carbon rod is the positive electrode, the zinc, negative. Cell e.m.f. is about 1.5 volts. The whole cell is usually contained in a glass jar. Because the electrolyte is liquid it is somewhat messy, hence this type is generally replaced by the so-called "dry cell".
(* Cell, Primary Cell, Electrolyte, Positive, Negative)

LED   Abbreviation of Light-Emitting Diode — see this term.

LENZ'S LAW (after Henrich Friedrich Lenz, a German-Russian physicist).   This is concerned with electromagnetic induction, i.e. the production of an electromotive force (e.m.f.) in a conductor when there is a change in magnetic flux through it. The Law states that: "the e.m.f. induced in any circuit acts in such a direction that its effect tends to oppose the motion or change producing it".
    Such opposition is to be expected for if the e.m.f. were to aid the original cause, this would grow cumulatively.
(* Electromotive Force, Magnetic Flux, Electromagnetic Induction, Back E.M.F.)

LIFETIME   When in a semiconductor an electron receives sufficient energy for release from an atom orbit, an electron-hole pair is produced. The free electrons and holes act as charge carriers but it is almost inevitable that recombination will occur, that is a given carrier will combine with its opposite number or with an ionized impurity atom. The mean time interval between generation and recombination of the charge carriers is known as the *lifetime*. Practical values are of the order of a fraction of a nanosecond.

(* Semiconductor, Atom, Orbit, Electron, Hole, Charge Carrier, Energy, Electron-Hole Pair, Recombination)

LIGHT is an electromagnetic phenomenon and as such needs no medium for its transmission. It occupies a band of frequencies running from about 4.1×10^{14} Hz (red) to 7.9×10^{14} Hz (violet) — see Figure L5 for the full colour spectrum. The position of this band within the full electromagnetic spectrum is shown in Figure E5. These frequencies are capable of stimulating the millions of light receptors on the retaina of the eye which are interpreted by the brain as vision.

Light is sometimes perceived as a wave, hence we can place it in the frequency spectrum as shown above. However, Planck has concluded that it can also be considered as minute bursts of energy known as photons.

As with all other electromagnetic waves, the speed of light in free space is 2.998×10^8 metres per second — always.
(* Electromagnetic Radiation, Wave, Photon, Diffraction, Interference, Visible Spectrum)

LIGHT-EMITTING DIODE (LED)   This is a p-n junction which emits visible radiation when forward biased. It is usually recognized as a tiny electric lamp which has no filament. Under forward bias conditions, electrons fed into the n-type material find an easy passage into the p-type via the reduced depletion layer [see Fig. P10(iii)]. Once in the p-type, the electrons meet a good supply of holes and recombination takes place. These conduction electrons have energies in the conduction band so when combining with holes with energies in the valence band, the additional energy of the electron is released. The amount of energy (E_g) is at least that represented by the width of the forbidden band or gap [see Fig. E12(iv)]. Hence each time an electron combines with a hole, a photon of energy E_g is released.

Taking the most widely used red LED as an example, from Planck's formula:

$$E_g = hf$$

where h is Planck's constant and f is the frequency of the radiation — and from Figure L5, taking f as, say 4.6×10^{14} Hz:

$$E_g = (6.626 \times 10^{-34}) \times (4.6 \times 10^{14}) \text{ joules}$$

therefore:

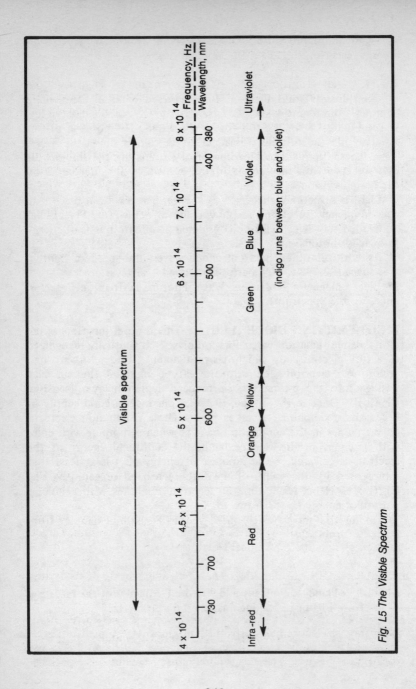

Fig. L5 The Visible Spectrum

$$E_g = \frac{6.626 \times 10^{-34} \times 4.6 \times 10^{14}}{1.602 \times 10^{-19}} \text{ eV} = 1.9 \text{ eV}.$$

Any semiconducting material can therefore be used provided that it has a sufficiently wide energy band gap. This rules out silicon and germanium for they have $E_g = 1.1$ and 0.7 eV respectively, both being too low. Taking the silicon electron as an example, if it gives up its 1.1 eV of energy, f is only 2.7×10^{14} Hz, this is well down in the infra-red region and therefore does not produce visible light. However, gallium arsenide and other gallium compounds have wider energy gaps and are suitable.

LED's are normally connected in series with a resistance to limit the forward current.

As a lamp, compared with the filament type which dissipates most of its input power in the form of heat, the LED is very efficient.

The graphical symbol is shown in Figure L6.

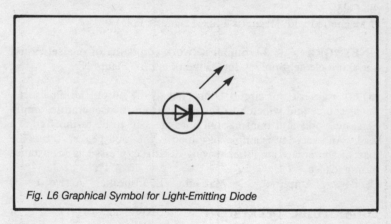

Fig. L6 Graphical Symbol for Light-Emitting Diode

(* Electron, Hole, P-N Junction, Recombination, Energy, Energy Bands, Valency, Photon, Planck Constant, Visible Spectrum, Direct Gap Semiconductor >> Optical Isolator)

LINEAR   Of or in line, the term is generally used to describe any system which provides an output directly proportional to the input.

LINE OF ELECTRIC FLUX is a notion which is used to represent or portray an electric field. It is the line which a free positive charge traces out as it moves, the direction of movement being shown by one or more arrows. The idea is purely imaginary but it is especially

241

useful in drawings on which the closeness of the lines is used to give a rough idea of the strength of the field (see Fig.E1 as an example). As the figure also shows, the lines are not necessarily straight. At any point along its length the direction of the line indicates the direction of the force acting on a positive charge placed at that point.
(* Electric Field, Electric Field Strength, Charge, Positive)

LINE OF MAGNETIC FLUX is a notion which is used to represent or portray a magnetic field. It is the line which a free North pole traces out as it moves, the direction of movement being shown by one or more arrows. The idea is purely imaginary but it is especially useful in drawings on which the closeness of the lines is used to give a rough idea of the strength of the field (see Fig.M2 as an example). Note that lines of magnetic flux never intersect one another. As the figure also shows, the lines are not necessarily straight. At any point along its length the direction of the line indicates the direction of the field.
(* Magnetic Field, Magnetic Flux, Magnetic Pole)

L-NETWORK   A 4-terminal network consisting of one series and one shunt element only — see Network and/or Figure N2.

LOAD is a device or circuit connected to the output terminals of a signal source and which absorbs power from it. Generators, amplifiers, networks and transmission lines are said to be terminated in a load. An everyday example of a load is the loudspeaker, this is the load of the power amplifier driving it. It is expressed as a resistance or impedance.
(* Power, Amplifier >> Matching, Loudspeaker, Active Load)

LOGARITHMIC DECREMENT is an expression of the rate of decrease of amplitude in a damped oscillation. The *damping coefficient*, δ, is the ratio of the amplitude of any one of the damped oscillations to the amplitude of the one following. The *logarithmic decrement* is simply the natural logarithm of the damping coefficient, i.e. $\log_e \delta$.

In a resonant circuit containing inductance L, capacitance C and resistance, R, the logarithmic decrement can be shown to be very nearly equal to:

$$\log \text{dec.} = \frac{R}{2f_r L} = \pi R \times \sqrt{C/L}$$

since:

$$f_r = \frac{1}{2\pi\sqrt{LC}}$$

where f_r is the frequency of oscillation. This shows that as R increases, the damping coefficient and logarithmic decrement also increase.

(* Resonance, Damping, Oscillation, Free Oscillation)

LORENTZ CONTRACTION is an important part of the *Lorentz transformation* originally proposed in the early nineteen hundreds by Heinrike Anton Lorentz (a Dutch physicist) as an explanation as to why some of the earlier equations of physics were failing in their predictions. Here we look at that part of Lorentz's work which helps in understanding better the link between current flow and magnetism, it is known as the *Lorentz contraction*.

Considering the two observers A and B in Figure L7(i), let A be stationary and B be moving at a speed v in the x direction and suppose that both measure the position of point P. A's measurement of the distance to P, d_A is always the same but B's depends on the position at any given time, say at t. After this time t, B's position has moved a distance vt so if both A and B were originally at the position of A, then designating the distance to P as seen by B, d_B:

$$d_B = d_A - vt$$

Lorentz in his transformation however took note of Einstein's formula showing that the mass of a body increases with its velocity and modified the above relatively simple equation to:

$$d_B = \frac{d_A - vt}{\sqrt{1 - (v^2/c^2)}}$$

where c is the velocity of light. This formula is known as the Lorentz contraction. In more general terms it can be expressed as:

$$L = L_0 \sqrt{1 - (v^2/c^2)}$$

where L is the length measured from a body in motion, L_0 is the length measured from the body at rest and v is the velocity of *relative* motion. Clearly because $c^2 = 9 \times 10^{16}$ the Lorentz contraction is ineffective in everyday life but at high particle speeds where v may even approach the speed of light, scientists must take

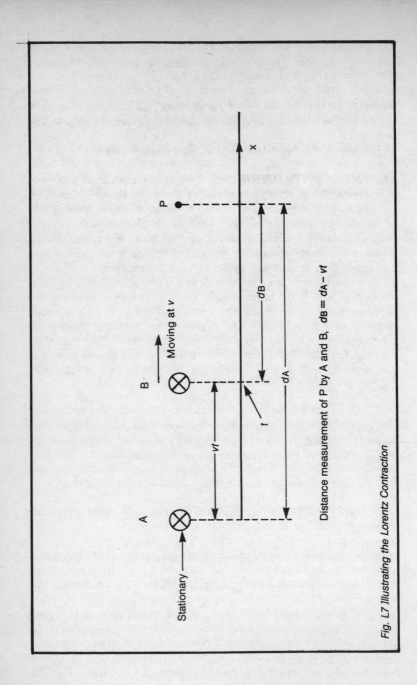

Fig. L7 Illustrating the Lorentz Contraction

Distance measurement of P by A and B, $d_B = d_A - vt$

this into account. Of interest is the fact that at a particle velocity equal to c, $L = 0$. Things cannot disappear so the formula indicates that nothing travels as fast as light.

The Lorentz contraction is basic to our understanding of what magnetism really is — see Electromagnetism.

(* Relativistic Effect, Light, Current, Magnetism)

LORENTZ FORCE EQUATION is an equation showing the force, F, on a moving charge in a combined electric and magnetic field. Each field will tend to impart its own direction of motion on the charge and let ϕ be the angle between the two fields. The total force acting on the moving charge is the vector sum of the electric and magnetic forces F_e and F_m so for a charge of q coulombs:

$$F = F_e + F_m = q(E + vB \sin \phi) \text{ newtons}$$

where E is the electric field strength in volts per metre, v is the velocity of the charge in metres per second and B is the flux density of the magnetic field in teslas.

When $\phi = 90°$, i.e. the electric and magnetic fields are at right angles, $F = q(E + vB)$. The force is perpendicular to both the direction of particle motion and the flux density.

(* Force, Newton, Charge, Coulomb, Electric Field, Electric Field Strength, Magnetic Field, Magnetic Flux Density, Tesla)

LOSS ANGLE is a term mainly referring to capacitors and dielectrics. In an alternating current circuit with a perfect capacitor, the current leads the voltage by $90°$. Practical capacitors have some losses so the current leads the voltage by an angle less than $90°$. The loss angle is the angle by which the angle of lead of the current is less than $90°$ — see Dielectric Loss Angle, Dielectric Phase Angle.

LOW PASS FILTER   An electrical filter passing only frequencies below a predetermined *cut-off* value — see Filter.

LUMEN   This is a unit of power in the measurement of light and it is defined as the luminous flux per unit solid angle from a uniform source of one *candela*. The unit symbol is lm. To understand the lumen it is therefore first necessary to define the candela.

If we consider light in terms of power spread over a given area (e.g. in watts per square metre) then we find that the sensitivity of the eye in these terms varies with colour. As an example, the eye is more sensitive to green than to blue or red. Accordingly for standardization of measurements, a light frequency is chosen. This for the S.I. System is 5.4×10^{14} Hz (555 nanometres, in the yellow-green part of the spectrum – see Fig.L5) and this happens to be the frequency at which the eye is most sensitive. The candela (cd in the S.I.) is defined as the luminous intensity in a given direction of a light source at 5.4×10^{14} Hz which has an intensity in that direction of 1/683 watts per *steradian*. A steradian (sr) is a unit employed in considerations of point sources of energy, it is the *solid angle* (as at the apex of a cone) which, having its vertex at the centre of a sphere, subtends a surface area equal to the square of the radius (see Fig.L8).

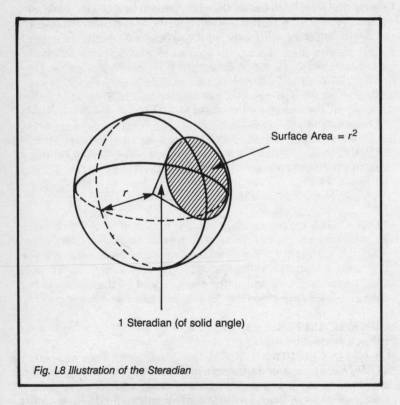

Fig. L8 Illustration of the Steradian

At this standard light frequency therefore, one watt of radiant power is equivalent to 683 lumens of luminous power. Put in other words, an *illuminance* or illumination of 1 lm/m² is equivalent to 1/683 watts of 5.4×10^{14} Hz light falling on an area of 1 m².

To get the lumen into perspective, some (very approximate) values of illumination at the earth's surface in lm/m² follow:

direct sunlight (midday)	10^5
dull day	10^3
full moon	0.25
starlight	10^{-3}

(* S.I., Derived Units, Visible Spectrum)

LUMINESCENCE is the emission of light without heat. Light is emitted when certain materials are irradiated by energy of a higher frequency or when they are bombarded by high energy electrons. One of the everyday uses of the phenomenon is the conversion of electron energy into radiant energy in cathode-ray tubes. In these the screen is coated internally with luminescent crystals, generally known as *phosphors*. These emit light when electrons strike them at high speed. In the process the electron kinetic energy is transferred to the electrons of the phosphor crystals. These are therefore excited to a higher energy level and on reversion to the ground state the energy is emitted as photons (light).

Emission of light *during* excitation is known as *fluorescence*, persistence after this is termed *phosphorescence*.
(* Light, Electron, Energy, Kinetic Energy, Energy Levels, Photon, Quantum Theory, Persistence >> Cathode-Ray Tube)

MAGNETIC AXIS – see Magnetic Pole.

MAGNETIC CIRCUIT   This is the closed path of the magnetic flux originating from a permanent magnet or a coil carrying a current. Fortunately it is possible to use an electrical circuit as a guide to what goes on in a magnetic circuit. Magnetic flux is analogous to current although it does not flow as current does. The magnetic circuit offers resistance to the creation of magnetic flux, this is known as the *reluctance*. A driving force is required to set up the flux which is called the *magnetomotive force* (m.m.f.), this has a parallel with the electrical circuit e.m.f. With Ohm's Law in mind, the magnetic circuit formula is:

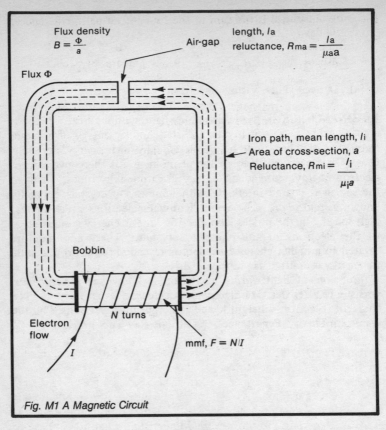

Fig. M1 A Magnetic Circuit

$$\text{magnetic flux} = \frac{\text{magnetomotive force}}{\text{total reluctance}}$$

or using symbols,

$$\phi = \frac{F}{R_{\mathrm{m}}} \text{ webers}$$

where F is in amperes (or ampere-turns) and R_{m} is in amperes per weber.

As an example, a typical series magnetic circuit (a record/replay head) is shown in Figure M1. The core is of iron having a length l_{i}, on it is wound a coil of N turns carrying a current, I amperes. The magnetomotive force is therefore $F = NI$ amperes (or ampere-turns).

The total reluctance is the sum of the iron and air-path reluctances, i.e.:

$$R_m = R_{mi} + R_{ma} = \frac{l_i}{\mu_i a} + \frac{l_a}{a} \text{ amperes per weber}$$

($\mu_a = 1$). Then magnetic flux, $\phi = F/R_m$ webers. Therefore, m.m.f. required to produce a given flux, ϕ:

$$F = \phi \times R_m \text{ amperes (or ampere-turns)}$$

and current, I required:

$$I = \frac{\phi \times R_m}{N} \text{ amperes}.$$

(* Magnetic Flux, Reluctance, Magnetomotive Force, Current, Weber, Ampere-Turn)

MAGNETIC CONSTANT is synonymous with Permeability of Free Space. It has a value of $4\pi \times 10^{-7}$ henries per metre — see Permeability.

MAGNETIC DIPOLE MOMENT is a measure of the strength of a magnet — see Magnetic Moment.

MAGNETIC FIELD   As with force and gravity a magnetic field is an invisible something, charged with energy and permeating air, space or materials. We do not fully understand what it is so have to describe it mainly in terms of what it does. It is set up by a magnet or by current flowing in a conductor and gives rise to certain forces which act on some materials but not others. As an example, the earth's magnetic field affects a compass needle but generally has no effect on non-metals (there are exceptions, lodestone is one). Within a magnetic field certain other magnetically inclined elements experience forces on them.

A magnetic field can be made to reveal itself through the standard school experiment of placing a piece of paper over a magnet and then sprinkling iron filings on the paper. The filings arrange themselves in lines looping between the two ends of the magnet as shown in Figure M4. We label the *poles, North* and *South* (N and S), they are different magnetically and always exist in pairs, a N or S pole cannot exist on its own. The poles have a similar rule governing them as do charges, i.e. "like poles repel, unlike attract". In order to

249

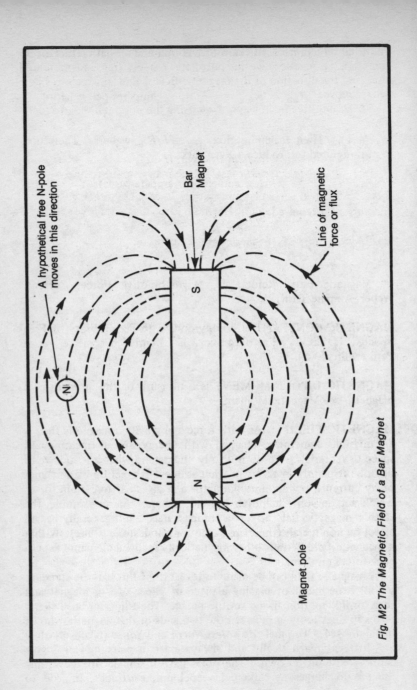

A hypothetical free N-pole moves in this direction

Bar Magnet

Line of magnetic force or flux

Magnet pole

Fig. M2 The Magnetic Field of a Bar Magnet

state the *direction* of a field, although admitting that a field has no direction in practice, we do postulate a single free and mobile N pole and the direction of the magnetic field is that in which this pole would move.

There are three main ways of assessing the potential of a magnetic field:

(i) by the *magnetic flux density, B*
(ii) by the *magnetic field strength, H*
(iii) by the *magnetisation, M* of the magnetic substance.

Each has its own particular application — see these terms.
(* Field, Magnetism, Line of Magnetic Flux, Magnetic Pole)

MAGNETIC FIELD INTENSITY — see Magnetic Field Strength.

MAGNETIC FIELD STRENGTH at any point is the strength of the field in the direction of the line of force at that point. It is defined as the magnetomotive force (m.m.f.) per unit length of the magnetic circuit and is denoted by the symbol H with the unit, amperes per metre:

$$\text{magnetic field strength}, H = \frac{\text{m.m.f.}}{l} = \frac{F}{l} = \frac{IN}{l} \text{ A/m}$$

where l is the length of the path in metres, I the current in amperes and N the number of turns.

Thus, for example, a long air-cored coil carrying a current will have a lower magnetic field strength than a shorter coil of the same number of turns and with the same current simply because the m.m.f. is distributed over a greater length.
(* Current, Magnetism, Magnetomotive Force, Magnetic Field)

MAGNETIC FLUX   In our ignorance of what a magnetic field really is, *magnetic flux* is an expression used in an attempt to describe what it consists of and how much of it there is. In Figure M2 the line traced out as the hypothetical free N-pole moves is known as a "line of magnetic force or flux". The magnetic flux is related to the number of lines passing between the two poles, more lines (i.e. the closer they are together) indicates a stronger magnetic field. It must be emphasized that this is our way of handling a magnetic field, lines of flux do not actually exist, nor is anything in a state of flux (flowing). With permanent magnets or direct current in coils, the field is stationary.

Magnetic flux is given the symbol ϕ and the S.I. unit is the weber (Wb).
(* Magnetism, Magnetic Field, Line of Magnetic Flux, Magnetic Pole, Weber)

MAGNETIC FLUX DENSITY is the magnetic flux per unit area normal to the direction of the flux. It is recognized by the symbol B with the unit, the tesla:

$$\text{magnetic flux density} = \frac{\text{magnetic flux}}{\text{area}} = \frac{\phi}{a}$$

where ϕ is the magnetic flux in webers and a is the area in square metres (one tesla = one weber per square metre).

Magnetic flux density is also known as magnetic induction.
(* Magnetism, Magnetic Flux, Tesla)

MAGNETIC HYSTERESIS   This occurs in *ferromagnetic* materials (easily magnetised) in that the magnetisation (M) or flux density (B) lags behind the applied magnetic field strength (H). M and B also vary non-linearly with H. A typical magnetic hysteresis set of curves or loop is shown in Figure M3. By such curves as these many of the characteristic properties of the material are displayed.

Consider an unmagnetised specimen of iron, steel or other iron alloy, placed within a coil carrying a current. Variation of the current varies the magnetic field strength as plotted on the x-axis in the figure. Initially with no H there is no B or M (these are related so we can plot either), this is at point 0. As H is increased the initial magnetisation curve is followed up to point a where saturation is reached. It is suggested that this is because all magnetic domains are fully aligned so further increases in H are ineffective. Next let H be reduced whereupon the curve does not retrace its original path but falls back to point b, i.e. with no magnetic field through it, the specimen still remains magnetised. The magnetisation at this point is known as the *remanence* with the corresponding value of B called the *residual induction.*

The curve shows that it requires a certain value of H in the opposite direction to reduce B or M to zero, i.e. to demagnetise the sample. This value is known as the *coercive force* and brings us to point c. Thereafter, increasing H in the negative direction eventually brings saturation with B or M also reversed in direction, to point d. Reducing the negative value of H to zero again brings remanence at e, demagnetisation as H is then increased positively taking the curve to f. Again the value of H at f is the coercive force.

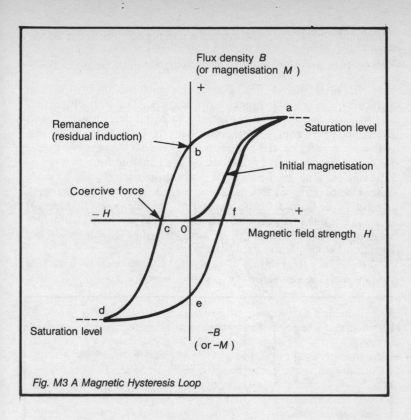

Fig. M3 A Magnetic Hysteresis Loop

The area enclosed by the loop represents the work required to take the sample through one complete cycle, this is the *hysteresis loss*, hence the wider loops indicate higher losses. Magnetically soft materials have thin loops showing that lower coercive forces are required for demagnetisation, this makes them suitable for transformer cores, electric motors etc. in which alternating currents take the iron through the full loop once per cycle. Magnetically hard materials (steels and iron alloys) have wide loops showing that demagnetisation is not so easy, i.e. the metal is suitable for permanent magnets.

(* Magnetism, Magnetisation, Magnetic Flux Density, Magnetic Field Strength, Domain >> Saturable Reactor)

MAGNETIC INDUCTION is the fundamental magnetic force defined as the magnetic flux per unit area — see Magnetic Flux Density.

MAGNETIC LEAKAGE is the loss of magnetic flux from a magnetic circuit due to its leaking around unintended paths — see Leakage Flux.

MAGNETIC MOMENT   This is one answer to the thorny question as to how to assess the strength of a magnet. The difficulty is that in order to line up with the point charge in electrostatics, point sources of magnetism in permanent magnets are needed. This does not occur in practice, the magnetic power is distributed, nevertheless for our purposes it can be considered as emanating from two points called poles. The precise location of these theoretical poles however cannot be determined so a quantity such as magnetic pole strength has not so far been defined. Instead of this, the *magnetic moment* is used, not quite so neat and tidy but it does give us a satisfactory way of assessing the strength of a magnet when in fact we do not even know where its so-called poles are.

A *moment* is the product of a force tending to cause rotation (the torque) and the distance from its line of action to a point, hence

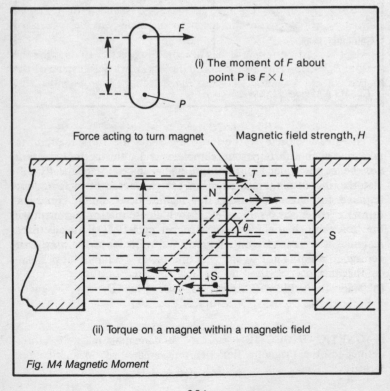

(i) The moment of F about point P is $F \times L$

Force acting to turn magnet

Magnetic field strength, H

(ii) Torque on a magnet within a magnetic field

Fig. M4 Magnetic Moment

expressing the power the force has of causing rotation about that point. This is illustrated in Figure M4(i) where a force, F acts to turn the bar about the point P. Here the moment of F is $F \times l$ showing clearly that the moment increases with l. In this case it is also known as the *turning moment* or *torque*. When a magnet is freely suspended within a magnetic field, it experiences a torque as shown in Figure M4(ii), hence a *magnetic* moment may be defined as that property of a magnet which interacts with an applied field to produce a *mechanical* moment. If the magnet pole strengths are labelled p and the magnetic field strength, H, then the force acting on each pole is $H \times p$ and the turning moment or torque, T is $H \times p \times l/2$ per pole. For the two poles therefore, $T = Hpl$, tending to align the magnet with the magnetic field. When the magnet is at an angle θ with the field, the torque is reduced to $Hpl \sin \theta$ which is zero when the magnet is fully aligned and therefore $\theta = 0$.

The product pl (i.e. the hypothetical pole strength multiplied by the distance between the poles) is known as the *magnetic moment* of the magnet. It is given the symbol j, hence $T = j \times H$ and by measuring the torque on a given magnet suspended in a known magnetic field strength, the magnetic moment can be calculated (weber metres).

More recently however it has become the practice to describe the magnetic field in terms of the magnetic flux density, B instead of the magnetic field strength, H. The *magnetic (area) moment* is now given the symbol m.

$$T = m \times B \text{ newton metres,}$$

where B is in webers per square metre and now the unit for m is ampere metres^2.

If instead of a permanent magnet, a small current-carrying loop is suspended within the field, similar conditions apply. Equal and opposite forces act on opposite sides of the loop tending to turn it into line with the field and if the loop is in a field of flux density, B, and has an area A with a current, I flowing, then the maximum torque, $T = IBA$.

The product of the current and the area of the loop is the magnetic moment, hence:

$$m = I \times A$$

and again

$$T = m \times B \text{ newton metres,}$$

255

with B and m in the same units as above.

(* Magnetism, Magnetic Field, Magnetic Field Strength, Magnetic Flux Density, Magnetic Pole, Force, Newton, Weber)

MAGNETIC POLE   Any specimen of magnetised material is known as a magnet and it gives rise to a magnetic field around it. There are two points near the opposite ends of the magnet from which the magnetism appears to originate. These points are known as the *magnetic poles* and the line joining them is the *magnetic axis*. The two poles are different and are governed by a similar rule as for electric charges: "like poles repel, unlike poles attract".

The earth is like a giant magnet and has two magnetic poles which have been labelled North (N) and South (S). The poles of any other magnet therefore experience forces arising from the earth's poles. The end of a freely swinging bar magnet that points towards the north is called its *north-seeking* pole or just north pole (N). Similarly the opposite end of the magnet is the *south-seeking* pole or south pole (S). Be warned here, a north pole is only attracted by a south pole hence the earth's north pole is in our terms, a south pole. However, this topsy-turvy arrangement does at least mean that the N end of a compass points to the north.

All magnets have these two unlike poles and it is a fact that an isolated pole cannot exist for it has no physical meaning. Nevertheless we sometimes visualize one as an aid in the manipulation of formulae. As an example, if two isolated opposite magnetic poles could exist having pole strengths m_1 and m_2, then there is sufficient evidence to show that the inverse square law is followed (again as in electrostatics), i.e. the force acting between them:

$$F \propto \frac{m_1 \times m_2}{d^2}$$

where d is the distance between them.

Because the "strength" of a magnet pole is not concentrated at a point, it is difficult to pin it down and quote a value. Use is therefore made nowadays of a quantity called *magnetic moment* which measures the strength of a magnet by the effect a known magnetic field has on it.

(* Magnetism, Magnetic Field, Magnetic Flux Density, Magnetic Moment, Charge)

MAGNETIC POTENTIAL   Same as Magnetomotive Force — see this term.

MAGNETIC RESISTANCE – see Reluctance.

MAGNETIC SATURATION   When a specimen of a ferromagnetic material is subjected to an increasing magnetising force of magnetic field strength H, the flux density B at first also increases but eventually reaches a saturation level where further increases in H result in no corresponding increase in B. This is illustrated in Figure M3 where the two saturation levels (according to the direction of H) are indicated on the curve.

Magnetic saturation must be avoided in for example, transformers carrying speech or music signals otherwise distortion of the waveform is introduced. On the other hand, magnetic saturation is the basis on which the saturable reactor is founded.
(* Ferromagnetism, Magnetic Field Strength, Magnetic Flux Density, Magnetic Hysteresis, Distortion >> Saturable Reactor)

MAGNETIC SUSCEPTIBILITY – see Susceptbility, Magnetic.

MAGNETISATION   This is the process of inducing magnetism in a material. It is given the symbol M (or H_i), is measured in amperes per metre and is defined as the magnetic moment per unit volume. Magnetic moment can be looked upon as indicating the strength of a magnet. Furthermore it can be shown to be the product of the magnetic field strength, H and the magnetic susceptbility, X, i.e. $M = H \times X$. From this a second formula for M can be derived for since magnetic susceptbility is given by $(\mu_r - 1)$, where μ_r is the relative permeability, then:

$$M = H \times (\mu_r - 1)$$

and since

$$\mu = \mu_0 \mu_r, \quad M = H \times (\mu/\mu_0 - 1) = H \times \frac{(\mu - \mu_0)}{\mu_0}$$

and since $\mu = B/H$, where B is the magnetic flux density,

$$M = \frac{(B - \mu_0 H)}{\mu_0}$$

where μ_0 is the permeability of free space and μ is the permeability of the material. Magnetisation only applies to materials subjected to magnetic stress and is zero for free space because for

this $\mu_r = 1$.
(* Magnetism, Magnetic Moment, Magnetic Field Strength, Susceptibility, Permeability)

MAGNETISING FORCE – see Magnetic Field Strength.

MAGNETISM This is a very complex subject in which the various effects are thought to arise from atomic movements in slightly different ways but all basically from the motions of charged particles. In materials electrons, apart from orbiting the atom nucleus, spin (like a top) in a complicated way a spinning and moving electron acts as though it were a microscopic magnet having North and South poles and the force which arises is transverse to its movement. Figure M5 illustrates the basic idea. From the figure it is evident

Fig. M5 A Spinning Electron behaves like a Tiny Magnet

that if two electrons attached to the same atom have opposite spins, their magnetic effects cancel out because they create a closed magnetic loop (N to S to N to S). Accordingly atoms exhibit no overall magnetism if they possess an even number of electrons with half spinning in one direction, the other half in the opposite direction. When this condition does not arise there is an overall magnetic effect.

Take iron as an example. Its shell occupancy is as follows:

$$K = 2, \quad L = 8, \quad M = 14, \quad N = 2$$

The two electrons in the N shell give the metal its conductive properties. From the point of view of the magnetic properties, the K, L and N shells each have an equal number of electrons with opposite spins, hence cancelling magnetically. However, shell M has 9 electrons spinning in one direction, 5 in the opposite direction, hence 4 electron spins remain uncancelled and the atom exhibits magnetism. To a lesser extent the same happens in nickel and cobalt.

A single iron crystal does not normally exhibit magnetism simply because its constituent atoms do because the atoms form groups having closed magnetic paths (N to S to N etc.), known as *domains*. However, when an external magnetic field is applied, those domains with magnetic axes already in the direction of the field grow at the expense of the others and the domain then exhibits N and S poles. It is when more domains are aligned in one particular direction than any other, that the material itself exhibits N and S poles along this direction.

Permeability is a measure of the degree to which this happens or can be forced to happen so generally materials can be assessed for their possibilities of magnetisation by this characteristic.

For magnetism arising from electric current, see Electromagnetism.

See also Ferromagnetism, Paramagnetism, Diamagnetism.

(* Atom, Electron, Orbit, Spin, Shell, Permeability, Domain)

MAGNETOMOTIVE FORCE   Very simply, this is the force which produces a magnetic field. It arises from the movement of charges in current flow. Because all electrons carry the same charge, then clearly the magnetomotive force (m.m.f.) is proportional to current. Also when a conductor is wound as a coil, the magnetic fluxes produced by each turn are additive, hence the m.m.f. varies as the number of turns (N), i.e.:

$$\text{m.m.f.}, F = I \times N \text{ ampere-turns (At)}$$

where I is the current in amperes.

(Strictly the unit for F is the ampere (A) rather than the ampere-turn. The latter is perhaps more descriptive and is a reminder that we are dealing with m.m.f. and not simply current.)

(* Magnetism, Magnetic Field, Magnetic Flux, Electron, Charge)

MAGNETOSTRICTION refers to the minute change in dimensions of a magnetic material when it is subjected to magnetic stress. A magnetic domain has its North and South poles and this in itself produces a stress between the poles and therefore the domain experiences a mechanical strain. If an external magnetic field is applied, the stress and its direction are changed, consequently the strain directions are also changed. Thus groups of domains may tend to lengthen or shorten and the crystal lattice becomes distorted. Magnetostriction is assessed for a particular material by the *magnetostriction stress constant*, quoted in newtons per weber. Some materials such as pure nickel contract with increasing flux density, the constant therefore being negative (about -20×10^6 newtons/weber) whereas for others, for example nickel-iron compounds, the constant is positive so these particular metals expand ($2 - 3 \times 10^6$ newtons/weber).

Magnetostriction which in effect converts magnetic field energy into mechanical energy can be used in the driving unit of loudspeakers. The effect is also used to control frequency in a *magnetostriction oscillator*.

(* Magnetism, Domain, Magnetic Field, Newton, Weber >> Loudspeaker)

MAJORITY CARRIER   This is the type of charge carrier in an extrinsic (doped) semiconductor which outnumbers the alternative type (minority carrier). In p-type materials the majority carriers are holes, in n-type electrons.

(* Semiconductor, Doping, P-N Junction, Electron, Hole, Charge Carrier)

MASER   Transitions occur between the atomic energy levels in matter through the interaction with electromagnetic radiation and for this process to occur, "packets" of energy known as photons are either absorbed or emitted. An undisturbed atom normally rests at its lowest energy level, the *ground state* and if we label this energy level E_1 as in Figure M6(i), then it can be raised to an energy level E_2 by the absorption of one photon of energy hf joules where h is Planck's constant and f is the frequency of the radiation providing the energy. Atoms can only have certain "allowed" energy levels so assuming that E_2 is one, for the photon to be of the correct energy to excite the atom from E_1 to E_2 :

$$hf = E_2 - E_1$$

that is, it must be provided by an electromagnetic radiation of frequency $(E_2 - E_1)/h$.

Atoms show no desire to remain in an excited state so they normally revert to the ground state within about 10^{-8} seconds with emission of the photon which has just been absorbed as illustrated in (ii) of the figure. It is possible for this emission to be stimulated by the arrival of another photon of the correct frequency and this is shown in (iii) where an atom has received one photon and risen to energy level E_2, then a second photon stimulates it to emit the first photon in which case both stimulating and stimulated

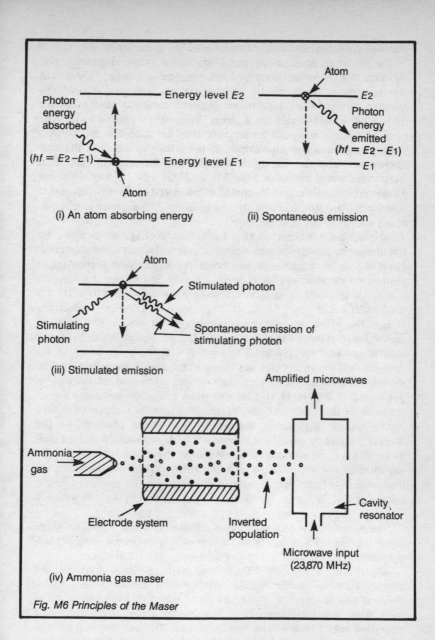

(i) An atom absorbing energy

(ii) Spontaneous emission

(iii) Stimulated emission

(iv) Ammonia gas maser

Fig. M6 Principles of the Maser

photons are emitted together in phase, so are *coherent*.

Generally at equilibrium there are more atoms at energy level E_1 than at E_2. However, if by some means the number of atoms at E_2 (n_2) could be increased to the extent that they exceed the number at E_1 (n_1) then further incident radiation at the correct frequency would result in a large increase in emission, i.e. the incident radiation would be amplified. The condition $n_2 > n_1$ is known as *population inversion* and the whole process has the title Microwave Amplification by the Stimulated Emission of Radiation from which the acronym MASER is obtained. Obviously some power must be delivered to maintain an inverted population and it is essential that the lifetime should be long at the upper level compared with that at the lower level.

A practical outcome of this basic two-level system is given by the ammonia gas maser, one which is relatively easy to understand. Level E_2 in an ammonium molecule corresponds to a microwave photon of frequency 23 870 MHz. A few figures may be helpful:

Energy required to raise an atom to $E_2 = hf = (6.626 \times 10^{-34})$ $\times$ $(23\,870 \times 10^6) = 1.58 \times 10^{-23}$ joules or 9.87×10^{-5} electronvolts. Therefore the minimum number of photons which must be emitted per second for the atom to fall to energy level E_1 for 1 watt of power $= 1/(1.58 \times 10^{-23}) = 6.3 \times 10^{22}$.

Ammonia gas molecules are pumped through a specially arranged electric field which separates excited and unexcited molecules as illustrated in Figure M6(iv), the excited molecules tending to concentrate in the centre of the beam, they are then directed into a cavity resonator. Inside the cavity microwave photons of the correct frequency exist hence there is a high probability that excited molecules will be stimulated to return to the ground state with the emission of photons. There is therefore amplification. It so happens that ammonia has a low density of atoms hence the amplified power output is low, however the device works extremely well as a highly stable oscillator.

There are many different types of maser, some based on three energy levels. There are also solid-state masers employing a paramagnetic material such as ruby or a compound of chromium.

Microwave maser amplifiers are used in many systems for amplification of weak signals with a poor signal-to-noise ratio. Because the energy levels are sharply defined, the frequency band of a maser can be extremely narrow, hence a desired signal can be amplified with much of the noise rejected. The maser is often maintained at a very low temperature which reduces the noise still further. Typical applications are radar, astronomy and satellite communication.

See also Laser.
(* Energy, Energy Levels, Molecule, Microwave, Photon, Ground State, Planck Constant, Coherence, Phase, Lifetime, Joule, Electron-Volt, Paramagnetism, Noise >> Cavity Resonator, Signal-to-Noise Ratio)

MASS is the quantity of matter in a body. This is measured by the acceleration when acted upon by a given force. The S.I. unit of mass is the kilogram. Mass is used in electronics in preference to weight because the latter varies with height above earth (and to a lesser extent with latitude). As an example, astronauts in space have the same mass as on earth but their weight is practically zero.
(* Force, Momentum)

MASS DEFECT The equivalent mass of the energy required in an atomic nucleus to bind the nucleons (neutrons and protons) together – see Binding Energy.

MATCHED TERMINATION is a component or circuit acting as the load (or termination) of a transmission line or network of such value that there is no reflection. This implies that the termination impedance is the same as the characteristic impedance of the line or network.
(* Transmission Line, Network, Reflection, Characteristic Impedance >> Matching)

MATTHIESSEN'S RULE is concerned with electrical resistivity. The conductivity σ (which is the reciprocal of resistivity) of a metal can be expressed in terms of the mobility μ of its electrons, each of mass m as:

$$\sigma = ne\mu$$

where e is the electron charge and n is the number of free electrons per unit volume. Also $\mu = e\tau/m$ where τ is the relaxation time (see Drift Velocity), then:

$$\sigma = (ne^2\tau)/m .$$

There are two ways in which free electrons lose their drift velocity (i) by collisions with the lattice for which the relaxation time τ_1 varies with the lattice temperature and (ii) by collisions with impurities and imperfections in the lattice for which the relaxation time τ_i depends mainly on the impurity concentration. The *rates* of collision in these two cases are therefore $1/\tau_1$ and $1/\tau_i$, hence the net rate of collision is given by $1/\tau = 1/\tau_1 + 1/\tau_i$.

The net resistivity, $\rho = 1/\sigma$ is therefore:

$$\rho = \frac{m}{ne^2} \; [1/\tau_1 + 1/\tau_i]$$

which can be written more simply as $\rho = \rho_1 + \rho_2$, showing that the resistivity is the sum of two components, the *thermal resistivity* ρ_1 and that due to the scattering of electrons by impurities and by imperfections in the lattice, the *residual resistivity, ρ_2*. This rule was published by A. Matthiessen in 1863. At very low temperatures therefore, the residual resistivity predominates, as temperature rises, the thermal resistivity takes over.

(* ·Electron, Charge, Resistivity, Conductivity, Drift Velocity, Relaxation Time, Lattice Structure)

MAXIMUM POWER TRANSFER THEOREM This is an important theorem which provides the guiding principles for interconnecting networks, amplifiers, lines, antennas, transducers etc. The full theorem states that the maximum power will be obtained from a generator of internal impedance $ZL\phi$ if its load has the conjugate impedance, $ZL-\phi$. If the modulus only can be varied, the power will be maximum when the moduli of generator and load are equal irrespective of the values of ϕ.

For purely resistive conditions therefore the load resistance must be equal to the internal resistance of the generator or source. The available power is then equal to $E^2/4R_g$ where E is the electromotive force (e.m.f.) of the generator and R_g its internal resistance. When the condition for maximum power transfer is obtained, the generator is said to be *matched* to its load.

It can be seen from the example in Figure M7 in which a $100 \, \Omega$ generator feeds a variable load up to $200 \, \Omega$ that it is possible for considerable *mismatch* to occur before the power falls significantly from the maximum.

Transferrence of maximum power into a load from a generator should not be confused with maximum efficiency. When a generator is matched to its load, as much power is lost in the generator as is gained in the load. Higher efficiencies are obtained as load impedance is increased above the matched value but the power into the load actually decreases (see Fig.M7).

(* Polar Coordinate, Impedance, Conjugate Impedance, Power, Electromotive Force, Internal Resistance >> Load, Generator)

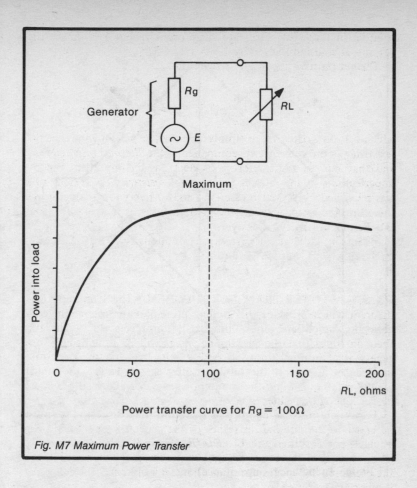

Fig. M7 Maximum Power Transfer

MAXWELL BRIDGE is an a.c. bridge network widely used for accurate measurement of inductance but also suitable for the measurement of capacitance. The circuit is shown in Figure M8. L_x and R_x represent the inductor being measured, C_s is a standard (calibrated) capacitor. When the bridge balances (i.e. when there is no deflection on the meter), then:

$$L_x = R_1 R_3 C_s \qquad R_x = R_1 R_3 / R_2$$

Alternatively, if the bridge is used for measuring capacitance and a known inductance, L_s is substituted in the inductive arm, then:

265

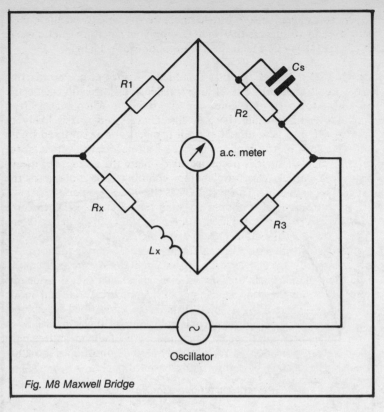

Fig. M8 Maxwell Bridge

$$C = L_s/R_1 R_3$$

(* Bridge, Inductance, Capacitance)

MAXWELL'S EQUATIONS   Maxwell's series of fundamental equations are more than a little complicated so are not quoted here. However, we should at least understand what their message was so many years ago. In the 1860's James Clerk Maxwell, the distinguished Scottish physicist, managed to combine the existing known laws of electricity and magnetism with those of light. In doing so he realized that something was missing from his equations to account for the fact that somehow electric and magnetic fields did not obey the normal inverse square law but instead the first power of the distance. He decided from this that electric currents in one place can affect other electric charges at a great distance and so he was able to predict the existence of electromagnetic waves with which we are so familiar today. Furthermore he was able to calculate their velocity and to suggest that light is simply an electromagnetic wave. (* Charge, Magnetic Field, Electromagnetic Wave, Light)

MEAN FREE PATH   In a conductor free electrons are darting about in all directions and in such a mêlée collisions with each other or with atoms or molecules are inevitable.   When an electron "collides" with another, because like charges repel, it is likely to bounce off in a new direction until it meets and is captured by an ion.   Because of the random nature of all particle movements, for certain calculations it is necessary to estimate the average (or mean) distance a particle can travel before colliding with another for the particular conductor. This is known as the *mean free path.*

As an example, for copper at room temperature, the mean free path for electrons is calculated to be about 4×10^{-8} metres (some $100 - 200$ times the copper atom diameter).

With gases things are very different because atoms and molecules are not tightly packed as they are in a metal. We are particularly interested in the mean free paths in devices such as gas discharge tubes which for this purpose can be considered as cathode and anode electrodes separated by a small distance in a gas-filled glass tube. Gas discharge tubes rely on particle collisions for their operation. A formula has been developed giving the length of the mean free path (l) of an electron. It of course is only a guide but it does show the order of things and can lead to quite sensible conclusions:

$$ l = \frac{4kT}{\pi d^2 p} $$

where k is Boltzmann's constant (1.38×10^{-23} J/K), p is the pressure of gas in newtons per square metre (N/m^2), T is the absolute temperature and d is the molecular or atomic diameter.

Consider first practical vacuum conditions within the tube where $p =$ (say) 0.15×10^{-3} N/m^2 and suppose that the only gas there is nitrogen for which d is quoted as 0.36×10^{-9} m. At $T = 293$ (room temperature), the formula shows the mean free path, l to be 265 metres, meaning simply that under high vacuum conditions an emitted electron is almost certain to make its journey unimpeded. However, at the gas pressures used in practical tubes, say at $p = 1.5$ N/m^2 for the popular neon gas with $d = 0.2 \times 10^{-9}$, l becomes 86 mm.   Hence, considering that the path of an electron is anything but straight, this indicates that the chances of collision are now appreciable.   In fact it can further be shown that for a distance between anode and cathode of 1 cm, 1 in 9 electrons are *likely* to experience a collision (at 2 cm it becomes 1 in 5). These results are borne out in practice.

(* Atom, Electron, Charge, Collision, Ion, Gas Discharge, Boltzmann's Constant, Drift Velocity, Newton, Electrode, Anode, Cathode)

MERCURY CELL (MERCURIC OXIDE CELL)   This is a primary cell of comparatively high capacity, especially useful in "button" form for camera and hearing aid batteries. The positive plate is formed of compressed mercuric oxide, the negative is of amalgamated zinc (coated with mercury). The electrolyte is an alkaline hydroxide producing ions which carry charges across the cell but which take no part in the chemical action. A mercury cell has a voltage of about 1.4 which it maintains throughout most of its life.
(* Cell, Primary Cell, Electrolyte)

MESFET is an acronym from metal-semiconductor field-effect transistor. The introduction of metal is at the gate electrode which becomes a reverse-biassed Schottky junction instead of a normal semiconductor junction. The substrate is gallium arsenide and an aluminium gate is deposited directly on it. The current-voltage characteristic is little different from that of the more usual junction f.e.t. but the fact that the device is small and that gallium arsenide has an electron mobility 3 − 4 times that of silicon, gives the mesfet the advantage of better performance at microwave frequencies. Useful gains can be obtained up to about 10 GHz.
(* Semiconductor, Field-Effect Transistor, Schottky Effect, Schottky Diode, Gallium Arsenide, Mobility, Microwave)

MESH   In a network it is a group of elements which are connected as a closed loop. The three resistors of the π network of Figure N2 comprise a single mesh, also the four resistors shown as a bridge — see Network.

METALLIC BOND   When a number of atoms in a metal are close together their valence electrons become free and shared by the group, i.e. no electron can be considered as belonging to any one atom. Taking copper as an example, nearly all its atoms contribute one valence electron resulting in a "cloud" or "gas" of electrons moving between the positive ions (i.e. the atoms which have each lost one electron). The ions can be considered as being fixed within the cloud of freely moving electrons and the attraction between the ionic lattice and the negative space charge of the free electrons

provides the weak bonding force of the metal. Elements which have this weak metallic bond are therefore ductile and because of the presence of ample free electrons, have good electrical and thermal conductivity.
(* Atom, Electron, Ion, Charge, Space Charge, Bond, Valency)

METRE is a unit of length in the metric system, adopted as the S.I. unit of length, symbol m. An international prototype was formerly used but the metre is now defined exactly and unvaryingly with time in terms of a number of wavelengths in vacuum of the radiation associated with a particular krypton atom. It is also defined as the "length of the path travelled by light in vacuum during a time interval of $1/299\,792\,458$ of a second" (the speed of light is not exactly 3×10^8 as is generally used but is $2.997\,924\,58 \times 10^8$ m/s).
(* S.I., Wavelength)

MHO   An earlier name for the unit of conductance, now replaced by the *siemens.* It is the reciprocal of the ohm and accordingly has the symbol Ω^{-1}.
(* Conductance, Resistance, Siemens)

MICA is a complex mineral which contains various proportions of different elements but that for electrical work, mainly aluminium and potassium. It is known as a *sheet silicate* because it occurs as thin flaky sheets. Mica is used as an insulator and is especially useful as a capacitor dielectric because it has a large dielectric constant and has high dielectric strength.
(* Element, Capacitor, Dielectric, Permittivity)

MICRON is a unit of length equal to one micrometre (μm, 10^{-6} m). The latter name is now preferred.

MICROWAVE is an electromagnetic wave of very high frequency. At such frequencies it is frequently more convenient to work in terms of wavelength rather than frequency. Limits for the micro-wave range as quoted by various authorities differ, but not widely. One range frequently used is 3 mm – 1.3 m (100 GHz – 230 MHz), another is 1mm – 10 cm (300 – 3 GHz). As a rough guide however we might simply work to "wavelengths around and below 30 cm" (frequencies above 1 GHz), extending to the infra-red region (see Fig.E5).
(* Electromagnetic Wave, Wavelength, Frequency)

MILLER EFFECT   In electronic amplifying devices such as transistors and thermionic valves the interelectrode capacitance creates an effective feedback path from output to input. In a single stage, depending on the nature of the output load and therefore the phase relationship between the output and input signals, it is possible for a circulating current to flow through the interelectrode capacitance and clearly the greater the gain of the stage, the higher the current will be. Because the input signal has to provide this current it therefore sees a capacitance equal approximately to the interelectrode capacitance multiplied by the stage gain. This is in addition to the normal input capacitance. The effect was first discovered by J. M. Miller.

(* Transistor, Thermionic Valve, Capacitance, Feedback, Phase, Phase Angle >> Load, Interelectrode Capacitance)

MINORITY CARRIER   This is the type of charge carrier in an extrinsic (doped) semiconductor which is outnumbered by the alternative type (majority carrier). In p-type materials the minority carriers are electrons, in n-type, holes.

See Doping.

(* Semiconductor, P-N Junction, Charge Carrier, Electron, Hole)

MOBILITY   This refers to moving charges. It is designated by μ and may be defined as the ratio of the *drift velocity* (v) of charge carriers to the strength of the electric field (E) accelerating them, i.e. $\mu = v/E$ — see Drift Velocity.

MODE is a term which describes the form in which an electromagnetic wave is propagated, more specifically it describes the electric and magnetic field patterns, usually with regard to waveguides. The three main classifications are:

(i)   *TE Waves* — these are *transverse electric waves* in which the electric field vector (E) is always perpendicular to the direction of propagation.

(ii) *TM Waves* — are *transverse magnetic waves* in which the magnetic vector (H) is always perpendicular to the direction of propagation.

(iii) *TEM Waves* — are *transverse electromagnetic waves* in which both the electric and the magnetic vectors are perpendicular to the direction of propagation. However, it can be shown that they cannot exist in a waveguide.

To these main classifications subscripts are added to indicate different modes of transmission within each. Only a certain number

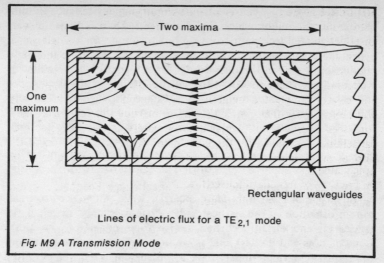

One maximum

Two maxima

Rectangular waveguides

Lines of electric flux for a TE$_{2,1}$ mode

Fig. M9 A Transmission Mode

are possible, depending on the guide shape, its dimensions and the wave frequency.

A single example of the TE$_{2,1}$ mode may help to make this clear. The subscript 2 indicates that the electric field has two maxima occurring across the width of the guide and the second subscript (the 1) indicates one maximum across the height. The E lines for this particular mode at a certain instant might be as sketched in Figure M9 (magnetic lines not shown for clarity). Note that the two maxima across the width of the guide are made up of one complete pattern plus two halves. For the height there are two half patterns. Circular waveguides have their transmission modes classified similarly.

(* Electromagnetic Wave, Waveguide, Electric Field, Magnetic Field)

MODULATION   The need for this arises from the fact that baseband frequencies, i.e. the range of frequencies initially generated (e.g. directly from a microphone or tv camera) cannot be transmitted as they exist over a radio or line system. The reasons for this are perhaps obvious, lower frequencies cannot be transmitted successfully by radio and even if they could, there is no way of sorting out the various transmissions. The technique is therefore to impress the baseband frequencies onto a higher frequency wave which can be transmitted. In medium wave broadcasting for instance, speech and music frequencies occupying a frequency range of a few Hz up to some 10 kHz are impressed on and transmitted by a higher frequency wave of perhaps 1 MHz. Modulation is the method by which this is achieved. On reception the wave is then *demodulated.*

Modulation is accordingly a method of altering the amplitude, frequency or phase of a *carrier wave* by a wave of lower frequency. The lower frequency wave is the signal carrying information and is termed the *modulating wave.* The carrier wave is so called because it transports (carries) the modulating wave and the composite signal of carrier wave and modulating wave is known as a *modulated wave.* Generally, but not exclusively, in radio transmission the carrier is a sine wave and is therefore of a single frequency only but when modulated it occupies a range of frequencies of bandwidth according to the type of modulation used.

Any type of change made to a carrier wave can be used to transmit information. The earliest radio systems simply switched the carrier on and off in accordance with some code (e.g. the Morse Code of dots and dashes) and as we now see it this is the equivalent of a carrier wave modulated by a rectangular wave. Apart from merely switching on and off, the other types of change which can be impressed on a sine wave carrier are:

(i) *amplitude* – in which the amplitude of the carrier wave is varied in accordance with the amplitude of the modulating wave and at its frequency;

(ii) *frequency* – in this the frequency (but not the amplitude) of the carrier wave is varied in accordance with the amplitude of the modulating wave. This variation is at the frequency of the modulating wave;

(iii) *phase* – the phase of the carrier is varied about its unmodulated value according to the amplitude of the modulating wave and at its frequency. The amplitude of the carrier wave remains constant.

There is also *pulse modulation* in which the carrier consists of a series of pulses which again can be changed in various ways.

See also Amplitude . . . , Frequency . . . , Phase . . . , Pulse . . . , Velocity Modulation, Demodulation.
(* Frequency, Bandwidth, Phase, Pulse >> Baseband, Balanced Modulator, Cross Modulation)

MODULATION FACTOR   This expresses the depth to which the carrier is modulated in an amplitude modulation system – see Amplitude Modulation.

MODULATION INDEX   This expresses the depth to which the carrier is modulated in a frequency modulation system — see Frequency Modulation.

MODULATOR   An electronic circuit which accepts as inputs (i) a carrier wave and (ii) a modulating wave. The output is the modulated wave which is the product of the two input waves. See for example Figure A4(vi).
(* Waveform, Carrier Wave, Modulation)

MODULUS — see Polar Coordinate.

MOLE is one of the base units of the S.I., but perhaps more widely used in chemistry than in electronics. The name of the unit is the *mole* but the symbol used is *mol* and it is basically a unit of a number of molecules.   A mole of any substance is the quantity whose mass is equal to its *mole*cular mass (or atomic mass if it is an element) expressed in grams instead of atomic mass units (u).   As an example, a water molecule has a mass of 18.02 atomic mass units (18.02 u) therefore a mole of water has a mass of 18.02 grams. Since an atomic mass unit is equivalent to 1.66043×10^{-27} kg it follows that there are 6.023×10^{23} molecules per mole.
The S.I. definition however is in terms of a known substance and it is that quantity of the material which contains as many "elementary entities" as there are atoms in 0.012 kg of the isotope carbon 12.   The elementary entities must be specified and may be atoms, molecules, ions, electrons, etc.
The usefulness of the mole arises from the fact that a mole of any substance contains the same number of molecules etc. as any other substance.
(* S.I., Atom, Molecule, Atomic Mass Unit, Isotope)

MOLECULE   Just over 100 different elements exist, each typified by its own particular atom, such as sulphur, nickel, carbon, silicon, zinc. When any two or more atoms combine chemically, another material substance is formed, usually bearing no resemblance whatever to its constituents. As an example, oxygen and hydrogen are elements and gases but when their atoms combine chemically, *molecules* of water are produced (the chemist's H_2O — 2 hydrogen atoms combined with one of oxygen per molecule). Figure M10 shows how, in a rather inadequate way, we might picture the molecules of water. A molecule is therefore the smallest particle of a substance which displays the characteristics of that substance. If the molecule is split up, only the atoms of the

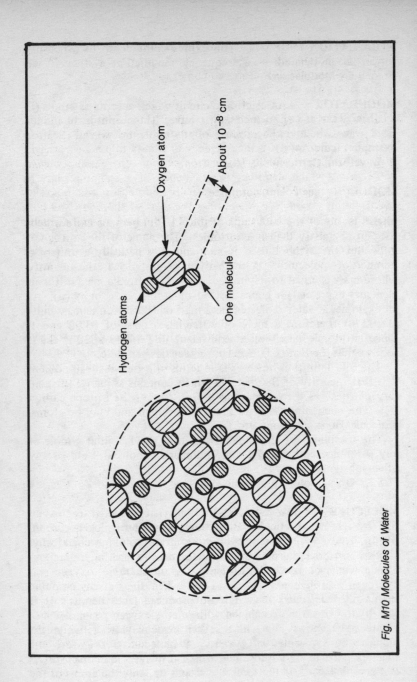

Fig. M10 Molecules of Water

constituent elements remain and the substance no longer exists. See Figure E2(i).

For examples of how atoms combine, see Bond.
(* Element, Atom)

MOMENTUM is one of the terms relating to the motion of a body. In a way it describes the vigour underlying the velocity of the body but more technically it is the tendency of a body to pursue a straight path at a constant velocity (*linear momentum* — there is also *angular momentum* which describes the tendency of a spinning body to continue to spin). Momentum is usually denoted by p with a value given simply by $m \times v$ where m is the mass of the body and v its velocity, the unit is therefore kg m/s. Note that momentum and energy are not the same, momentum is proportional to the velocity of a body, energy is proportional to the velocity squared. Velocity is a vector quantity, hence momentum is also.
(* Mass, Energy, Vector)

MOS TRANSISTOR (MOST)   This is an alternative term used for an insulated-gate field-effect transistor but in this case it describes the structure rather than the principle of operation. The metal gate is insulated from the channel hence the description "field-effect" and the insulator (the dielectric) is of silicon dioxide. This type of transistor is eminently suited to integrated circuit production — see Field-Effect Transistor.

MOTIONAL IMPEDANCE is perhaps best explained by considering the moving coil of a loudspeaker. When not in operation, the impedance of the coil (now not moving) is simply its resistance, generally of a few ohms. In operation however as the coil moves in the magnetic field, the back e.m.f. generated opposes the coil current and hence increases the coil impedance. Clearly the effect is frequency sensitive.

Motional impedance is therefore the difference between the impedance of a transducer under working conditions and that when it is motionless.
(* Impedance, Current, Back E.M.F. >> Loudspeaker)

MUTUAL CONDUCTANCE is a term used with active devices working on the basis of a changing voltage at the input giving rise to a changing current at the output. Two devices which fall into this category are the field-effect transistor and the thermionic valve, both of which have high input impedances and are therefore voltage driven. Mutual conductance is defined as the ratio between the incremental change in output current and the incremental change in input voltage causing it (with the output voltage held constant).

Mutual conductance is also known as *transconductance* or *forward transfer admittance*. It has the symbol g_m and is usually quoted in mA/V but as it is a conductance it can also be quoted in siemens (A/V).

As an example, drain current (I_d) versus gate voltage (V_{gs}) characteristics of field-effect transistors are shown in Figure F3. The mutual conductance is given by the slope of the curve at any chosen operating point, i.e. $g_m = \delta I_d / \delta V_{gs}$, where δ means "a small change in".

(* Conductance, Thermionic Valve, Field-Effect Transistor, Characteristic $\gg$ y-Parameters)

MUTUAL INDUCTANCE   Coils are said to have the property of mutual inductance when a change of current in either of them induces a voltage in the other — see Inductance.

N

NANOTECHNOLOGY is the manufacture to dimensions or tolerances from 0.1 nanometre (10^{-10} m — roughly the size of an atom) to 100 nm (10^{-7} m). The technique is essential in the development of improved electronic and optoelectronic components.

NATURAL FREQUENCY   If an electrical circuit or mechanical system is capable of vibrating and is given a short duration pulse of energy, free oscillations or vibrations are set up at a frequency determined by the constants of the circuit or system and known as the *natural frequency*. In practice the damping effect of resistance or friction causes the oscillations to die away. When an alternating voltage is impressed on an electrical oscillating circuit the current is maximum when the voltage has a frequency equal to the natural frequency.

(* Frequency, Resonance, Damping, Forced Oscillation $\gg$ Shock Excitation)

n-CHANNEL is the conducting path of n-type material through which the main current flows in a field-effect transistor (f.e.t.). Figure F3(i) shows such a channel. The term is also used to classify MOS integrated circuits and field-effect transistors when an n-type conducting path is used. Most f.e.t devices are n-channel since in n-channel the charge carriers are electrons which have higher mobility (and therefore higher operating speeds) compared with p-channel devices in which the charge carriers are less mobile holes. (* Field-Effect Transistor, Electron, Hole, Mobility >> Integrated Circuit, MOS Integrated Circuit)

NEGATIVE   If a glass rod is rubbed with silk, electrons are transferred from the rod to the silk. The charge accumulated by the silk due to the surplus electrons is labelled *negative* (–ve or –). (* Atom, Electron, Charge)

NEGATIVE FEEDBACK is a system in which a fraction of the output energy delivered by a circuit is returned to the input in opposition to the signal there – see Feedback.

NEGATIVE RESISTANCE   This term applies to any two-terminal circuit which has a negative real part to its impedance. More simply, the current increases as the voltage decreases and vice versa. The current/voltage characteristic exhibits negative resistance only over a certain part, it must be bounded on either side by regions of positive resistance. If this were no so, the device would be self-destructive.

Negative resistance devices deliver energy to the circuit terminals, this energy is in fact provided by the device power supply. In general there are two categories, classed as N and S because of the shapes of the current/voltage characteristics, typically as in Figure N1. As examples, the N shape is found in tunnel diodes, while the S occurs in thyristors.
(* Impedance, Characteristic, Energy, Gunn Effect, Tunnel Diode >> Thyristor)

NEON is an inert gas, symbol Ne, atomic number 10. When ionized, neon glows with the characteristic red light so often seen in neon signs.
(* Atom, Ionization, Gas Discharge)

NEPER is a unit of attenuation or gain which was introduced by John Napier, a Scottish mathematician. It is given the symbol Np. In everyday life the neper has been overtaken by the *decibel* but it

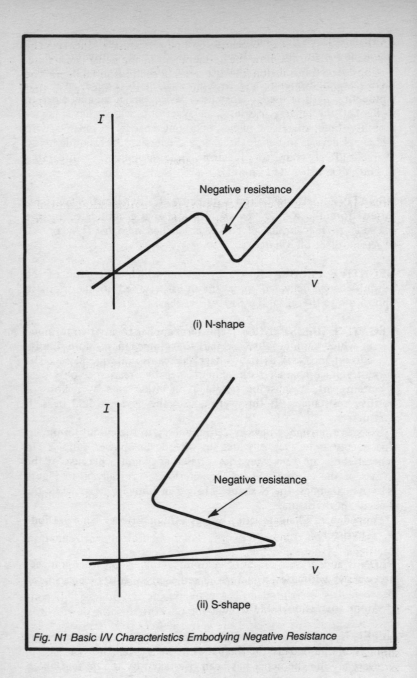

(i) N-shape

(ii) S-shape

Fig. N1 Basic I/V Characteristics Embodying Negative Resistance

still has its part to play, especially in line transmission theory. The following brief notes show the development of the neper and its use.

Consider a transmission line as a series of sections in tandem. The theory requires that the ratio of the current entering (I_1) to that leaving a section (I_2) is expressed by e^α where α is the attenuation coefficient, i.e. $(I_2/I_1) = e^\alpha$ from which:

$$\alpha = \log_e \frac{I_2}{I_1} \text{ nepers (Np)}$$

Put simply, the number of nepers (n) is the natural logarithm of a current or voltage ratio. To work in power instead, it follows that the number of nepers:

$$n = \log_e (I_2/I_1) = \log_e \sqrt{P_2/P_1} = \frac{1}{2} \log_e (P_2/P_1)$$

where P_1 is the power input and P_2 is the power output, from this

$$e^{2n} = P_2/P_1 .$$

Attenuation in nepers can be converted directly to decibels provided that the resistive components of the terminating impedances are equal for:

$$\text{number of decibels} = 20 \log_{10} I'$$

where I' is the current ratio and equals:

$$29 \log_e I' \times 20 \log_{10} e = \text{number of nepers} \times 8.686 ,$$

i.e. attenuation or gain in decibels = 8.686 × attenuation or gain in nepers.

One tenth of one neper is known as a *decineper*.
(* Transmission Line, Network, Polar Coordinate, Attenuation Coefficient, Decibel)

NETWORK is a system of components interconnected in such a way that overall a specific electrical characteristic is obtained. If consisting of impedances only so that the network absorbs power, it is classed as *passive*, if one or more active devices (e.g. transistors) are included, the network is said to be *active*. If there is a linear relationship between the voltages and currents within the network it is classed as *linear*, if not it is said to be *non-linear*. General classification may

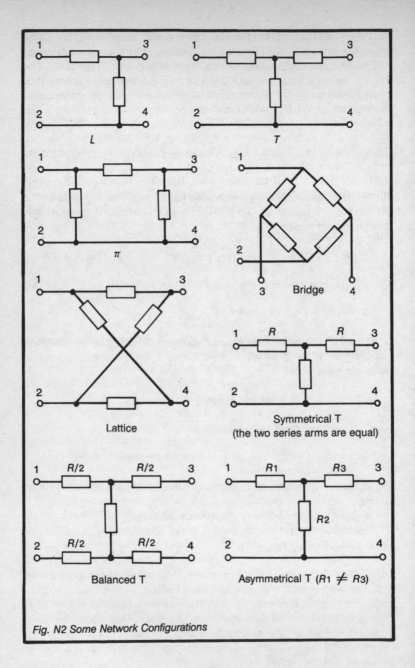

Fig. N2 Some Network Configurations

be by (i) component(s), e.g. resistance-capacitance or (ii) by shape on a drawing, e.g. L, T, π, bridge, lattice [these are illustrated by Fig.N2]. Networks designed as attenuators are frequently also known as *pads* and are available in *symmetrical* or *asymmetrical* form as shown in the figure. The network may also be *balanced* as shown for the T. *Unbalanced* is the term used when the series elements are in one wire only of the through circuit as in the L, T and π configurations shown in the figure. In this case terminals 2 or 4 are usually connected to the chassis or common of the equipment in which the network is used.

Those shown are basic networks, there are others more complicated. As an example, ladder networks are built up of a number of sections of L, T or π or again of these in balanced form. Most networks as shown in the figure are of the 4-terminal (quadripole) type and are designed for insertion in a 2-wire circuit.

Fortunately we have several theorems which help in analysis of networks and of course, Ohm's Law is basic to all. Some of the terminology associated with network analysis is as follows (in alphabetical order). Each is considered separately and in more detail as a term.

(1) *Compensation Theorem* – this deals with the replacement of any impedance in a network by a generator.

(2) *Iterative* and *Characteristic Impedance* – these terms refer to the impedance measured at one pair of terminals when the opposite pair is terminated in a special way.

(3) *Kirchhoff's Laws* – these enable equations to be derived for calculating the values of currents in a network.

(4) *Maximum Power Transfer Theorem* – shows the conditions required for maximum power transfer from a network to a terminating impedance.

(5) *Norton's Theorem* – is similar to Thévinin's Theorem (see below) but substitutes an equivalent current generator.

(6) *Reciprocity Theorem* – considers interchange of voltage or current in different parts of a linear circuit.

(7) *Star-Delta Transformation* – shows how to transform a star (or T) network into the equivalent delta (or π) and vice versa.

(8) *Superposition Theorem* – is a help when a linear network contains more than one generator.

(9) *Thévenin's Theorem* – applies to linear networks and enables load currents to be calculated by replacing a network by an equivalent voltage generator.

(* Impedance, Attenuation, Attenuator, Ohm's Law, Propagation Coefficient, Bridged-T Network, Ladder Network, Lattice Network, Mesh)

NEUTRAL is used to indicate the condition when positive and negative charges are in balance, i.e. there is no net charge.
(* Charge, Positive, Negative)

NEUTRON is one of the particles contained within an atomic nucleus. It has a mass of 1.67495×10^{-27} kg which is almost the same as that of a proton. Unlike the proton however, it has no electric charge. Neutrons are present in all atomic nuclei except that of hydrogen and their number is equal to or greater than the number of protons. It is considered that one of the functions of the neutrons is to hold the protons together within a nucleus for otherwise because of their like (positive) charges, they would fly apart.
(* Atom, Nucleus, Proton, Charge, Binding Energy)

NEWTON   This is the S.I. unit of force. It is that force which when applied to a mass of one kilogram gives it an acceleration of one metre per second per second (m/s^2). One newton is roughly equivalent to the weight exerted by 100 grams or about 3½ ounces.
(* Force, Mass)

NICKEL is a metal element, symbol Ni, atomic number 28. It is strongly ferromagnetic and is frequently alloyed with iron to improve the magnetic characteristics, especially the permeability.
   Nickel is also used in certain secondary cells.
(* Atom, Ferromagnetism, Permeability >> Nickel-Cadmium Cell, Nickel-Iron Cell)

NODE   The term is derived from the Latin, *nodus*, a knot and has two different uses in electronics:

(1)   in a network it is a point where three or more elements are connected together (see Fig.N3 for example);
(2)   of a standing wave, it is a point at which the voltage or current falls to a minimum or zero value. This is illustrated in Figure S8 which also shows the *antinodes*, the points of maximum value.

(* Network, Branch, Standing Wave)

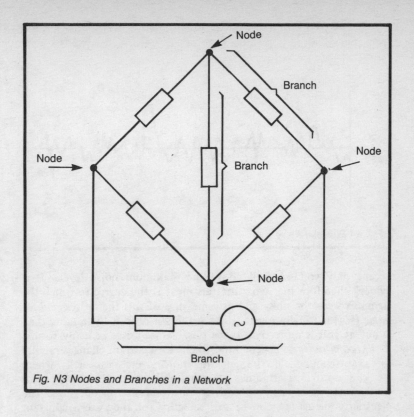

Fig. N3 Nodes and Branches in a Network

NOISE is the uninvited and generally unwanted guest. In tele-communications it is not only those sounds lacking in harmony and which offend our ears directly such as the pneumatic drill, the chatter at a party or the jet aircraft, but also the sounds heard from equipment as with the crackle on the radio or the hiss from a loud-speaker. But noise as defined in the telecommunications world goes further than that, it is *any* spurious electrical disturbance occurring within the effective frequency band of a circuit. This shows that noise need not be capable only of being heard. For example, even the white spots on a television screen are "noise".

Noise is present in all electronic systems and is one of the limiting factors to the usefulness of a communication channel. This is illustrated graphically in Figure N4 which shows how in a trans-mission channel carrying digital information, the pulse at A has little chance of being recognized above the general noise level, whereas the one at B is better off because equipment can be arranged to

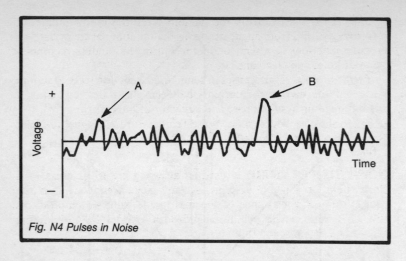

accept only voltages well above the maximum noise level. It is evident therefore that what matters most is the degree to which the signal exceeds the noise and as a measure of this the ratio *signal-to-noise* (s/n) is usually quoted. At **A** the s/n ratio is little more than 1 but at **B** it is more than twice this. Noise arises in many forms:

External noise — is generated whenever a current changes rapidly as in automobile electrics, electric motors, etc., especially where sparking occurs. Harmonics are generated and these enter systems or channels via capacitive, inductive or even resistive couplings. The electricity mains are also in this category for they are a constant source of "hum" and also carry voltage "spikes".

Random noise — as its name implies, arises from any randomly occurring disturbance which may be external to a system, e.g. lightning or occurring within the system, e.g. a poor connection. It is also used as a general term to describe noise arising from the random movements of large numbers of particles, especially electrons so giving rise to net charges which vary at random over a mean level. Subdivisions of this are thermal, shot and partition noise as described below.

Thermal noise — is everywhere, it arises from the random movement of electrons in a conductor. It has a constant power per unit of bandwidth with a frequency range extending to infinity. The graph of Figure N4 shows how a thermal noise voltage waveform might appear on an oscilloscope over a very short duration of time. Thermal noise, however, is probably the only type which has a practical use — it can be used for the generation of random numbers and for testing electronic equipment.

Shot noise — arises from the random variations in the number of electrons emitted from an electrode, in the random nature of carriers crossing junctions in a semiconductor and in the random recombination of holes and electrons.

Partition noise — also arises in semiconductors due to the random nature of the division of currents between electrodes, e.g. emitter current dividing between base and collector of a transistor.

(* Thermal Noise, White Noise, Noise Temperature >> Signal-to-Noise Ratio, Noise Factor, Noise Figure, Sky Noise, Psophometer)

NOISE TEMPERATURE is used in assessing electrical noise of a single item or a whole system. At any given frequency it is the temperature of a resistance of the appropriate value which produces the same noise power per unit bandwidth as does the noise being assessed. The reasoning follows from:

$$P_n = kTB$$

for thermal noise when the noise generator feeds into a matched load. P_n is the available noise power, k is Boltzmann's constant, T is the temperature in $^\circ$K and B is the bandwidth in hertz. Therefore noise temperature, T_n is calculated as follows:

$$T_n = P_n/kB$$

which shows that for a given bandwidth (e.g. 1 Hz), T can be used as an expression of the magnitude of noise. This refers to thermal noise but in many systems (e.g. satellite communication) all sorts of noise can be measured and quoted as an *equivalent noise temperature*.

(* Noise, Thermal Noise, Matching, Boltzmann's Constant, Kelvin, Bandwidth >> Satellite Television)

NON-LINEARITY If two quantities are related in such a way that by plotting one against the other on a simple graph the result is a straight line, then they are in a linear relationship. If, however, the graph is not a straight line but exhibits curvature anywhere, then the relationship between the two quantities is *non-linear*. Figure F3 shows at (iv) and (v) two examples of non-linearity. Its effects are classed under the general heading "distortion".

Perfect linearity is hard to achieve in electronic systems, hence it is important that we know where non-linearity arises and what its effects are:

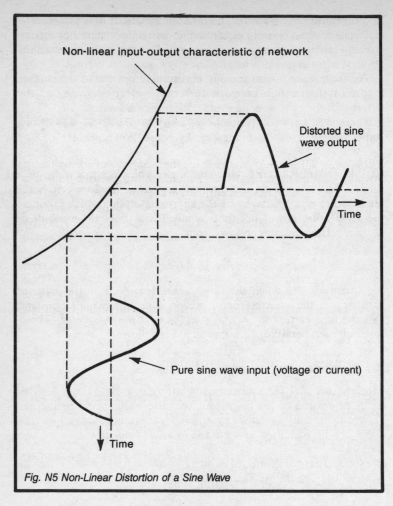

Non-linear input-output characteristic of network

Distorted sine wave output

Time

Pure sine wave input (voltage or current)

Time

Fig. N5 Non-Linear Distortion of a Sine Wave

(i) a sine wave is "pure" because it consists of one frequency only. However, if it meets non-linearity then its shape changes as demonstrated in Figure N5. Fourier analysis shows us that it then no longer consists of a single frequency but in addition, harmonics of this frequency. Usually the effect is undesirable and the harmonics are removed by filtering;

(ii) when two voltages of different frequency meet non-linearity together, the resulting current consists not only of these two frequencies but also others equal to their sum and difference. This is *modulation* which is essential in line and radio transmission. However, if, for example, such sum and difference frequencies are generated in an audio system, the intermodulation products as they are called can make the output sound unpleasant. Intermodulation products are not as easy to remove as are harmonics; accordingly it is essential to make the system as linear as possible.

(* Frequency, Distortion, Sine Wave, Fourier Analysis, Harmonic, Modulation)

NORTON'S THEOREM is used in the analysis of complicated networks containing generators. To understand this theorem it is preferable to read Thévenin's theorem first because Norton's is simply a modification of it. Whereas Thévenin's theorem replaces a network by a single generator plus its internal impedance, Norton's does the same except that the replacement is by a constant-current generator shunted by an admittance.

Generally Thévenin's theorem is the easier to apply especially as most engineers are happier working with impedance rather than with admittance. Nevertheless Norton's theorem is more useful when the network impedance is high compared with that of the load.

See Thévenin's Theorem.
(* Network, Impedance, Admittance >> Generator, Constant Current Source)

N-TYPE SEMICONDUCTOR   This is a semiconductor to which a donor impurity has been added so that the free electron density exceeds the hole density. Current flow through the device is therefore mainly by electrons.

For the basic technique, see Doping. See also P-type Semiconductor.
(* Semiconductor, Donor, Electron, Hole)

NUCLEON   A collective name for both neutrons and protons in an atomic nucleus — see Nucleus.

NUCLEUS is the centre of the atom and generally we leave it at that since it is electron behaviour which is the basis of electricity while the nucleus seems to do nothing more than hold the electrons in place. Nevertheless it is worth considering the nucleus because some nuclei are responsible for *radioactivity*. We may develop a respect for this tiny particle on learning that whereas energies of only a few electron-volts keep electrons in their orbits, any change in nuclear structure involves energies millions of times greater as demonstrated so distressingly by the atomic bomb.

Except for the hydrogen nucleus which consists of one proton only, all elements have nuclei containing both neutrons and protons (see for example, Fig.A7). The neutron has no charge, hence its name, it has a mass of $1.674\ 95 \times 10^{-27}$ kg. The proton has a charge equal to that of the electron but positive (i.e. $+1.602 \times 10^{-19}$ coulombs), its mass is $1.672\ 65 \times 10^{-27}$ kg. Both neutrons and protons are also called *nucleons*. As a rough guide the diameter of a nucleus is some 10^{-15} m.

The *atomic number, Z,* of an element is equal to the number of protons in the nucleus and for a *neutral* atom it is also equal to the total number of electrons in orbit. The total positive charge carried by a nucleus is therefore equal to *Ze* where *e* is the fundamental electronic charge. Except for hydrogen, the number of neutrons in a nucleus is equal to or greater than the number of protons and generally the likelihood of an excess of neutrons over protons increases with the atomic number.

From the above in which we picture a group of protons each with a positive charge comes the question as to why they do not fly apart. Obviously this does not happen and this is because there are extremely strong forces acting between all the nucleons in a nucleus binding them together (the *binding energy*). The forces are considered as a *nuclear field* and because the nucleons are tightly packed, these forces are of very short range. Even if they were not, they would have no effect on the electrons outside because these are only affected by positive or negative fields arising from charges. (* Atom, Electron, Orbit, Radioactivity, Energy, Electron-Volt, Charge, Mass, Binding Energy, Nucleon, Positron, Positive, Negative)

OHM   This is the standard unit of electrical resistance, reactance and impedance. It is that resistance which when subjected to a potential difference of one volt allows a current of one ampere to flow. The symbol used is the Greek capital omega (Ω).
(* Resistance, Reactance, Impedance, Potential Difference, Current, Ohm's Law)

OHM-METRE is the S.I. unit of electrical resistivity and is given the symbol Ω m — see S.I., Resistivity.

OHM'S LAW   In the early 1800's Georg Simon Ohm, a German physicist, studied how an electric potential caused current to flow through a wire and he was able to show that the magnitude of the current was directly proportional to the magnitude of the potential applied to the ends of the wire. He went on to show that (using our modern symbols) $I = G.V$ where G is the conductance, I and V are current and potential difference respectively. Ohm used the idea of *resistance* (R), so moving on to talking in terms of this instead of conductance, since:

$$G = 1/R , \quad \text{then } I = V/R$$

and when I is the current in amperes, V the potential difference in volts, R becomes the resistance in ohms. A practical arrangement linking voltage, current and resistance is illustrated by Figure O1(i), how this is shown as a circuit diagram is in (ii).

For a particular value of resistance, that the current through it is proportional to the voltage across it is easily demonstrated by means of a test circuit as shown in Figure O2(i). The resulting graph which for direct proportionality must be a straight line, is shown in (ii).

Naming the unit of resistance after him has honoured his name throughtout the world for giving us what is perhaps the most fundamental law in electronics.
(* Potential Difference, Current, Conductance, Resistance, Internal Resistance >> Ohmmeter)

OPEN-CIRCUIT IMPEDANCE refers to a 4-terminal network and is the impedance measured at one pair of terminals when the other pair of terminals is on open circuit.
(* Impedance, Network)

OPTICAL FIBRE   In the drive for higher and higher carrier frequencies to accommodate wider bandwidths it has been possible to jump several orders of frequency from the e.h.f. band (around 10^{11} Hz — see Fig.E5) to the visible spectrum, i.e. into a range extending approximately from 3×10^{14} to 8×10^{14} Hz (1000 — 375 nm). The system is based on the waveguide properties of the *optical fibre* which itself relies for its operation entirely on the phenomenon of *total internal reflection.*

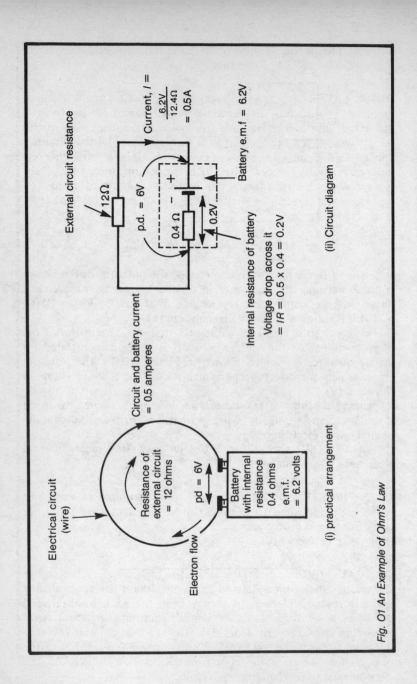

Fig. O1 An Example of Ohm's Law

External circuit resistance

12Ω

p.d. = 6V

Current, $I =$

$\dfrac{6.2V}{12.4\Omega}$

$= 0.5A$

Battery e.m.f = 6.2V

+
−

0.4 Ω

0.2V

Internal resistance of battery

Voltage drop across it
$= IR = 0.5 \times 0.4 = 0.2V$

(ii) Circuit diagram

Electrical circuit
(wire)

Resistance of
external circuit
= 12 ohms

pd = 6V

Circuit and battery current
= 0.5 amperes

Electron flow

Battery
with internal
resistance
0.4 ohms
e.m.f
= 6.2 volts

(i) practical arrangement

290

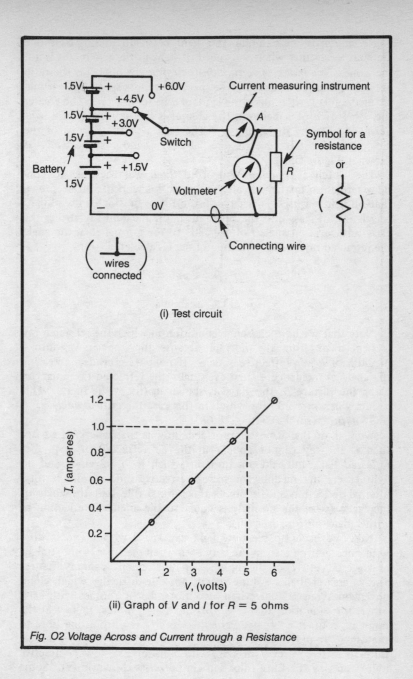

(i) Test circuit

(ii) Graph of V and I for R = 5 ohms

Fig. O2 Voltage Across and Current through a Resistance

Refraction is the bending of a light beam on passing from one medium to another when the speed of light in the two media is not the same. The *index of refraction* (or *refractive index*) is the ratio between the speed of light in free space (c) and its speed in a particular medium (v). It is given the symbol n hence $n = c/v$. The greater the value of n of a medium, the greater is the deflection of a light beam on entering or leaving it. The angles to the normal of the incident and refracted rays are labelled i and r respectively as shown in Figure O3(i).

The Dutch astronomer Willebrord Snell was the first to consider refraction mathematically and from his work it can be shown that $\sin i/\sin r = n_2/n_1$. Hence in the figure in which a ray of light travels out of glass into the open air, if the incident ray strikes the glass surface at an angle i of, say $30°$ to the normal then the angle the refracted ray makes with the normal is calculated from:

$$\sin r = n_1/n_2 \sin i = 0.31$$

$\therefore \qquad\qquad\qquad r = 53.1° \text{ as shown.}$

Note that we have chosen a condition in which the refracted ray is bent *away* from the normal because the light moves into a medium of *lower* refractive index. If next we consider increasing the angle of incidence, i then eventually the refracted ray must run along the surface of the glass as shown in (ii) of the figure. This occurs when $r = 90°$ for which in this case the *critical angle, i_c* = $\sin^{-1} n_2/n_1 = \sin^{-1} 0.625 = 38.68°$.

What is of the utmost importance now is that when i is greater than i_c the ray cannot appear in the air refracted, it is in fact *reflected* back into the medium in which it is travelling and no light enters the medium of lower refractive index. This is total internal reflection and it obeys the normal rule that the angle of incidence (with the normal) is equal to the angle of reflection as with a plane mirror – see (iii).

Now we begin to see how light can travel within a glass fibre with none getting lost on the way even when the fibre is not straight as suggested in (iv) of the figure. The requirement is simply that i is always greater than i_c. Fine so far, but one difficulty which could be encountered is that when two fibres lie in contact with each other, the condition that $n_1 > n_2$ no longer holds, in fact at the point of contact $n_1 = n_2$, light therefore travels from one fibre to the other. In practice therefore for communication purposes optical fibres consist of a core of glass with a cladding of lower refractive index, making the fibre fully self-contained as shown in (v). Some

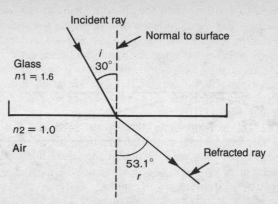

(i) A ray of light entering a medium of lower refractive index

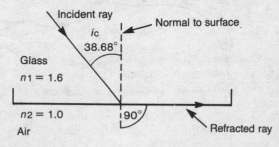

(ii) Critical angle

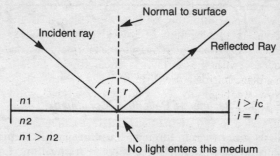

(iii) Refraction changes to reflection

Fig. O3 Total Internal Reflection

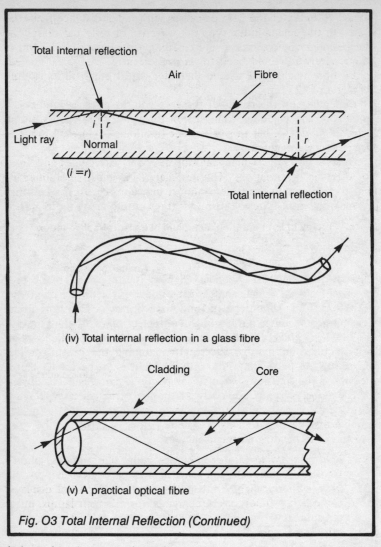

Total internal reflection

Air   Fibre

Light ray   Normal

$(i = r)$

Total internal reflection

(iv) Total internal reflection in a glass fibre

Cladding   Core

(v) A practical optical fibre

Fig. O3 Total Internal Reflection (Continued)

light is lost however through scattering and absorption by impurities in the glass, i.e. the fibre exhibits attenuation. Low attenuation has been one of the keys to success for optical fibres and it is achieved through the use of ultra-pure silica glass. Practical attenuations are only a fraction of a decibel or so per kilometre.

Progression radially from the core into the cladding may be either *step* in which the transition is abrupt or *graded* in which the refractive index of the core decreases with radial distance from the axis. In the graded-index type the wave is not reflected sharply at the boundary between core and cladding as in Figure O3(iii) but is progressively refracted back towards the centre. A typical graded-index fibre might have a core diameter of 50 μm with a cladding diameter of 125 μm.

Depending on the radius of the core and the refractive indices of both core and cladding, transmission through a fibre occurs in one or more *modes*, either in single mode (monomode) or multimode as occurs in a waveguide.

Optical fibres have many advantages over waveguides and wires for carrying information. The raw material is cheap and abundant and the bandwidth available is almost unbelievable. It is a fact that a single hair thin fibre is capable of transmitting many thousands of telephone calls simultaneously.

(* Visible Spectrum, Bandwidth, Waveguide, Attenuation $\gg$ Optoelectronics, Fibre Optic Transmission)

OPTOELECTRONICS is concerned with the transmission and processing of optical signals and the use of devices to convert them into their electronic counterparts and vice versa. Two important developments which have brought optoelectronics to the fore are the low-loss optical fibre and the semiconductor laser which can be manufactured to have a wavelength matching the low-loss wavelength of the particular fibre with which it is to be used. Optoelectronic transmission systems have many advantages over conventional copper systems especially at the high frequencies which are required for large bandwidths and in their requirement of a smaller number of repeaters for a given system.

Under this heading we might include:

(1)   *light detectors:* photoconductive cells, photodiodes, phototransistors, solar cells and other light actuated devices;
(2)   *light emitters:* light emitting diodes, liquid crystal displays, cathode-ray tubes, gas discharge lamps, filament lamps, infrared sources;
(3)   *optical isolators.*

(* Optical Fibre, Laser, Bandwidth $\gg$ Repeater, Fibre-Optic Transmission, Optical Isolator)

ORBIT is the path taken by one body round another. Usually the moving body is the smaller and the path is through space. The inescapable example of this is the earth which moves in a circular orbit round the sun. The orbits of comets and most artificial

satellites, however, are elliptical, one exception being the *geostationary* artificial satellite which has a circular orbit. Electronics is greatly concerned with the orbit of the electron round its atom nucleus. This is in space and for any particular orbit, the centrifugal (centre-fleeing) force which tends to move the electron out of the orbit is exactly balanced by the attractive force tending to pull the electron back towards the nucleus (the centripetal force). This latter force arises from the unlike charges possessed by the nucleus (positive) and the electron itself (negative).
(* Atom, Electron, Charge >> Satellite)

OSCILLATION   The term is derived from Latin, *oscillare*, to swing and hence applies to anything which swings to and fro. In electronics we define oscillation as a periodic variation of an electrical quantity (usually current or voltage).

Generation of oscillations is frequently achieved by use of a resonant circuit, i.e. one containing capacitance (C), inductance (L) and the inevitable resistance (R). If a closed LC(R) circuit is excited by a pulse of energy from an external source, oscillation is set up within. The energy which was originally supplied by the excitation is alternately stored as the charge of the capacitor, then in the magnetic field of the inductor. This energy swinging between capacitor and inductor is an electrical oscillation at the *natural frequency* of the circuit which is given by $f_r = 1/2\pi\sqrt{LC}$. Resistance losses take their toll and the oscillation quickly dies away. Such an oscillation is said to be *free*. If however an active device such as an amplifier or a negative resistance component can replace the energy which is lost on each cycle by feeding in the right amount at the right time, then the oscillation can be maintained and many oscillators work on this principle. On the other hand an *LC* circuit may experience *forced oscillations* if connected to an external alternating electromotive force (e.m.f.). The circuit then contains a mixture of oscillations at its natural frequency plus oscillations at the frequency of the applied e.m.f. The oscillatory current is maximum when the two frequencies coincide — this is the basic principle used in tuning radio receivers. LC oscillation is generally sine wave.

Oscillation is also achieved without the help of inductance, a significant advantage when integrated circuits are required. The oscillation frequency is controlled not by a resonant circuit but by the time constants or phase shifts of resistance-capacitance networks. In phase-shift oscillation circuits, feedback over an amplifier is made positive by interposing an RC network between input and output. Again the oscillation is sine wave.

When waveforms other than sinusoidal are required, *relaxation* circuits are usually employed. In these the control is exercised by one or more *RC* networks (*RL* may also be used but in practice this is less likely owing to the bulk of the inductor). There is a rise in output voltage while the capacitor is being charged (the "relaxing" time) but a sudden fall when it is rapidly discharged. A typical waveform is the "sawtooth" but very many other shapes can also be generated. The multivibrator is a type of relaxation oscillator, e.g. the astable version is *RC* controlled, working on the basis of continual sudden switching between two states, consequently it generates square waves. The frequency of oscillation is inversely proportional to the time constants of the built-in RC networks. (* Resonance, Natural Frequency, Oscillator, Feedback, Forced Oscillation, Sine Wave, Time Constant, Phase Shift, Negative Resistance >> Oscillator, Relaxation Oscillator, Multivibrator)

OWEN BRIDGE is an a.c. bridge network which is used for measuring a wide range of inductance values in terms of resistance and capacitance. The circuit is shown in Figure O4 and in this L_x and R_x represent the unknown inductance. At balance (i.e. when there is no deflection on the meter), then:

$$L_x = R_1 R_3 C_2 \qquad R_x = R_1 C_2 / C_3$$

By connecting a d.c. voltage source through a large series inductor (with blocking capacitors as required), the bridge can be made suitable for measurement of the incremental permeability of iron-cored inductors which are subject to alternating current superimposed on a direct current.
(* Bridge, Inductance, Permeability, Core, Incremental Permeability)

OXIDE is formed by the chemical composition of an element with oxygen. The term is prefixed by di, tri, etc. according to the number of oxygen atoms which are contained in each molecule. The oxide we are mostly concerned with in electronics is *silicon dioxide* (silica — $Si + O_2 = SiO_2$) and it is worth noting that frequently it is called silicon oxide, thus mention of the "oxide layer" really means "silicon dioxide layer". It is fortunate that the element silicon is one which has a great affinity for oxygen hence silicon dioxide is comparatively easily formed on a silicon layer. The technique is to pass oxygen or steam over the heated layer. (* Silicon, Molecule, Bond >> Planar Process, Photolithography, Integrated Circuit)

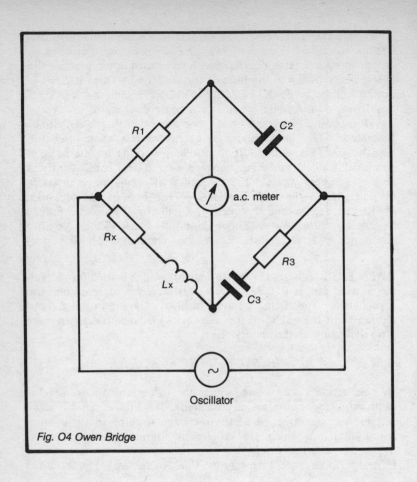

Fig. O4 Owen Bridge

P

PARABOLA is a particular form of *conic section*, it is the shape revealed when a cone is sliced parallel to its side. Mathematically a parabola is described by the function $y^2 = 4fx$ where f is known as the *focal length* and is the distance along the principal axis as shown in Figure P1 in which the focal length is chosen as 20 units.

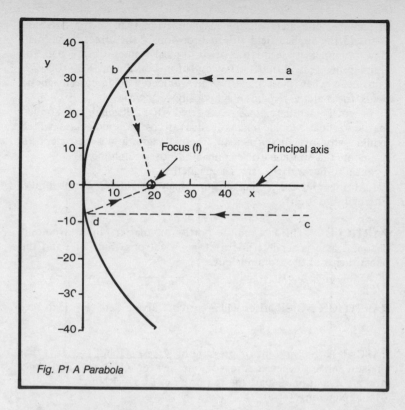

Fig. P1 A Parabola

The important feature of the parabola of which we make much use in antenna design is that as a receiving antenna all electromagnetic energy arriving parallel to the principal axis is directed to the focus, equally on transmitting, energy launched at the focus is radiated as a parallel beam as with a searchlight. A parabolic antenna is therefore highly directional. Two wave paths to illustrate this are shown in the figure as abf and cdf.
(* Antenna >> Parabolic Antenna)

PARALLEL RESONANCE   The condition of resonance which arises when a circuit comprises a capacitor and inductor in parallel as shown in Figure R8 (iii) — see Resonance Frequency.

PARAMAGNETISM is a property exhibited by certain materials, both metals and compounds, for which the relative permeability is very slightly greater than 1. The relative permeability, μ_r can be used as a guide to the effect of a magnetizing field on a material.

In paramagnetic materials the magnetization is in such a direction as to aid the applied field although obviously the effect is minimal. How minimal is seen from two typical values of μ_r, e.g. for aluminium it is 1.000 000 65 and for beryllium, 1,000 000 79. Thus even when these materials are subjected to intense magnetic fields, the material remains magnetically very weak.

In such materials it is considered that although an applied magnetic field would tend to align atoms and molecules which exhibit any overall magnetism, thermal agitation is sufficient to overcome this so the particles remain disposed randomly.

See also Ferromagnetism, Diamagnetism.
(* Atom, Molecule, Magnetism, Magnetic Field, Permeability, Thermal Agitation)

PARTICLE   This is a minute portion of matter. In electronics it is found as a general term for atoms, electrons, molecules and the constituents of the atom nucleus.
(* Atom, Molecule)

PARTITION NOISE arises when currents divide between electrodes — see Noise.

PASCAL is the S.I. unit of pressure or stress, symbol Pa. It is that pressure arising when a force of one newton (1N) acts uniformly over an area of one square metre (m^2), i.e. 1 Pa = 1 N/m^2.
(* S.I., Newton, Metre)

PASCHEN'S LAW refers to a discharge between two electrodes in a gas. It states that the voltage required for breakdown is a function of the product of the gas pressure and the electrode separation. As an example, if the gas pressure is doubled, the distance between the electrodes must be halved for the same breakdown voltage and vice versa.
(* Gas Discharge, Breakdown)

PASS BAND   The range between the highest and lowest frequencies passed by a filter — see Filter.

PASSIVE is a term generally applied to a component or circuit which does not introduce gain. Components such as resistors, capacitors and inductors are passive. The opposite is *active* as exemplified by the transistor.

See also Active.

PAULI EXCLUSION PRINCIPLE   Through quantum theory an electron within an atom is completely specified by four quantum numbers:

(i)   the *principal* number, n, which specifies the shell, i.e. for the K, L, M . . . shells, $n = 1, 2, 3$ . . .

(ii)   an *azimuthal* number, l, which specifies the angular orbital momentum of the electron. Values of l of 0, 1, 2, 3, 4 and 5 are generally referred to by s, p, d, g and f (see Fig.S4). They indicate the orbital shape;

(iii)   a *spatial* number, m, which specifies the orientation of the magnetic field of the electron orbit. This is important in considerations involving the application of an external magnetic field;

(iv)   a *spin* number, s, specifies the direction of spin of an electron on its own axis (see Fig.M5). There are two spin directions, these have values of $\frac{1}{2}h/2\pi$ and $-\frac{1}{2}h/2\pi$, where h is Planck's constant.

There are therefore many different electron states and in 1925 Wolfgang Pauli (an Austrian physicist) proposed his Exclusion Principle which simply says that no two electrons in an atom can have the same full set of quantum energy numbers. In accordance with this, if two electrons are described by the quantum numbers, n, l and m, then they can occupy the same orbital provided that their spins are opposing.

(* Atom, Electron, Orbit, Shell, Planck's Constant, Spin)

p-CHANNEL is the conducting path of p-type material through which the main current flows in a field-effect transistor. The term is also used to classify MOS integrated circuits and field-effect transistors when a p-type conducting path is used. Generally p-channel devices are less used compared with n-type since in p-type the charge carriers are holes which have lower mobility (and therefore operating speed) compared with n-type in which the charge carriers are the more mobile electrons.

(* Semiconductor, Field-Effect Transistor, Electron, Hole, Mobility >> MOS Integrated Circuit)

P.D. — see Potential Difference.

PEAK FACTOR is a feature of an alternating waveform. It gives the relationship between the peak value and the root mean square (r.m.s.) value and is helpful in describing the shape of a waveform, especially when used in conjunction with the *form factor*.

Let the peak voltage of a sinusoidal waveform $= V_{max}$. The r.m.s. value is then $V_{max}/\sqrt{2}$, hence:

$$\text{peak factor} = \frac{\text{peak value}}{\text{r.m.s. value}} = \frac{V_{max}}{V_{max}/\sqrt{2}} = \sqrt{2} = 1.414 .$$

For a square wave, however, the r.m.s. value is equal to V_{max}, the peak factor is therefore 1.0.

See also Form Factor.

(* Alternating Current, Sine Wave, Square Wave, Root Mean Square)

PEAK VALUE is the maximum positive or negative value of an alternating quantity over a specified period — see for example, Sine Wave.

PELTIER EFFECT   If two different metals are placed in contact, because the energy distribution among the electrons in each of them is different, a contact potential is set up. If a current flows across the junction, heat is absorbed or released depending on whether the current flows with or against the contact potential. The effect is named after its discoverer — see Thermoelectric Effect.

PENTODE is any electronic device containing 5 electrodes but the term is usually reserved for describing a certain type of thermionic valve. It is equivalent to a triode (cathode, control grid and anode) with the addition not only of a screen grid but also an open-mesh *suppressor grid*. This is situated between the screen grid and the anode. Normally with a tetrode secondary electrons flow from anode to screen and this is shown by a kink in the output characteristics. The suppressor grid is held at cathode potential hence is negative relative to both screen and anode. It therefore repels (or suppresses) secondary electrons released at the anode and the tetrode kink is eliminated.

(* Thermionic Valve, Tetrode, Characteristic)

PERIOD (PERIODIC TIME) is the time required to complete one cycle of a regularly recurring waveform. It is labelled by the symbol T, with the second (s) as the unit. For a given waveform having a frequency f hertz and therefore an angular frequency, $\omega = 2\pi f$ radians per second, the period is

$$T = 1/f = 2\pi/\omega \text{ seconds.}$$

(* Waveform, Cycle, Frequency, Angular Frequency, Radian)

PERIODIC   Briefly this means recurring at regular intervals. Generally in electronics it refers to a wave which repeats regularly with respect to time. Sine waves and most musical notes are periodic, speech waves are hardly in this category because except for very short intervals, the fundamental frequency is constantly changing.

PERMEABILITY is a measure of the ease with which a material is magnetised. It has a parallel in the electrical circuit where conductance expresses the ease with which a material (or circuit) passes an electric current when a given voltage is applied. In the magnetic sense, permeability expresses the ease with which magnetic flux is set up in a substance when a magnetic field is applied. The magnetic flux is quantified by the *magnetic flux density* (B) and the field by the *magnetic field strength* (H). Permeability is designated by μ with the unit the henry per metre (H/m). Its value for any path is given by the ratio of the flux density B to the magnetic field strength H producing it, i.e. $\mu = B/H$.

The *permeability of free space* or *magnetic constant* is that of a vacuum and is given the symbol μ_0. It is a constant which is necessary in electronics to link theoretical calculations with practical observed values. The permeability of air is almost the same as that of free space. The value of μ_0 in the S.I. system is $4\pi \times 10^{-7}$ H/m.

Relative permeability is the amount by which the magnetic flux density is increased or decreased when a particular material is substituted for free space. It is given the symbol μ_r. Hence $\mu = \mu_0 \times \mu_r$.

Relative permeabilities range from a little less than 1 up to many thousands.

The link between permeability and permittivity (ϵ_0) was found by James Clerk Maxwell to be $\mu_0 \epsilon_0 = 1/c^2$ where c is the velocity of light in metres per second.

When a small alternating magnetic field is superimposed on a larger, steady one, the ratio of the change in magnetic flux to the small change in magnetising force which gives rise to it, is known as the *incremental permeability*. The effect mainly concerns windings on magnetic cores where a small alternating current flows through the winding together with a larger direct current (e.g. in some audio output transformers). Increasing the direct current towards the level of saturation of the magnetic core, reduces the incremental permeability.

(* Magnetism, Magnetic Flux, Magnetic Flux Density, Magnetic Field Strength, Free Space, Core >> Electromagnet, Permeability Tuning)

PERMEANCE is a feature of the magnetic circuit. It expresses for a material the ease with which a given magnetomotive force can create a magnetic flux. It is analogous to *conductance* in the electrical circuit and is the reciprocal of *reluctance* (R_m) in the magnetic circuit. The symbol used is Λ (Greek, capital lambda) and the unit the weber per ampere, i.e. the henry. In a magnetic circuit therefore:

$$\text{Permeance}, \Lambda = \frac{\text{magnetic flux}}{\text{magnetomotive force}} = \frac{\Phi}{F}$$

Also:

$$\Lambda = 1/R_m = (\mu \times a)/l$$

where μ is the permeability of the material, l, the length of the path in metres and a the area of cross-section in square metres.
(* Magnetism, Magnetomotive Force, Reluctance, Magnetic Flux, Permeability, Conductance)

PERMITTIVITY is a measure of the ability of a material to store electrical energy in an electric field. Permittivity is designated by ϵ. It has a parallel in the electrical circuit where conductance expresses the ease with which a material (or circuit) passes an electric current when a given voltage is applied. In electrostatics permittivity relates to the electric flux developed (as measured by the flux density, D) by a given electric field strength, E. Hence:

$$\epsilon = D/E \text{ farads per metre (F/m)}$$

(The unit for D is coulombs/metre^2 and that for E is volts/metre, hence the unit for D/E becomes coulombs per volt per metre, i.e. farads per metre.)
(Compare also with $\mu = B/H$ for the magnetic circuit.)

The *permittivity of free space* or *electric constant* is that of a vacuum and is given the symbol ϵ_0. It is a constant which is necessary in electronics to link theoretical calculations with practical observed values. The permittivity of air is almost the same as that of free space. The value of ϵ_0 in the S.I. system is $10^{-9}/36\pi$, i.e. 8.854×10^{-12} farads per metre.

Relative permittivity or *dielectric constant* is a more practical consideration and usually refers to the amount by which the capacitance of a capacitor is increased when a particular material is substituted for free space. It is given the symbol ϵ_r. Hence:

$$\epsilon = \epsilon_0 \times \epsilon_r \ .$$

Relative permittivities range from less than 10 for mica, glass, polystyrene, etc. to over 1000 for certain ceramics.

The link between permittivity and permeability (μ_0) was found by James Clerk Maxwell to be $\mu_0 \epsilon_0 = 1/c^2$ where c is the velocity of light in metres per second.

(* Energy, Charge, Field, Electric Flux Density, Electric Field Strength, Free Space, Farad)

PHASE   A term mainly used with regard to electrical waveforms and in this respect defined as a point within the cycle relative to a fixed datum point, measured in degrees or radians (the phase angle).
(* Cycle, Radian, Phase Angle)

PHASE ANGLE   A sine wave can be represented by a rotating phasor (see Fig.S5). When two such waves act together the angle between their phasors is known as the *phase angle*. This is illustrated in Figure P2 where at a certain time t, $\angle$BOP represents the phase of wave B relative to the fixed datum point at t_0. Similarly $\angle$AOP is the phase of wave A relative to the same datum. The angle ϕ between these two phasors is the phase angle and it is also known as the *phase difference* between the two waves. Wave B is said to be *lagging* on wave A by ϕ (degrees or radians), equally wave A is said to be *leading* wave B by ϕ. If the waves have the same frequency, the phase angle between them remains constant, when $\phi = 90°$ ($\pi/2$ radians), they are said to be *in quadrature*, when $\phi = 180°$ (π radians), the waves are said to be *in opposition*. If the two waves are of different frequencies, the phase angle varies continually.
(* Sine Wave, Phase, Phasor, Lag, Lead, Radian)

PHASE-CHANGE COEFFICIENT   This is part of the *propagation coefficient* of a line or network. The propagation coefficient is a complex quantity comprising a real part known as the attenuation coefficient and an imaginary part, β, the *phase-change coefficient*. β is expressed in radians per metre (for degrees per metre multiply by 57.3) so that for any transmission line the phase of the voltage (or current) l metres away relative to that at the sending end is βl radians (lagging).

β is calculated from the primary coefficients of a line or network – see Propagation Coefficient.
(* Transmission Line, Radian, Network, Phase Angle)

PHASE CONSTANT is synonymous with Phase-Change Coefficient – see this term.

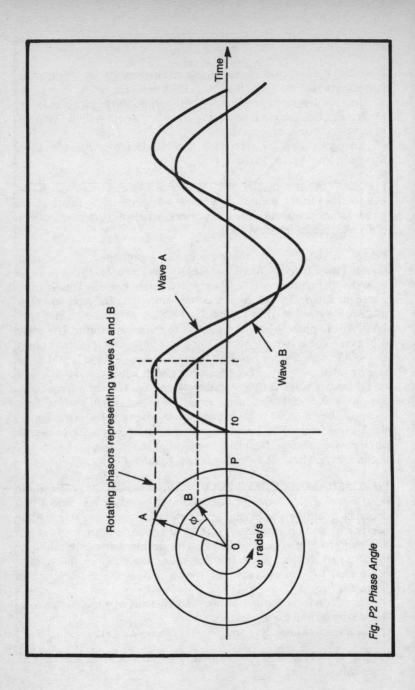

Fig. P2 Phase Angle

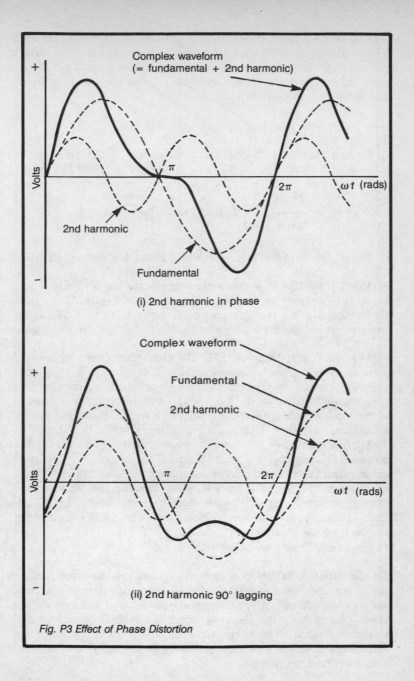

Complex waveform
(= fundamental + 2nd harmonic)

2nd harmonic

Fundamental

(i) 2nd harmonic in phase

Complex waveform

Fundamental

2nd harmonic

(ii) 2nd harmonic 90° lagging

Fig. P3 Effect of Phase Distortion

PHASE DELAY refers to an alternating waveform and is an expression of the phase difference between the input and output waveforms of a system on a time basis. It is given the symbol t_ϕ. If the phase difference or shift is ϕ radians and the frequency of the wave is ω radians per second, then:

$$\text{phase delay}, t_\phi = \phi/\omega \text{ seconds}.$$

We can also work in degrees, for example if the phase shift introduced by a system is $60°$ at a frequency of 1000 Hz, then:

$$t_\phi = \frac{60}{360 \times 1000} \text{ seconds} = 167 \text{ microseconds}.$$

(* Waveform, Frequency, Phase Shift, Phase Difference, Radian)

PHASE DIFFERENCE is the angle representing the time difference between two waves of the same frequency. In Figure P2 the two waves A and B are represented by the vectors OA and OB. The angle ϕ between them is the phase difference — see Phase Angle.

PHASE DISTORTION arises when the phase shift over a system or network is not directly proportional to frequency. In this case some frequency components in the output of the system do not have the same phase relationship with other frequencies as existed at the input of the system. This therefore creates distortion of the waveform. A simple demonstration of this is given in Figure P3. This shows in full line the complex waveform arising from a fundamental frequency together with its second harmonic. In (i) the two are in phase but in (ii) the second harmonic has been shifted so that it lags on the fundamental by $90°$. The effect on the overall waveform is perhaps surprising but it must be remembered that phase shifts generally are of lower order and that higher harmonics usually have lower amplitudes.
(* Distortion, Phase Shift, Harmonic)

PHASE MODULATION is a method of angle modulation in which the phase angle of a carrier wave is varied about its unmodulated value in accordance with the instantaneous value of the modulating wave. Accordingly the phase variation is at the frequency of the modulating signal. The carrier wave has constant amplitude and the system therefore has a better signal-to-noise performance compared with amplitude modulation.

Consider a sine wave modulating signal of frequency f_m, phase modulating a carrier wave, f_c of maximum amplitude E. The instantaneous amplitude e of the modulated wave is given by:

$$e = E \sin(2\pi f_c t + \beta \sin 2\pi f_m t)$$

where β is the peak phase variation.

The *phase deviation* is the maximum difference between the instantaneous phase angle of the modulating wave and that of the carrier. Because the phase deviation must be relative to something, a reference phase must be generated in the demodulation process and this is one complication which frequently makes frequency modulation preferable. In the latter a reference is automatically transmitted to the receiving end in the form of the one component carrying no information, the unmodulated carrier.

(* Phase Angle, Carrier Wave, Angle Modulation, Amplitude Modulation, Frequency Modulation, Demodulation >> Phase Discriminator)

PHASE SHIFT   Simply implies a change in the phase angle existing between any two periodic quantities. Take Figure P3 as an example. In (ii) of this figure, the second harmonic passes through zero (or reaches maximum) one quarter of a cycle ($90°$ or $\pi/2$ radians) later than it does in (i). It has therefore undergone a phase shift of $90°$.

Phase shifts occur when there are reactances present in networks, they may be unwanted and so give rise to *phase distortion*, equally they can be deliberately introduced by means of a *phase shifting network*.

(* Sine Wave, Phase Angle, Impedance, Reactance, Radian)

PHASE VELOCITY refers to a single wave travelling through a medium. It is the velocity at which an *equiphase front* travels in the direction of the normal. Put more simply, it is the velocity at which any particular point on the waveform travels (e.g. a maximum or zero). The phase velocity, $v_P = \lambda/T$ where λ is the wavelength and T is the period (periodic time). It is also given by $v_P = f \times \lambda$ since $f = 1/T$ where f is the wave frequency.

If the phase velocity is independent of frequency, then all components in a group of several waves travel at the same velocity, hence the *group velocity* is equal to the phase velocity.

See also Group Velocity.

(* Electromagnetic Wave, Wavelength, Frequency, Phase, Period)

PHASOR   A *vector* is described as a quantity possessing both magnitude and direction. It can be represented by a line whose length and angle with some reference axis correspond to this magnitude and direction. When such a line is used in electronics to indicate magnitude and relative phase of, for example, a current, voltage or impedance, it is then known as a *phasor*.

For ease of manipulation, phasors can be resolved into two components at right angles as shown in Figure P4(i). Here the reference axis is the horizontal one and the direction of the phasor OP is given by the angle ϕ it makes with the reference axis (this is normally at 3 o'clock as shown). The phasor is described as OP$\angle\phi$, (e.g. $5\angle20°$, $9.6\angle87°$ etc.). The two components are simply projections of the phasor onto the horizontal and vertical axes. As an example, for OP = 10 units and $\phi = 30°$, the horizontal component, OPcos $\phi = 8.66$ and the vertical component, OPsin $\phi = 5.0$. These components have special names in electronics and are used in complex algebra – see Complex Notation.

The resultant of two phasors can be determined by completion of the parallelogram which has these phasors as two of its sides. The resultant is the diagonal. However, to make sure that we get the right diagonal it may be better to work with only half a parallelogram, i.e. a triangle. Figure P4(ii) shows this way of doing the job. The arrows on the two phasors must run in the same direction round the triangle, the arrow on the third side (the resultant) is then placed running in the opposite direction. In the drawing the resultant of the two phasors V_1 and V_2 is V, leading V_1 by 30°. Its two components at right angles are OP the in-phase and PQ the quadrature. The latter is shown in the figure as having a magnitude V_2 sin 60° but it could equally be V sin 30°.

(* Phase, Phase Angle, In-Phase Component, Quadrature Component)

PHONON   In a crystal of say, silicon or germanium, heat causes atoms to vibrate about their mean positions with energies proportional to the temperature. These vibrations create elastic waves wihin the crystal which travel at the speed of sound (in this type of solid some 10 times the speed in air). If an elastic wave has a frequency f, then according to quantum theory, its energy can be quantized as hf joules where h is Planck's constant; the quantum is known as a *phonon*. The number of phonons traversing a crystal therefore rises with temperature.

We can look upon phonons which are transmitted through a crystal as particles which are analogous to *photons* which exist in electromagnetic waves. For both the energy is given by hc/λ so

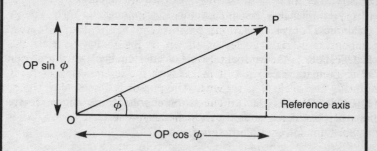

(i) Components of a phasor

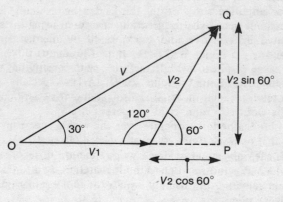

(ii) Finding a resultant phasor

Fig. P4 Phasors and Components

because the velocity c for a phonon is very much less than that for an electromagnetic wave, the energy of a phonon is only about one-tenth of that of a photon. Nevertheless, phonons in a crystal lattice are said to be the cause of additional electron collisions hence are important in the deep down physics of semiconductors.

(* Crystal, Planck Constant, Photon, Electromagnetic Wave, Energy, Quantum Theory)

PHOSPHOR   A material capable of emitting light when irradiated — see Luminescence.

PHOSPHORESCENCE is the emission of light from a phosphor after its atoms have been excited to a higher energy level.

See Luminescence, Persistence.

PHOTOCATHODE   This is a cathode which accepts photons and emits electrons into the space at its surface. The basic theory of this action is known as the *photoelectric effect*. Briefly, photons are absorbed into the photocathode material and excite free electrons. If the total kinetic energy of an excited electron exceeds the work function of the material the electron can escape from the surface (it is then known as a photoelectron). If the cathode is mounted within an evacuated tube, as soon as the photoelectrons escape they can be collected or amplified.

Photocathode sensitivity is generally measured using a standardized tungsten light source and is expressed in microamperes per lumen ($\mu A/1m$ — a lumen is the S.I. unit of luminous flux). There is a wide range of photocathode materials with sensitivities ranging from a few $\mu A/1m$ up to some 2000 $\mu A/1m$ (specially treated gallium arsenide). Each material is also rated by its "dark current", typically between 10^{-9} and 10^{-17} amperes per cm^2.

For a photocathode to operate over the visible spectrum, it can be shown that its work function must be small (around 2 eV or less). Caesium is the only metal having a work function of less than 2 eV (actually 1.92 eV) and so photocathode materials used for example, in television camera tubes usually have a caesium coating on a base such as silver oxide.

(* Cathode, Photon, Photoelectric Effect, Space Charge, Work Function, Electron-Volt, Lumen >> Image Intensifier, Image Converter, Camera Tube)

PHOTOCELL is a general name for a device with electrical characteristics dependent on light falling on its input electrode. Some cells use the photon energy to develop an electromotive force, they are known as *photovoltaic*, others use the light energy to release electrons from a *photocathode*, these are generally classed as *photoelectric cells*. Another type of cell reduces its resistance according to the intensity of the light reaching it, this type is *photoconductive*.

The graphical symbols for photovoltaic and photoconductive devices are shown in Figure P7.

(* Light, Visible Spectrum, Electromotive Force, Photovoltaic Cell, Photoelectric Cell, Photoconductive Cell >> Solar Cell)

PHOTOCONDUCTIVE CELL is a light-sensitive resistor of a type widely used for control and photometric (light measurement) purposes. The cell consists of a semiconductor material contained between two conducting electrodes. The material may be rod or bar shaped or a polycrystalline film on a glass substrate. The material exhibits photoconductivity in that when light of a certain wavelength falls on it, its conductance increases, hence if it is part of a circuit containing an electromotive force, the current through it also increases. Cadmium sulphide and cadmium selenide are frequently used as the semiconductor, these have maximum response to radiation of wavelength 600 − 700 nm (orange/red light − see Fig.L5). For a response to infra-red light lead sulphide or lead selenide is used (about 2 μm).

The graphical symbol is given in Figure P7(ii).

(* Light, Visible Spectrum, Wavelength, Semiconductor, Photon, Photoconductivity, Electromotive Force)

PHOTOCONDUCTIVITY This is additional conductivity created in certain semiconductors when irradiated. Light can be considered as a stream of photons, each of which can give up its energy to an electron of the semiconductor. Accordingly, given sufficient photon energy, an orbiting electron in the valence shell of an atom can be freed and an electron-hole pair is created. Explained energy-wise, an electron in the valence band can be excited by the radiation across the forbidden band into the conduction band if the photon energy supplied is sufficient. The photon energy needed is therefore equal to or greater than the forbidden band or gap energy, E_g. From Planck's work we find that the photon energy is equal to hf where h is Planck's constant and f is the frequency of the radiation. Hence for photoconductivity to occur, hf must be greater than E_g and under this condition the material conductivity increases noticeably.

E_g for silicon is 1.1 eV and for germanium, 0.7 eV, hence photoconductivity arises in silicon for example, at frequencies at or above:

$$E_g/h \text{ Hz , i.e. } \frac{1.1 \times 1.602 \times 10^{-19} \text{ J}}{6.626 \times 10^{-34} \text{ J s}} = 2.66 \times 10^{14} \text{ Hz}$$

(1128 nanometres), which as Figure L5 shows, is in the infra-red region. (Note that in the numerator E_g is converted from electron-volts into joules.) All visible frequencies are therefore also effective. For germanium the lowest frequency is 1.7×10^{14} Hz, effective therefore at even lower infra-red frequencies.

The above merely increases the number of charge carriers (electron-hole pairs) available. For electrons to escape from the surface of the semiconductor the photon energy must exceed the work function, when this happens it is known as the *photoelectric effect.*
(* Atom, Electron, Visible Spectrum, Photon, Energy Bands, Planck Constant, Work Function, Electron-Volt, Joule, Charge Carrier, Electron-Hole Pair, Valency, Silicon, Germanium, Photoelectric Effect)

PHOTODIODE   This is a p-n junction which has a reverse current dependent on the amount of light falling on it. The energy of a photon is given by hf where h is Planck's constant and f is the radiation frequency. If photons act on the depletion layer of a p-n junction, electron-hole pairs are created. An electric field existing across the depletion region is able to separate the electrons and holes and although recombination takes place continually, ample charge carriers remain free and are set in motion, i.e. a current flows. The basic circuit is shown in Figure P5(i). The reverse bias is, of course, less than the breakdown voltage. The normal diode reverse saturation current is known as the *dark current* and the photo-current is superimposed on it as shown in (ii).

As an example, for silicon which has an energy gap of 1.1 eV, photons with energies greater than this are effective, then:

$$1.1 \text{ eV} = hf$$

i.e.
$$f = \frac{1.1 \times 1.602 \times 10^{-19}}{6.626 \times 10^{-34}} = 2.66 \times 10^{14} \text{ Hz (1128 nanometres)}$$

(Note that in the numerator electron-volts are converted into joules.)

This frequency is in the infra-red region. Below it therefore a silicon diode will not operate as a photodiode. Above (and this includes part of the visible spectrum) the diode has a response as

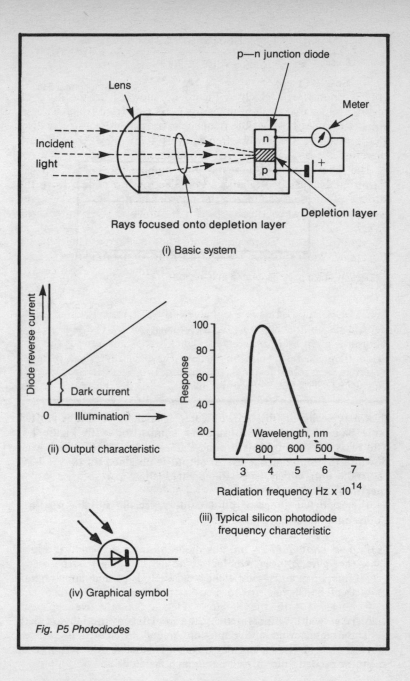

p—n junction diode

Lens

Meter

Incident light

n

p

Rays focused onto depletion layer

Depletion layer

(i) Basic system

(ii) Output characteristic

Diode reverse current

Dark current

0   Illumination →

(iii) Typical silicon photodiode frequency characteristic

Response

Wavelength, nm
800   600   500

Radiation frequency Hz x 10^{14}

(iv) Graphical symbol

Fig. P5 Photodiodes

315

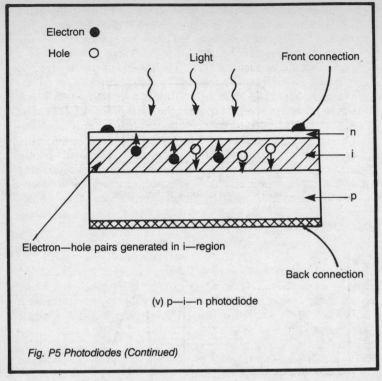

Electron ●

Hole ○

Light

Front connection

n

i

p

Electron—hole pairs generated in i—region

Back connection

(v) p—i—n photodiode

Fig. P5 Photodiodes (Continued)

shown typically in (iii) of the figure. The characteristic is plotted on a base of frequency to simplify comparison with Figure L5. The maximum response is around 3.75×10^{14} Hz (800 nm), well down in the infra-red but useful output is obtained up to 5×10^{14} Hz (600 nm) which is in the orange/yellow part of the visible spectrum).

There are two types of photodiode especially suitable for fibre optic communication:

(1)   *p-i-n photodiode* – in this diode an intrinsic region is added (i.e. pure, although in fact some light doping may be used). This i-region is sandwiched between a p- and an n-region. Depletion layers are formed at the junctions of both p- and n-regions with the i-region. Hence the effective depletion layer width is increased by the insertion of the i-region with the result that the depletion layer capacitance is reduced compared with a normal diode. This makes the response of the diode to modulated light much faster.

Photons reaching the i-region create electron-hole pairs. Under reverse bias the n-region is made positive hence the liberated electrons cross the depletion layer into it. Equally holes move into the p-region as indicated in the sketch of a typical diode in Figure P5(v). The net result of the electron and hole movement is an increase in reverse current.

(2) *avalanche photodiode (a.p.d.)* – this is a photodiode which is operated with a reverse bias near the breakdown voltage (some 100–200 V). A greater gain is obtained than for normal photodiodes because both leakage and photocurrents are internally amplified by avalanche multiplication. Liberated photoelectrons are accelerated by the intense electric field existing across the junction and they gain sufficient energy to create new electron-hole pairs by impact ionization. The photodiode therefore has high sensitivity. It also has a relatively low noise performance.

The graphical symbol of a photodiode is given in (iv).

(* Atom, Electron, Photovoltaic Effect, Charge Carrier, Energy, Electric Field, Photon, Planck Constant, P-N Junction, Joule, Electron-Volt, Impact Ionization, Recombination, Infra-Red, Electron-Hole Pair, Depletion Layer, Avalanche >> Fibre Optic Transmission)

PHOTOELECTRIC CELL is a light sensor comprising basically a photocathode and an anode mounted in an evacuated glass envelope. The anode is positively charged. Illumination of the photocathode releases electrons from it which are collected by the anode, a current therefore flows in the external circuit controlled by the intensity of the light.

Sometimes referred to as a *photocell*.
(* Light, Emission, Photoelectric Effect, Photocathode)

PHOTOELECTRIC EFFECT Experimentally this can be demonstrated (as it was in early days) by a simple electroscope as shown in Figure P6. Light falling on the metal plate attached to the top electrode causes electrons to be emitted. The two leaves therefore become positively charged and fly apart. The phenomenon was first explained by Einstein on the assumption of the existence of photons. The energy of a photon is given by hf where h is Planck's constant and f is the frequency of the radiation. Provided that the photon energy exceeds the work function (ϕ) of the material, an electron near the surface which absorbs the energy of a photon gains sufficient energy to jump clear.

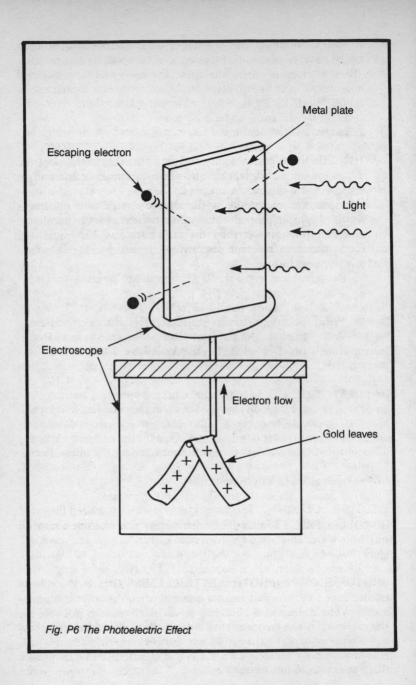

Escaping electron

Metal plate

Light

Electroscope

Electron flow

Gold leaves

Fig. P6 The Photoelectric Effect

Consider a photon of energy E acting on an electron. An amount of energy equal to the work function is used up in freeing the electron from the surface of the material. The energy left over $= E - \phi$ and this is still with the electron and hence represents an increase in its kinetic energy. Since $E = hf$, Einstein suggested that:

$$\text{maximum k.e. of emitted electron} = \tfrac{1}{2}mv^2 = hf - \phi$$

where v is the maximum velocity and m is the mass of the electron.

This is known as *Einstein's photoelectric formula* or *law* and an electron so emitted is known as a *photoelectron*.

It follows that when the whole of the energy of a photon is expended in fulfilling the work function, none remains to accelerate the escaping electron. It therefore falls back into the metal, the surface of which has become positively charged because of electron loss. Then:

$$hf - \phi = 0 \quad \therefore f = \phi/h$$

showing that for any particular material, there is a light frequency below which emission does not take place. Take zinc as an example, it has a work function of 3.73 eV (i.e. $3.73 \times 1.602 \times 10^{-19} = 5.98 \times 10^{-19}$ joules). The minimum frequency for photoemission is therefore $\phi/h = (5.98 \times 10^{-19})/(6.626 \times 10^{-34}) \simeq 9 \times 10^{14}$ Hz (0.33 μm).

This is in the ultra-violet range (see Fig.E5) hence visible light will not set free electrons from zinc but ultra-violet light will. This is confirmed by experiment.

(* Atom, Electron, Emission, Electroscope, Energy, Photon, Planck Constant, Work Function, Charge, Space Charge, Photocathode, Primary Electron, Electron-Volt, Joule, Visible Spectrum)

PHOTOELECTRON   This is an electron which has been liberated from the surface of a material by the energy gained from a photon of the incident light — see Photoelectric Effect.
(* Photon)

PHOTOEMISSION (PHOTOELECTRIC EMISSION) is the release of electrons from the surface of a material when the latter is illuminated. When a photon is absorbed by an electron, it is possible for the electron to acquire more than sufficient energy for escape across the surface potential barrier. This is the photoelectric effect which is summed up by Einstein's photoelectric equation stating in essence that the maximum kinetic energy of emitted electrons when absorbing photons of frequency f is given by:

$$E_{K(max)} = \tfrac{1}{2}mv^2 = hf - \phi$$

where h is the Planck constant, ϕ is the work function, m is the electron mass and v its maximum velocity.

Electrons are excited from different energy states, they have to travel through the material to the true surface and finally overcome the surface potential barrier. Photoemission from some metals is poor because excited electrons within the material suffer many collisions before reaching the surface. Some metals also reflect light at the surface, hence generally semiconductors and insulators have greater yields.

(* Emission, Photon, Energy, Energy Levels, Work Function, Charge, Space Charge, Photoelectric Effect, Planck Constant, Photocathode, Photocell, Collision)

PHOTOIONIZATION is the ionization of an atom or molecule of a gas or liquid resulting from incident electromagnetic radiation. The energy obtainable from a photon is given by hf where h is the Planck constant and f is the frequency of the radiation. If this energy is equal to or exceeds the first ionization potential of the particular fluid and is absorbed by an electron, the electron then has gained sufficient energy for escape from the parent atom or molecule. Hence the atom or molecule is ionized. The mechanism of photo-ionization is similar to that of the *photoelectric effect* except that whereas in the photoelectric effect the photon energy must be equal to or exceed the material work function, in photoionization it must be equal to or exceed the first ionization potential.

Take as an example, the gas nitrogen which has a first ionization potential, I_1 of 14.5 electron-volts, i.e. $14.5 \times 1.602 \times 10^{-19}$ joules. For nitrogen to be just ionized therefore:

$$hf = I_1$$

i.e. $\quad f = \dfrac{I_1}{h} = \dfrac{14.5 \times 1.602 \times 10^{-19}}{6.626 \times 10^{-34}} \text{ Hz} = 3.5 \times 10^{15} \text{ Hz},$

a frequency well into the ultra-violet range as Figure E5 shows. Below this frequency no ionization due to radiation will occur in nitrogen. In fact most photoionization requires ultra-violet light.

When the photon energy exceeds I_1 some is left over which is almost entirely monopolized by the electron, hence the kinetic energy E_K of the freed electron is given by:

$$E_K = hf - I_1$$

from which the velocity of the electron (v) can be calculated since $E_K = \frac{1}{2}mv^2$ where m is the electron mass.

It is also possible for the photon energy to be equal to or exceed the second ionization potential, in which case a second electron may be removed from an atom.

(* Atom, Molecule, Electron, Ion, Ionization, Ionization Potential, Planck Constant, Photon, Charge, Space Charge, Work Function, Photoelectric Effect, Kinetic Energy, Electron-Volt)

PHOTON   In early days scientists were unable to explain how colours of light were emitted by hot glowing metals such as iron which changes from "red-hot" to "white-hot" as its temperature is raised. The ideas then current about the nature of light were inadequate. Max Planck (a German physicist) began to get to grips with this by considering that light was emitted in tiny bursts or "packets" of energy. At this early stage (about 1900) another problem was also looking for a solution but this was left for Einstein to solve later in 1905. Planck had dealt with the emission of light but the *photoelectric effect*, i.e. the effect light can have on the emission of electrons from the surface of a metal, was still unexplained.

Einstein reasoned that somehow a light beam concentrated its energy on the individual electrons in the metal. For this to happen the light beam had to be made up of discrete amounts or *quanta* of energy as Planck had shown and he considered that all the energy of a quantum could be absorbed by a single electron. Where light is concerned we call these packets of energy, *photons*. Einstein's work agreed with that of Planck in that the energy (E) of a single photon is: $E = hf$, where f is the radiation frequency and h is Planck's constant (6.626×10^{-34} J s).

We can only describe a photon as a "packet" of energy, always travelling at the speed of light just as the electromagnetic wave does. If anything happens to it to change this speed, then it disappears and its energy is given up. As shown above, if a photon collides with an electron the latter takes up the photon energy and the photon no longer exists.

An interesting example may help our understanding of photons and their energies even though we are only proving something already well known. The medical profession has examined certain molecules of the skin and found that an energy of about 3.5 eV is required to break up these molecules and cause sunburn. The lowest light frequency to produce sunburn is therefore:

$$f = E/h \quad \therefore f = \frac{3.5 \times 1.602 \times 10^{-19} \text{ J}}{6.626 \times 10^{-34} \text{ J s}} = 8.48 \times 10^{14} \text{ Hz} .$$

(Note, E is expressed in joules.) Figure L5 shows that this frequency is just within the ultra-violet range. Frequencies below this have no effect, so to get an artificial suntan an ultra-violet lamp is needed. (* Atom, Electron, Emission, Planck Constant, Energy, Collision, Electron-Volt, Joule, Visible Spectrum)

PHOTOSENSITIVITY is the degree of response of a material to electromagnetic radiation especially infra-red, visible and ultra-violet. Such materials are capable of absorbing the energy of photons, so liberating electrons. If the liberated electrons are released from the material the process is known as *photoemission.* If the electrons are not directly released they may remain available as charge carriers, this gives rise to *photoconductivity.*

At a junction between two dissimilar materials electromagnetic radiation may create electron-hole pairs from which an electromotive force is set up — this is the *photovoltaic effect.*
(* Photon, Charge, Charge Carrier, Photoelectric Effect, Photo-emission, Photoconductivity, Photovoltaic Effect, Photoionization, Electron-Hole Pair, Visible Spectrum)

PHOTOTRANSISTOR is a bipolar transistor in transparent encapsulation in which the collector current is determined mainly by the intensity of light falling on the base region. Put simply, the collector-base junction acts as a photodiode and responds to the radiation with the benefit of transistor gain added. In use there is either no connection to the base, i.e. the base is "floating" or a high value resistor is connected between base and emitter. Basically the transistor operates as a 2-terminal device, connected in common-emitter configuration.

Under dark conditions the current in the collector-emitter circuit is the normal common-emitter leakage current. However, when light falls on the collector-base junction, provided that the photons have sufficient energy, electron-hole pairs are created in the base region. Accordingly a minority carrier *photocurrent* flows across the junction which is reverse biased. In an n-p-n transistor, because electrons flow out of the base region and holes are attracted into it, the forward base-emitter bias is increased according to the magnitude of the photocurrent. Forward bias increases the electron flow

322

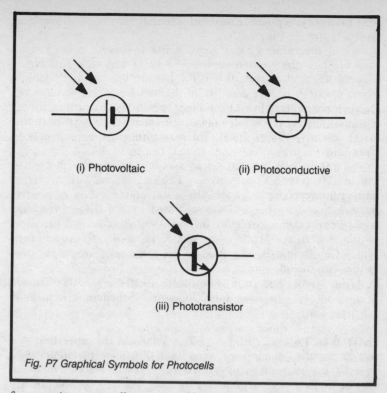

(i) Photovoltaic

(ii) Photoconductive

(iii) Phototransistor

Fig. P7 Graphical Symbols for Photocells

from emitter to collector so effectively the photocurrent of the collector-base diode is amplified by the current gain of the transistor. Hence greater sensitivity is obtainable from a phototransistor than from a photodiode.

The graphical symbol is given in Figure P7(iii).
(* Photovoltaic Effect, Photodiode, Photon, P-N Junction, Electron-Hole Pair, Transistor, Visible Spectrum >> Common-Emitter Connection)

PHOTOVOLTAIC CELL is one which generates an electromotive force (e.m.f.) from the energy of light. The e.m.f. is a function of the intensity of the light falling on the junction between two dissimilar metals, conductive and semiconductive. In the unbiased condition a potential barrier (the Schottky barrier) forms across the junction, hence the alternative name, *barrier-layer photocell.* Light photons pass through a very thin conductive layer to reach the junction. This creates electron movement across the normally unbiased junction and the potential existing across the barrier is able to drive a current round an external circuit. The graphical symbol is given in Figure P7(i).

One of the earlier types of cell is the *selenium.* It has an iron base which is the positive terminal, with a very thin coating of selenium (a semiconductor). Light passing through the selenium causes electrons to be ejected from the metal into the semiconductor, hence the metal base becomes positively charged with the selenium negative. The cell potential is approximately proportional to the intensity of the light. The maximum response is mainly to green light.

The *silicon cell* is based on an n-type silicon wafer in contact with a thin p-type silicon layer. Photons reaching the junction formed between the layer and the wafer create a flow of positive and negative charges which are separated by the field of the junction. Connection is made to the cell by plating around the edges of the materials. Maximum response is mainly to red/infra-red light. Germanium is also used in the same way with a response further into the infra-red.

(* Light, Visible Spectrum, Photovoltaic Effect, Schottky Barrier, Semiconductor, Photon, P-N Junction, Selenium, Germanium >> Solar Cell)

PHOTOVOLTAIC EFFECT   This results in the generation of a voltage at the junction between two dissimilar materials when exposed to electromagnetic radiation. Typical pairs of materials may be metal and semiconductor or more usually opposite polarity semiconductors. The radiation most effective is visible or infra-red and when this is incident on, for example, a semiconductor material, electron-hole pairs are generated by normal photoconductive action. Such additional charge carriers at or near a p-n junction become separated into electrons and holes by the electric field of the depletion layer. This is the normal action at the junction hence the radiation results in an additional forward voltage across the junction, resulting in an open circuit voltage, hence the description, *photovoltaic.*

If the p-n junction is forward biased, any photovoltaic current is swamped, accordingly the junction is usually reverse biased for which the reverse saturation current is sufficiently small to have little effect. Solar cells, however, are based on p-n junctions which are unbiased. Typically for a silicon junction, the "dark current" (no illumination) is around 0.1 μA and for "light current" up to 300 μA.

(* Light, Visible Spectrum, Semiconductor, Photon, Charge, Charge Carrier, Photoconductivity, Photodiode, Photocell, Electron-Hole

PIEZOELECTRIC CRYSTAL is one which has piezoelectric properties, i.e. pressure on the crystal produces a voltage across two of
its faces, alternatively when a voltage is applied to the crystal, it
becomes mechanically deformed. Certain crystals are piezoelectric,
most are not for example, common salt exhibits no such characteristics but Rochelle salt does. Ferroelectric crystals are also piezoelectric. Some commonly found piezoelectric materials are quartz,
Rochelle salt (sodium potassium tartrate), ammonium dihydrogen
phosphate (ADP), barium titanate.

In the study and use of piezoelectric crystals it has been found
advantageous to label a crystal slice according to three mutually
perpendicular axes as shown for the ADP crystal in Figure P8(i).
Note how the axis which is perpendicular to the main faces of the
plate denotes the type, e.g. in the figure the plate is known as
X-cut. Mechanical stress along the Y-axis of this plate results in a
voltage appearing along the X-axis.

Many different arrangements are used, commonly found is the
bimorph which consists of two plates cemented together as illustrated in (ii) of the figure. Each plate is sprayed on both faces with
a metallic coating and in the bimorph the pair of plates is arranged
so that when subjected to pressure the two inside coatings achieve
the same electrical polarity. The coatings are connected in parallel
as shown, in the figure the polarities are those for one direction of
plate stress, reversing if the stress is reversed. Attaching a sound
diaphragm to the centre creates a piezoelectric microphone.
(* Crystal, Piezoelectric Effect, Ferroelectricity >> Ceramic,
Microphone, Piezoelectric Microphone, Hydrophone)

PIEZOELECTRIC EFFECT occurs in certain crystals which when
under pressure or tension become electrically polarized in that
charges appear on the surfaces. Piezo is derived from a Greek
word meaning *to press*. Conversely, the crystal becomes mechanically deformed when a voltage is applied across two faces. If an
alternating voltage is applied, the crystal vibrates in a direction at
right angles to the applied electric field, it has a resonance frequency and the vibration is maximum when the applied voltage is
at this frequency.

The piezoelectric effect is found only in crystalline dielectrics in
which the distributions of positive and negative ions are asymmetrical, i.e. the crystal lacks a centre of electrical symmetry. When
a stress is applied there is a displacement of the ions in such a way
that there is a resulting dipole moment.

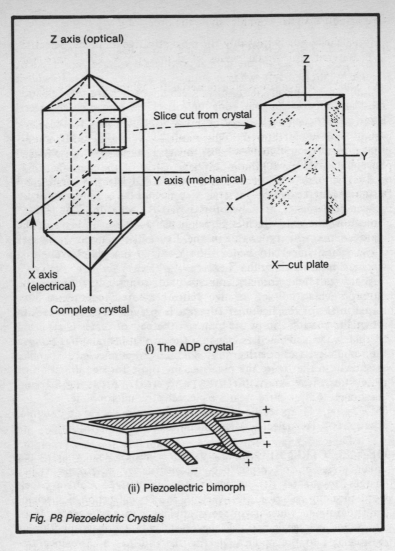

Z axis (optical)

Slice cut from crystal

Y axis (mechanical)

X axis (electrical)

Complete crystal

Z

Y

X

X—cut plate

(i) The ADP crystal

+
−
+
−
+

(ii) Piezoelectric bimorph

Fig. P8 Piezoelectric Crystals

The degree to which a material exhibits piezoelectric properties can be assessed by the *piezoelectric strain coefficient* (or *constant*), *d*. This relates the charge produced along a defined axis by a given force in coulombs per newton (C/N) or conversely the deflection caused by an applied voltage in metres per volt (m/V). There are many axes in a crystal and *d* is different for most or all of them, hence the axes concerned must be quoted, usually by a subscript on the constant d. Two examples show the order of d:

(i) Rochelle salt is probably the most sensitive of all piezoelectric materials for which values of d up to 5×10^{-10} m/V (or C/N) are possible.

(ii) Quartz is a more stable material for which d can be up to about 2.3×10^{-12} m/V (or C/N).

Piezoelectric materials may be broadly divided into two classes, natural and manufactured. The natural crystals include sodium potassium tartrate (Rochelle salt), quartz, ammonium dihydrogen phosphate (ADP) and lithium sulphate. Most of the manufactured ones come under the general title "poled ferroelectric ceramics". During manufacture the material is subjected to a strong electric field as it cools, it then becomes poled, i.e. the domains in the material are aligned in the direction of the field. Also certain characteristics of the material have similarities with those of ferromagnetic materials, hence the name "ferroelectric". Typical materials used are barium titanate and lead zirconate titanate. These crystals are especially versatile because they can be manufactured in a variety of ceramic (pottery-like) shapes, hence can be designed for applications for which natural crystals are not particularly suited.

(* Crystal, Dipole, Ion, Resonance, Electric Field Strength, Charge, Coulomb, Newton, Ferroelectricity, Piezoelectric Crystal)

PIEZOELECTRIC STRAIN CONSTANT (COEFFICIENT) – see Piezoelectric Effect.

P-I-N DIODE is a refinement of the ordinary p-n junction diode in that its special characteristics make it suitable for use at radio frequencies. In fact it becomes almost a pure resistance at these frequencies varying typically from some 10 kΩ down to less than 1 Ω depending on the bias current flowing through it.

The p-i-n diode is as its name suggests, a p-n diode with an intrinsic material sandwiched between the two regions. The p and n regions are heavily doped. With reverse bias the i-layer is depleted of mobile charge carriers, so leading to a high resistance diode. With forward bias, holes from the p-region and electrons from the n-region flow into the i-layer thereby causing its resistance to fall. The resistance of the layer is inversely proportional to the amount of mobile charge in it, hence it is also inversely proportional to the d.c. bias.

The high frequency performance of a p-i-n diode depends on the length of time required for the storage charge to become sufficiently depleted through recombination when the bias changes from forward to reverse. At low frequencies this time is such that a signal may experience varying resistance and in fact the diode exhibits normal p-n diode characteristics. At high frequencies the relationship from which the resistance can be determined approximately is:

$$R = \frac{d^2}{\mu I \tau}$$

where d is the i-layer thickness, μ is the combined mobility of electrons and holes, τ is their lifetime and I is the direct bias current. This looks reasonable but note that it only applies within certain limits (τ and d are interdependent).

The p-i-n diode is especially useful as a depletion layer photodiode.

(* Semiconductor, Intrinsic Semiconductor, P-N Junction, Diode, Doping, Charge, Charge Carrier, Recombination, Lifetime, Mobility, Depletion Layer, Photodiode)

P-I-N PHOTODIODE   A photodiode with a layer of intrinsic semiconductor material sandwiched between p- and n-regions — see Photodiode.

PINCH-OFF VOLTAGE refers to a field-effect transistor. It is the negative voltage at which the channel is cut off — see Field-Effect Transistor.

PLANCK CONSTANT   In 1900 Max Planck (a German theoretical physicist) published the first acceptable theory regarding the emission of thermal radiation. Previously scientists had been unable to explain why a very hot metal (e.g. iron) changes colour from "red-hot" to "white-hot" as its temperature is raised. Planck answered this by suggesting that radiation is emitted not continuously but in tiny bursts or "packets" of energy known as *quanta* (singular, *quantum*), the size of each being proportional to the frequency of the radiation. Where light is concerned the quantum is known as a *photon* (from Greek, *photos*, light). Planck's formula is simplicity itself: $E = hf$ where E is the quantum energy, f is the frequency of radiation and h is a constant, nowadays known as the Planck Constant and of value 6.626176×10^{-34} joule seconds (J s).

We can understand better the importance of Planck's work from the following example. Taking the lowest red light frequency as 4.1×10^{14} Hz and the highest violet as 7.9×10^{14} Hz, then the photon energy for the red from $h \times f$ is approximately 1.7 electron-volts (eV) and that for the violet, 3.3 eV. Hence because photon energy is proportional to the frequency of the light, it is possible for a weak violet light to have greater energy than a strong red one. Such considerations are of importance when considering the energy required for the emission of electrons from the surface of a metal.

Planck's ideas introduced the first relationship involving both energy and waves. They have since led to the development of *quantum theory* (also known as *quantum mechanics*).
(* Frequency, Energy, Joule, Electron-Volt, Work Function, Photon, Light, Visible Spectrum, Emission, Quantum Theory)

PLANE WAVE An electromagnetic wave in which the electric and magnetic fields and the direction of propagation are mutually perpendicular — see Electromagnetic Wave.

PLASMA is formed in the centre of a gas discharge. Consider the simple gas-discharge tube shown in Figure P9 and assume that V is greater than the breakdown voltage (i.e. that at which the gas fully ionizes). Under these conditions it is found that the fall in voltage between the two electrodes is not proportional to distance. There is a large potential drop in front of the anode because positive ions are repelled there, the net charge is therefore negative. Equally at the cathode electrons are repelled and again there is a potential drop. These potential changes are known as the *anode fall* and the *cathode fall.* In between them is the region with only a relatively small potential across it known as the *plasma.* The plasma consists of almost equal numbers of electrons and ions so there is very little net charge. Because of the many free charge carriers its resistance is very low, hence even though only a small potential exists across it, the current is large. Most of the current is carried by the electrons owing to their much higher mobility.
(* Gas Discharge, Breakdown, Ionization, Charge, Charge Carrier, Anode, Cathode, Electron, Potential Difference)

P-N JUNCTION As electrical conductors p- and n-type materials have no special features but when they are grown together and are therefore in intimate contact, something extraordinary happens which provides the basic operating characteristics of all junction semiconductor devices.

A representation of a p-n junction is given in Figure P10(i) in which only a few of each type of particle are shown to avoid over complication. In the immediate vicinity of the junction some of the excess holes of the p region (they are considered to be equal to

329

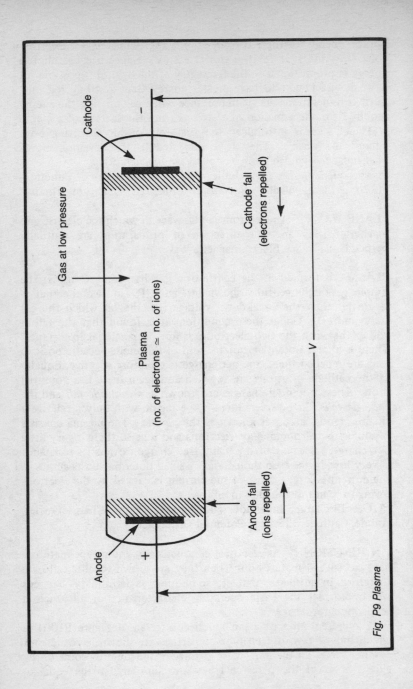

Fig. P9 Plasma

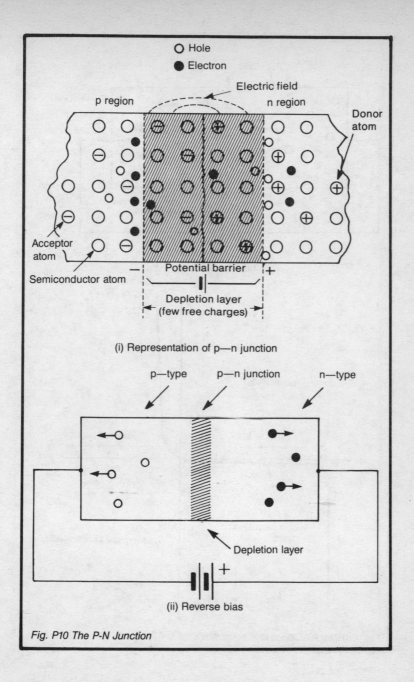

Fig. P10 The P-N Junction

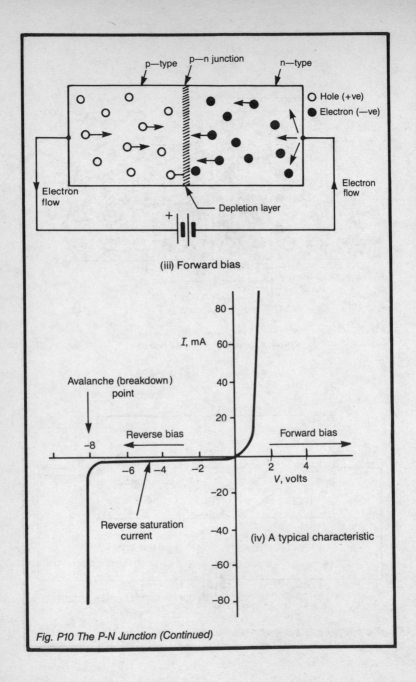

(iii) Forward bias

(iv) A typical characteristic

Fig. P10 The P-N Junction (Continued)

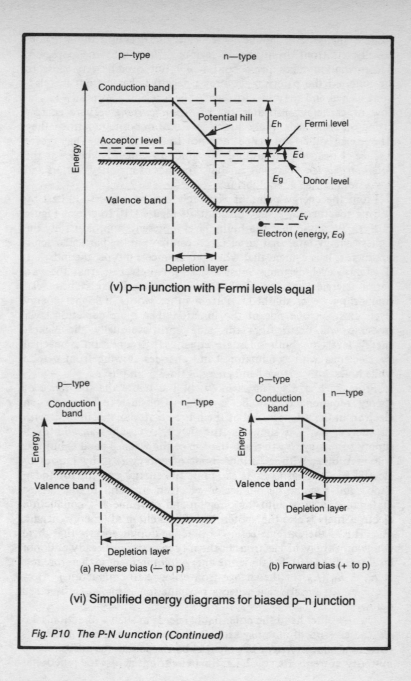

(v) p–n junction with Fermi levels equal

(a) Reverse bias (— to p)

(b) Forward bias (+ to p)

(vi) Simplified energy diagrams for biased p–n junction

Fig. P10 The P-N Junction (Continued)

positive charges and mobile — see Hole) diffuse into the n region. Equally electrons from the n region diffuse into the p region. Recombination takes place continually but overall, very close to the junction the p region acquires a negative charge from the electrons gained and the holes lost while the n region goes positive. The flow of carriers constitutes the *diffusion current*. These charges sitting on either side of the junction are of opposite polarities, they attract each other and hence tend not to diffuse away. They create a space-charged region around the junction which is known as the *potential barrier*. It repels further crossings of majority carriers and the system is then at equilibrium.

From the energy point of view this can be understood best by putting together the energy diagrams of Figure D10 to give us Figure P10(v). Recalling that the Fermi level represents approximately the highest energy level that an electron can have in the particular semiconductor, it is evident that when p-type meets n-type, the individual energy level diagrams must adjust themselves so that the two Fermi energies are the same for only under this condition can equilibrium be established. Put in other words, if higher energy levels exist on one side of the junction then more depletion layer crossings will occur from this side until eventually the highest energy levels on both sides are equal. This condition is reached by electrons with conduction band energies flowing from n to p while holes with valence band energies flow from p to n.

From such a diagram as in (v) of the figure the full range of energy requirements can be assessed. Consider for example, an electron in the valence band of the n-type material, it is in orbit with an energy, E_o. As shown in the figure, it requires an additional supply of energy, E_v to reach the top of the valence band — but it is still in orbit. With a further input of energy (e.g. by impact or electric field) equal to E_g it can jump the energy gap (the forbidden band) and become a conduction electron but still in the n-type material. To cross into the p-region and continue as a conduction electron there is also the "potential hill" to climb of (energy) height, E_h. This is the extreme case. In practice doping ensures that there is a good supply of electrons in the n-type material already at donor level (see Fig.D10), for these the energy requirement is therefore less at $E_d + E_h$ (E_d for the change from valence to conduction). How the energies are affected when a p-n junction is biased is discussed below.

On the other hand the potential barrier is in such a direction as to *aid* the crossing of minority carriers and the system therefore adjusts itself to a value or *height* of potential barrier so that the diffusion and minority currents are equal, i.e. the net current across the junction is zero. From this it is evident that around the junction few charge carriers are available, the region therefore has relatively high resistivity. It is known as the *depletion layer*. If however an external p.d. is applied across the junction, the equilibrium is disturbed and this is the practical way in which a p-n junction is used, generally known as a semiconductor diode.

Reverse Bias — this is the term used when an external p.d. applied across the two regions attracts the majority carriers away from the junction as shown in Figure P10(ii). Both the height of the potential barrier and the width of the depletion layer are increased, accordingly the resistivity of the region increases. Few majority carriers have sufficient energy for crossing the junction [note from Fig.P10(vi) at (a) the large supply of energy required], hence the majority current is low, down to practically zero when the applied potential difference is sufficiently great. The reverse bias, however, aids the flow of minority carriers so allowing a constant but small current flow across the junction. This is known as the *reverse saturation current* as shown on a typical characteristic in Figure P10(iv). The term *leakage current* is sometimes used because it represents a small leak in what otherwise would be a complete obstruction to current by the depletion layer.

If the reverse bias is increased sufficiently, a breakdown point is reached at which the current increases rapidly as shown. The voltage at which this happens is called the *breakdown voltage*. Electrons moving at high speed because of the high reverse potential collide with fixed atoms and break covalent bonds, thereby releasing further electrons. These are also accelerated by the electric field and release still more in the same way. The effect is cumulative, resulting in the release of electrons (and creation of holes) on a rapidly increasing scale. This is the *avalanche effect*, the main cause of breakdown.

Forward Bias — in this an external p.d. is connected as shown in Figure P10(iii). In the p-type material the electric field causes a drift of holes towards the junction, similarly with electrons in the n-type. This reduces both the height of the potential barrier and the width of the depletion layer [see Fig.P10(vi) at (b)], hence the resistivity of the latter is reduced. Majority carriers of low energy are able to cross the junction around which obviously there is considerable recombination. Because the depletion layer resistivity is greatly reduced, a comparatively large current is able to flow. The net current is constant throughout the crystal and is the sum of the hole and electron currents together. The minority current remains constant. It is in the opposite direction to that of the main current but much smaller. A typical forward bias characteristic is shown in

(iv) of the figure from which it is seen that the current increases rapidly with increase of bias voltage.

For a p-n junction, provided that the reverse current, I_0 is known, the theoretical current-voltage characteristic can be calculated from:

$$I = I_0 [\exp(eV/kT) - 1]$$

where I and V are the current and voltage, k is Boltzmann's constant, T is the thermodynamic temperature and e is the electron charge. e/k is equal to 11609 and by choosing a temperature of, say 305 K, to make the exponent of e a whole number:

$$I/I_0 = \exp(38V) - 1$$

i.e. for any given voltage the ratio of main current to reverse saturation current can be calculated. A curve plotted to this formula gives the *ideal* characteristic. Practical p-n junction characteristics differ slightly, usually conforming better to a reduced value of the exponent.
(* Atom, Electron, Orbit, Semiconductor, Doping P-type Semiconductor, N-type Semiconductor, Hole, Charge, Fermi Level, Valency, Boltzmann's Constant, Recombination, Thermodynamic Temperature, Potential Difference, Avalanche, Breakdown)

POCKEL'S EFFECT refers to the control by an electric field of the plane of polarization of a light beam passing through a piezoelectric material — see Kerr Effect.

POLAR is a term used to indicate a certain characteristic of a component, particle or system. The characteristic is usually a form of asymmetry, e.g. a molecule is said to be polar when it has opposite electric charges at its ends. A permanent magnet is, of course, polar. An electrolytic capacitor is also said to be polar when it can only be used with a voltage across it of a certain polarity.
(* Charge, Molecule, Magnetic Pole >> Electrolytic Capacitor)

POLAR COORDINATE   Any point on a plane can be defined relative to two axes (normally at right angles) by (i) the distance (r) the point is from the *origin* as shown in Figure P11 and (ii) the angle (ϕ) which the line joining the point to the origin makes with one of the axes (usually the x). r is known as the *modulus* (Latin, *measure*) and ϕ, the *argument* (a mathematical term for an angle on which the calculation of another quantity depends). In the figure, for example, the position of point P is determined relative to the x-axis by $5\angle30°$.

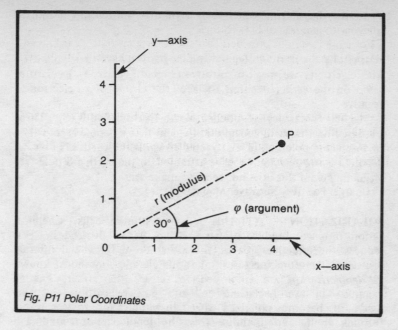

Fig. P11 Polar Coordinates

Phasors representing current, voltage, impedance and admittance may be expressed in polar coordinate form. To deal mathematically with the modulus separately from the argument, the modulus symbol is placed between two upright lines, e.g.:

$$|P| \text{ means "the modulus of the phasor } P \angle \phi \text{"}$$

Phasors are usually expressed in polar coordinate form when they are to be multiplied or divided, they are more easily handled this way than in cartesian form. When two phasors $r_1 \angle \theta_1$ and $r_2 \angle \theta_2$ are multiplied together the result is simply:

$$r_1 r_2 \angle (\theta_1 + \theta_2),$$

the rule being that the moduli are multiplied but the arguments are added. Conversely for division:

$$\frac{r_1 \angle \theta_1}{r_2 \angle \theta_2} = \frac{r_1}{r_2} \angle (\theta_1 - \theta_2),$$

the moduli are divided but the arguments are subtracted.

337

(* Phasor, Phase Angle, Complex Notation, Cartesian Coordinate
>> Polar Diagram)

POLARITY   Both electricity and magnetism have their polarities.
With electricity we speak of positive (+) and negative (−) polarities
based on the earlier decision to label the charge of an electron as
negative.

Magnetic polarities are labelled North (N) and South (S). These
are based on the earth's magnetic field in that a N pole is actually a
north-seeking pole, i.e. it is attracted towards the earth's N pole. A
S pole is *south-seeking*, i.e. it is attracted to the earth's S pole (see
Magnetic Pole if this does not seem to make sense).
(* Charge, Positive, Negative, Magnetic Pole)

POLARIZATION   (1) This occurs in primary cells. Chemical
action produces bubbles of gas on one of the electrodes. This
reduces the effective area of the electrode and the cell internal
resistance therefore increases. Various chemical methods, known
as *depolarization* are employed to reduce the effect. As an
example, in the Leclanché cell the positive carbon electrode
tends to become polarized through bubbles of hydrogen gas
forming on it. To minimize this, the depolarizer surrounding it
contains manganese dioxide which reacts with the hydrogen to
form water.

(2) is a term applied to electromagnetic waves. The electric
field of an electromagnetic wave has three main directions associated
with it, the x, y and z, as shown in Figure P12. If the direction of
travel is labelled z then the electric field vector can exist in directions x or y or any in between. If it is limited to one direction
only then it is said to be *linearly polarized* since it always points
along the same line. It is therefore possible for two waves to travel
together in the same direction but be independent of each other if
one is polarized in the x direction (vertical polarization − we always
refer to the electric vector, not the magnetic) while the other is
polarized in the y direction (horizontal polarization). This feature
is employed in satellite transmission so that the same frequency
can be used for two entirely different transmissions.

The term *mode* is used to indicate the different ways a wave can
travel, e.g. vertical mode, horizontal mode. In bounded transmission
lines such as waveguides and optical fibres many modes may exist
and these are labelled according to a special code (see Waveguide).

A wave is said to be *unpolarized* if the direction of the electric
vector various randomly.

(3) is short for Electric Polarization.

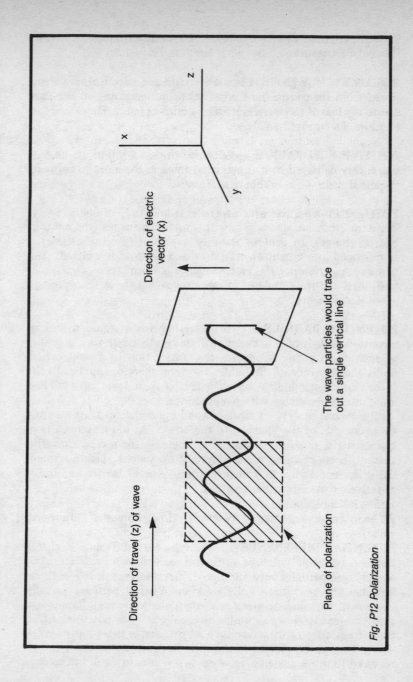

Fig. P12 Polarization

(* Cell, Primary Cell, Electrolyte, Wave, Electromagnetic Wave, Plane of Polarization >> Satellite, Satellite Television)

POSITIVE   If a glass rod is rubbed with silk, electrons are transferred from the rod to the silk. The charge remaining on the glass due to the loss of electrons is labelled *positive* (+ve or +).
(* Atom, Electron, Charge)

POSITIVE FEEDBACK is a system in which a fraction of the output energy delivered by a circuit is returned to the input to augment the signal there — see Feedback.

POSITRON is a particle which we meet in the study of radioactivity. When an atom nucleus is left with too few neutrons (the neutron has no charge), to achieve stability a proton (positive charge) is transformed into a neutron. To do this a *positron* is emitted. The name comes from *positive electron* since it resembles an electron in both mass and magnitude of charge except that the latter is positive — see Radioactivity.

POTENTIAL BARRIER   In general this is a region within an electric field in which accumulated charges give rise to a potential of such polarity that it opposes the normal flow of charge carriers under the influence of the field. The term therefore applies to the space charge surrounding the cathode of a thermionic valve but it is more usually associated with p-n junctions.
  The thermal energy of electrons and holes enables them to cross from one side of the junction to the other. At the junction the p-type material takes on a negative charge and the n-type a positive charge. These charges on either side of the junction create a potential difference across it, known as the *potential barrier* because it effectively prevents further crossings.
  See P-N Junction.
(* Semiconductor, Charge, Electron, Hole, Potential Difference)

POTENTIAL DIFFERENCE   When there is a difference in charge between two points it follows that there will be a force acting on any charged particles between them. The difference in charge therefore has the potential to do work on charged particles (usually electrons). In other words it has the potential energy required to cause current to flow. A unit which expresses the potential difference irrespective of the magnitude of the charge being moved is the volt. This can be defined as the ratio between the work or energy required to move a charge between two points in a uniform electric

340

field to the value of that charge, i.e. work per unit charge. (Note that the distance the charge is moved is accounted for in the formula for work.) Hence:

$$\text{potential difference (p.d.) or ``voltage''} = \frac{\text{work done}}{\text{charge}}$$

or in practical units,

$$1 \text{ volt} = \frac{1 \text{ joule}}{1 \text{ coulomb}} \text{ (J/C)}.$$

See also Electric Potential.
(* Charge, Coulomb, Force, Energy, Work, Joule, Current)

POTENTIAL ENERGY   This is probably best understood via the concept of *gravitational* potential energy first. Any object which can fall possesses potential (or stored) energy. Take, for example, a weight on the ground. Here we say that being at ground level, its potential energy is zero. Raise the weight to the top of a building and it is then said to possess potential energy simply because it has the energy to fall back to its original position. The gravitational potential energy (E_p) of a body is the product of its height (h) and weight (W), hence:

$$E_p = h \times W.$$

This leads to a similar reasoning for *electric potential energy*. The two plates of Figure P13 are charged to a voltage, V as shown, i.e. the *potential* difference between them is V volts. A small negative charge will be repelled by plate A and attracted towards plate B. Suppose that it is initially at B as shown. Then work must be done on it to force it over to plate A. This work is stored as potential energy in the charge and is equal to $V \times q$ (coulomb volts, i.e. joules). If the charge is now released, it has the energy required for it to travel back to plate B. Note the parallel with $h \times W$ above. The analogy is, of course, with lifting and lowering a weight, work is required to lift it but when released it falls back and gives up its potential energy.

When a body which has potential energy moves, then because of its motion some of its potential energy has changed into kinetic energy, the total energy remaining the same.

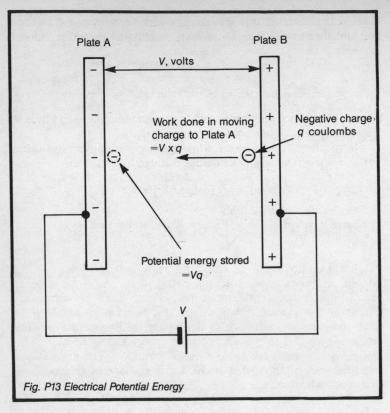

Plate A   Plate B

V, volts

Work done in moving
charge to Plate A
$= V \times q$

Negative charge
q coulombs

Potential energy stored
$= Vq$

V

Fig. P13 Electrical Potential Energy

The concept of potential energy is particularly useful in the study of atom orbits where an electron has associated with it differing values of potential energy plus kinetic energy according to the orbit number. From such calculations, orbit radius, electron velocity etc. can be readily derived.

(* Energy, Joule, Kinetic Energy, Work, Charge, Coulomb)

POWER   When a job of work has to be done, the time it takes is usually important. A small engine can move a motor car between two places in a certain time but with a large engine the time taken is less. This is because the larger engine has a faster work output, i.e. it does the same amount of work as does the small engine but completes it in less time. We say that the larger engine is more *powerful.* Summing up, the faster a device can do a certain amount of work, the more powerful it is, hence power is simply defined as the *rate* of doing work. It follows that it is also the rate at which energy is expended. Electrical power is designated by the symbol P and the unit is the watt (W — after James Watt, the English inventor). Hence:

$$\text{power} = \frac{\text{work done}}{\text{time interval}}$$

and in the S.I. system where work is measured in joules and time in seconds, a power of one watt = 1 joule per second.

Electrically, work is done when a charge is moved through a potential difference, say Q coulombs through V volts, then:

$$W \text{ (joules)} = Q \text{ (coulombs)} \times V \text{ (volts)}$$

hence power $= \dfrac{Q}{t} \times V$ watts (or joules per second) .

Now since one coulomb of electric charge flowing past a point in one second is equal to a current of one ampere, i.e. $I = Q/t$ where I is the current, then:

$$P = I \times V \quad \text{and from Ohm's Law,} P = I^2 R = V^2/R$$

where R is the resistance in the circuit.

In an alternating current circuit, if V and I are the root mean square values and they are not in phase, then:

$$P = VI \cos \phi$$

where ϕ is the phase angle between them.

Cos ϕ is known as the *power factor* and P is known as the *active power*.

If the power factor is ignored, i.e. the power is calculated from $V \times I$, then it is correctly known as the *apparent power*, measured in volt-amperes.

See also In-Phase Component, Quadrature Component.
(* Work, Charge, Joule, Coulomb, Resistance, Root Mean Square, Power Factor, Watt, Volt-Ampere, Potential Difference)

POWER COMPONENT   When current flows in a reactive circuit it becomes out of phase with the voltage. The current phasor can be resolved into in-phase and 90° out-of-phase components. The in-phase component is also known as the power component since it is only this one which dissipates power — see In-Phase Component.

POWER FACTOR   This applies to alternating current circuits only and is a correction applied to what is known as the *apparent* power (symbol S) to obtain the *active* power (symbol P). The apparent power is that given by the product of the root mean square (r.m.s.) values of voltage, V and current, I. Multiplying the apparent power by the *power factor* gives the active power.

When voltage and current are in phase, no correction is necessary for $V \times I$ is always positive (when V goes negative so does I so their product is always positive). That some correction is required when voltage and current are not in phase is demonstrated by Figure P14(i)

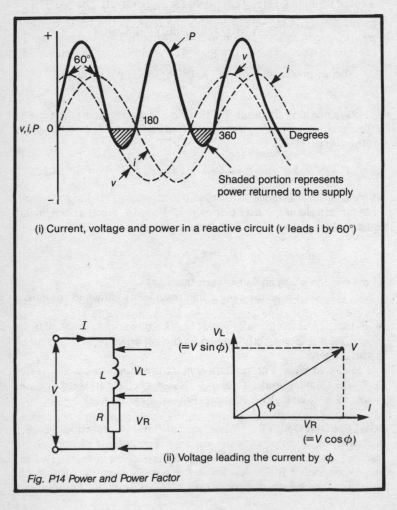

(i) Current, voltage and power in a reactive circuit (*v* leads i by 60°)

(ii) Voltage leading the current by ϕ

Fig. P14 Power and Power Factor

344

which shows how the power developed now has a negative component (below the axis). This represents power returned to the supply by the reactance which itself is creating the phase difference between the instantaneous values of v and i. If, for example, this reactance is inductive, some of the energy stored in the magnetic field is returned as the field collapses — twice per cycle. Hence simple multiplication of V by I does not give the active power, only the apparent power. The unit for the apparent power cannot be the watt, this only applies to power expended, the unit used is therefore the *volt-ampere* (V A).

The correction we need is called the *power factor* and when the apparent power is multiplied by this the result is the active power. In an a.c. circuit the average power dissipated is $I^2 R$ watts where I is the r.m.s. value of the current and R is the circuit resistance in ohms. The apparent power is VI volt-amperes, hence:

$$\text{active power} = \text{apparent power} \times \text{power factor}$$

and

$$\text{power factor} = \frac{I^2 R}{VI} = \frac{IR}{V}$$

From Figure P14(ii) which shows a phasor diagram for an inductive circuit, it is evident that $IR = V_R = V \cos \phi$

$$\therefore \quad \text{power factor} = \frac{V_R}{V} = \frac{V \cos \phi}{V} = \cos \phi$$

$\cos \phi$ is a ratio and therefore is not expressed in any units. Also the impedance, Z of the circuit is given by V/I, hence $I/V = 1/Z$:

$$\therefore \quad \text{since power factor} = IR/V \,,$$

it is also equal to R/Z showing that the power factor is also equal to the ratio of the resistance to the impedance which makes sense because it is only in the resistance that power is developed, not in the reactance. The average power in any circuit containing reactance is therefore expressed by:

$$P = VI \cos \phi \,.$$

The power factor has values from 0 to 1.

At the extremes therefore if the phase angle between voltage and current is 0, the power factor is cos $0° = 1$ and apparent and active powers are the same, this follows because only a completely resistive circuit can have such a phase angle. Conversely for a purely reactive circuit the phase angle $= 90°$; cos $90° = 0$, i.e. no power can be expended.

(* Alternating Current, Power, Root Mean Square, Impedance, Reactance, Phase, Phase Angle, Phasor $\gg$ Loss Factor)

POWER FLUX DENSITY is a term mainly used in assessing the strength of a radio signal. It is measured as the amount of power over a given area, i.e. in watts per square metre (W/m^2). Hence power flux density in vacuum or almost equally in air $= E^2/Z_0$ where E is the electric field strength in volts per metre and Z_0 is the intrinsic impedance of free space.

Power flux density is frequently quoted in decibels relative to one watt, i.e. in dBW/m^2, this makes it a convenient unit for calculating gains and losses over a radio transmission path.

(* Radio, Electric Field Strength, Impedance, Intrinsic Impedance, Electromagnetic Radiation, Power, Decibel $\gg$ Isotropic Antenna)

PRIMARY CELL   This is a device which produces electricity from a chemical reaction. Generally primary chemical cells are constructed on the basis of a pair of electrodes in contact with an electrolyte which is capable of moving electric charge through the agency of positive and negative ions. The electrolyte may or may not also be part of a chemical reaction. In use the chemicals and/or electrodes involved are consumed or alternatively the electrolyte may dry up, hence cell life is limited. Except in a few cases the process is not truly reversible. Primary cell e.m.f.'s are of the order of $1 - 2$ volts. Primary cells generally maintain a reasonably constant terminal voltage over the greater part of their life but the voltage is likely to fall as the cell nears exhaustion because of the rise in internal resistance. The earliest primary cell was the *Voltaic*, this was followed by the *Daniell*. Examples of primary cells in common use are:

(i)   the cylindrical 1.5 V cells used for hand torches;
(ii) the small 1.4 V mercury cells used in miniature equipment, including hearing aids and cameras.

(* Cell, Electrolyte, Electromotive Force, Internal Resistance, Voltaic . . . , Daniell . . . , Leclanché . . . , Mercury . . . , Weston Standard Cell $\gg$ Alkaline . . . , Dry . . . , Zinc-Air . . . , Zinc Chloride Cell)

PRIMARY COEFFICIENT of a Transmission Line. There are 4, the resistance (R), inductance (L), capacitance (C) and shunt conductance or leakage (G), usually quoted per metre of line – see Transmission Line.

PRIMARY ELECTRON   When the surface of a material is bombarded by a stream of electrons, other electrons are released. The bombarding electrons are the *primary electrons*, called this mainly to distinguish them from those released which are known as *secondary electrons*. Primary electrons are released for example by thermionic emission, by the photoelectric effect or from a cold cathode when a sufficiently high positive electric field is present.
(* Electron, Secondary Emission, Thermionic Emission, Electric Field, Photoelectric Effect, Cold Cathode, Secondary Electron)

PRIMARY WINDING is the winding of a transformer connected to the supply of energy as opposed to the secondary winding(s) which delivers energy to a load – see Transformer.

PROBABILITY is a term met frequently in electronics theory mainly because of the random nature of particle movements and of noise. Probability is the essence of *prediction* and it is a measure of the likelihood that something will or will not happen. The scale of measurement is simple. The impossibility of an event occurring is rated at zero and certainty as 1.0. Few events are in these categories but fall somewhere in between, hence a probability of between 0 and 1 is assigned. As an example, a coin tossed with no bias is as likely to produce a head as a tail. The probability of a head is expressed as $P(\text{H}) = 0.5$, equally that for the tail is $P(\text{T}) = 0.5$. $P(\text{H}) + P(\text{T}) = 0.5 + 0.5 = 1$, showing the certainty of either a head or a tail.
    Taking the roulette wheel as another example, we naturally assume that it has no bias, hence the numbers appear at random. With any of its numbers 0–36 as a possible result, the probability of any one turning up is 1 in 37, i.e. 0.027. Such a probability ensures that overall the operator wins, increase the probability slightly by reducing the numbers on the wheel (e.g. 0–24 gives a probability of 0.04) ensures that the operator goes bankrupt.
(* Random, Information Theory)

PROPAGATION COEFFICIENT   This is a quantity which expresses the rate at which the current falls as a sinusoidal wave progresses along a transmission line. The recommended symbol is γ (Greek lower case gamma) and the discussion below shows that the propagation coefficient can be calculated directly from the four primary coefficients to provide useful practical information about the line, the most important perhaps, being the attenuation. Theoretically the propagation coefficient refers to a uniform line of infinite length but it can be shown that a shorter line terminated in its characteristic impedance has similar characteristics. If the current at the beginning of a section of unit length of the line is I_1 and that at the end is I_2, then the propagation coefficient at a specified frequency:

$$\gamma = \log_e I_1/I_2 \text{ nepers}$$

which can be converted to decibels by multiplying by 8.686. γ is complex because the two currents are not in phase owing to the time taken for the wave to travel between the two points. From the formula above:

$$e^\gamma = I_1/I_2$$

this is for one section only hence for n sections where I_n is the current at the nth:

$$I_1/I_n = e^{n\gamma}$$

Accordingly if the sending current, I_1 and γ are known, I_n can be calculated from $I_1 \times e^{-n\gamma}$.

By considering each section as a T-network and knowing the primary coefficients per section (say, 1 metre or 1 kilometre), the propagation coefficient is calculated from:

$$\gamma = \sqrt{(R + j\omega L)(G + j\omega C)} \ . \qquad \text{(see Complex Notation for j)}$$

This is complex so if we substitute $\gamma = \alpha + j\beta$, then α is the *attenuation coefficient* in nepers and β the *phase-change coefficient* in radians. From β the wavelength, λ follows for if the phase change over each section is β radians, there are $2\pi/\beta$ sections per wavelength. Hence if, for example, the section is 1 metre and the primary coefficients used in the formula above are per metre:

$$\lambda = 2\pi/\beta \text{ metres} .$$

At a given frequency, f, the wave velocity:

$$v = f\lambda = (2\pi f)/\beta = \omega/\beta \text{ metres per second.}$$

To bring all these formulae into focus some practical figures may be helpful (the mathematics have been omitted for brevity). The figures are for an underground copper pair of wires used for telephony. The wires are 0.91 mm diameter and paper insulated. At 1600 Hz (which makes ω a convenient 10 000 rads/s):

$$R = 52.26 \; \Omega/\text{km}, \quad L = 0.69 \; \text{mH/km}, \quad G = 1.087 \; \mu\text{S/km},$$

$$C = 0.038 \; \mu\text{F/km}.$$

$$R + j\omega L = 52.26 + j6.9$$

$$G + j\omega C = 10^{-6}(1.087 + j380)$$

from which, after conversion to polar coordinates for easier calculation of γ:

$$\gamma = 0.141 \; \angle 48.68° \quad \text{or} \quad 0.93 + j0.106$$

hence:

$$\alpha = 0.93 \; \text{nepers per km (8.1 dB/km)}$$

$$\beta = 0.106 \; \text{radians per km},$$

from which:

$$\lambda = 2\pi/\beta = 59.3 \; \text{km}$$

and

$$v = \omega/\beta = 94\,340 \; \text{km/sec},$$

about one-third the speed of light.

A network terminated in its iterative impedances also has a propagation coefficient which again is the natural logarithm of the (complex) ratio of the input and output currents.

(* Transmission Line, Neper, Decibel, Impedance, Characteristic Impedance, Iterative Impedance, Network, Complex Notation, Polar Coordinate, Cartesian Coordinate, Radian)

PROTON   This is one of the particles contained within an atomic nucleus. It spins and has a positive charge of 1.602×10^{-19} coulombs, equal to that of the electron but of opposite sign. The proton mass $= 1.672 \times 10^{-27}$ kg, this is 1836 times the electron mass.

The number of protons within a nucleus determines the atomic number of the element.

Within the nucleus, the protons, which because of their like charges would normally fly apart, are bound to the neutrons by a strong interactive nuclear force.
(* Atom, Charge, Electron, Neutron)

PROXIMITY EFFECT arises when two or more conductors carrying the same alternating current run sufficiently close together so that each is within the influence of the electromagnetic field(s) of the other(s). The effect is similar to skin effect and results in an abnormal distribution of current across the cross-section of each conductor, therefore with a rise in effective resistance. As with skin effect, proximity effect increases with frequency. The effect is particularly noticeable in inductors used at high frequencies. (* Alternating Current, Effective Resistance, Electromagnetic Radiation >> Skin Effect)

P-TYPE SEMICONDUCTOR   This is a semiconductor to which an acceptor impurity has been added so that the mobile hole density exceeds the free electron density. Current flow through the device is therefore mainly by holes.
For the basic technique, see Doping. See also N-type Semiconductor.
(* Semiconductor, Hole, Donor)

PULSE is a voltage or current which increases from one value (the *base level*, usually zero) to a maximum value and then decreases to the original value, both transitions taking place in a short time, in a few words, a short burst of energy. However, pulses are best described graphically as in Figure P15(i) which shows an ideal *rectangular* pulse. The description "ideal" is used because no practical pulse can be of this form, transitions from minimum to maximum and back again need time, hence the two sides always slope. Pulses are described according to their graphical shapes, e.g. square, triangular, sawtooth, cosine, exponential, each can be analysed by Fourier waveform analysis.
Although pulse generators such as the multivibrator are capable of producing pulses of shape approaching the ideal, such a pulse subsequently meeting reactance or a limitation of bandwidth easily loses its intended shape. Taking the most common form of pulse, the rectangular as an example, Fourier analysis shows that to transmit such a pulse faithfully over any circuit requires an infinite bandwidth, a facility which is just not available. In fact as the bandwidth becomes more and more restricted a square pulse degenerates towards a sine wave, a clear indication that the pulse

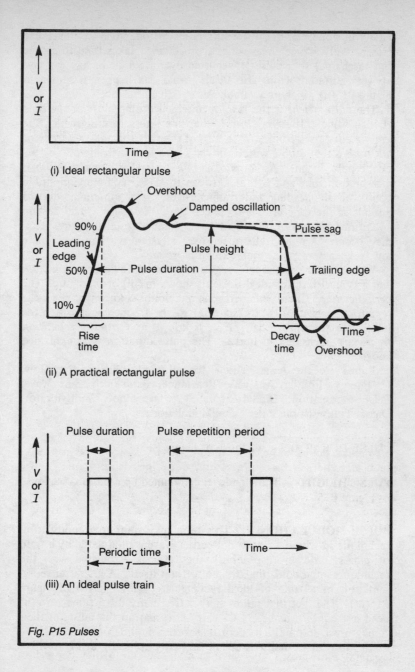

(i) Ideal rectangular pulse

(ii) A practical rectangular pulse

(iii) An ideal pulse train

Fig. P15 Pulses

sides will slope, i.e. the pulse suffers distortion. Also any reactance present adds a time delay (e.g. a capacitance takes time to charge and discharge) so a pulse transmitted over a circuit or line can end up very different from the ideal. What can happen is shown in Figure P15(ii) which now enables us to add all the labels.

The *pulse height* is the level maintained during most of the time at high value. The *rise time* is the time interval during which the *leading edge* rises from 10% to 90% of the pulse height, the *decay* or *fall time* is that during which the *trailing edge* falls from 90% to 10% of the pulse height. As shown the *pulse duration* or *pulse width* is measured in time and is that between the 50% maximum amplitude points on the leading and trailing edges. It is sometimes quoted instead as the time interval between the 90% levels. Under certain conditions *overshoot* followed by a damped oscillatory response may occur. A pulse transmitted over a system with an inadequate low frequency response may exhibit *pulse sag*.

When similar pulses recur regularly, this is known as a *pulse train* and a typical train of ideal pulses is shown in (iii) of the figure. The *periodic time, T* between corresponding points is known as the *pulse repetition period* (or *pulse spacing*) so the frequency at which the pulses are transmitted is $1/T$ or is known as the *pulse repetition frequency*, measured in hertz. The pulse duration is as explained above.

Pulses are the basic vehicle for all digital information flow. (* Energy, Fourier Analysis, Reactance, Bandwidth, Sine Wave, Pulse Modulation, Digital Signal >> Overshoot, Multivibrator, Digital Transmission, Pulse Code Modulation)

PULSE DURATION – see Pulse or Figure P15.

PULSE HEIGHT   The high level maintained by a pulse – see Pulse or Figure P15.

PULSE MODULATION   This term may refer to a modulation technique in which a sinusoidal carrier wave is modulated by a train of pulses. However, generally the term is associated with the techniques of modulating the pulse train itself. A graphical representation of a train of ideal rectangular pulses is given in Figure P15(iii). The fact that pulses may suffer many distortions as in (ii) need not concern us here. To carry information the pulses or their timing must be modified according to the modulating wave. Three of the four main methods are illustrated graphically in Figure P16. They are:

352

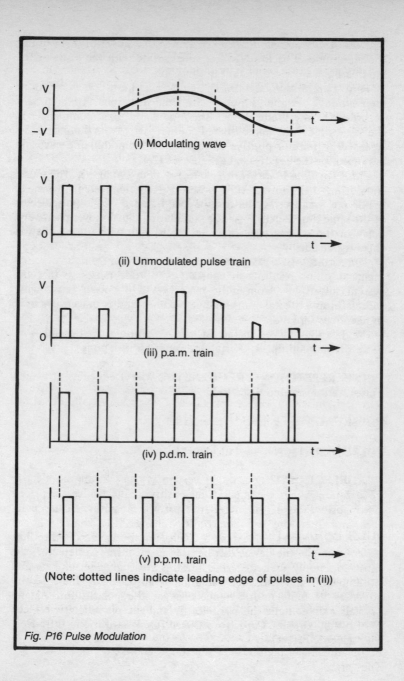

(i) Modulating wave

(ii) Unmodulated pulse train

(iii) p.a.m. train

(iv) p.d.m. train

(v) p.p.m. train

(Note: dotted lines indicate leading edge of pulses in (ii))

Fig. P16 Pulse Modulation

Pulse Amplitude Modulation (p.a.m.) – is shown in (iii). In this the amplitude of each pulse is commensurate with the value of the modulating wave at the instant of sampling.

Pulse Duration Modulation (p.d.m. – also known as *pulse width modulation*) – employs pulses, the time durations of which vary according to the modulation. The modulated pulse commences at the same time as its unmodulated counterpart but its trailing edge is retarded in time for positive excursions of the modulating wave and advanced for the negative excursions, see (iv).

Pulse Position Modulation (p.p.m.) – is shown in (v). The pulses shift from their normal time positions. In the system shown, at maximum negative modulation the leading edge of the pulse occurs at the same time as in (ii). As the modulating signal moves positively, delay in the leading edge increases, thus even with no modulation there is some delay.

Pulse Code Modulation (p.c.m.) – this is an ingenious development of p.a.m. resulting in constant amplitude pulses so that the system suffers less from pulse distortion and noise. It is highly successful as a digital transmission medium and is universally used in telephony circuits.
(* Modulation, Pulse, Digital Signal >> Pulse Code Modulation, Time Division Multiplex, Digital Transmission, Sampling)

PULSE REPETITION FREQUENCY is the frequency at which pulses are transmitted – see Pulse.

PULSE SAG – see Pulse or Figure P15.

PULSE WIDTH – see Pulse or Figure P15.

PYROELECTRICITY occurs in certain crystals having an electric polarization which is temperature sensitive. Electrodes are placed on opposite faces of the material to form a capacitor. As temperature and therefore the polarization change, the charge on the electrodes becomes evident as a change in voltage across the slice. As an example, the device can be used as an infra-red detector, the most commonly used materials for this are triglycine sulphate and lithium tantalate. Infra-red radiation is absorbed by the slice and so raises its temperature, hence changes the polarization. Many crystals exhibit both the pyroelectric and the piezoelectric effects.
(* Crystal, Dipole, Capacitor, Dielectric, Polarization, Infra-Red, Piezoelectric Effect)

Q

Q FACTOR   In most resonant circuits resistance is detrimental and it is especially so in the tuned circuits of radio receivers where resistance impairs the "sharpness" of tuning. Accordingly, some way is needed for expressing the goodness of a component or circuit for this purpose. In most resonant circuits reactance (X) is required but resistance (R) is not because it creates power losses so a sensible measure is the ratio between them, i.e. X/R. This ratio is termed the *quality factor*, more generally known as the Q *factor*, or often just plain Q and this is the symbol used. Q is used therefore to assess capacitors, inductors and resonant circuits. Hence $Q = X/R$ and:

$$\text{for a capacitor: } Q = \frac{(1/\omega C)}{R} = \frac{1}{\omega CR}$$

where ω radians per second $= 2\pi \times$ frequency and C is the capacitance in farads.

$$\text{for an inductor: } Q = \omega L/R$$

where L is the inductance in henries.

Theoretically therefore Q varies from 0 to infinity. Practical values of Q for inductors range from tens up to a few hundreds. Q's for capacitors are generally higher because resistance and other losses are much smaller. Note that even when R is constant with frequency, Q is not constant but itself varies with frequency.

The inherent resistance of a capacitor is usually sufficiently small compared with its reactance that Q is seldom used as a measure of quality. The opposite applies for inductors which are plagued with resistance losses in windings, core, etc.

The Q factor also expresses the ability of a resonant circuit to produce a high output at the resonance frequency, f_r, i.e. a high resonant rise in voltage. As a by-product this also is an indication of the selectivity of the circuit for high Q means good selectivity. In a tuned circuit nearly all the resistance lies within the inductor, hence, designating the value of Q at resonance, Q_r and for ω at resonance, ω_r:

$$Q_r = \frac{\omega_r L}{R} \quad \text{and since } \omega_r = \frac{1}{\sqrt{LC}}$$

355

where $\omega_r = 2\pi f_r$ and R is the *effective resistance:*

$$Q_r = \frac{1}{R} \sqrt{L/C} \, ,$$

so Q_r is inversely proportional to R as would be expected. It is also directly proportional to $\sqrt{(L/C)}$, accordingly Q_r can be increased by making L/C high. For any given resonance frequency the product of L and C is fixed so any combination having the same product will suffice. Thus to a certain extent we can change the L/C ratio at will provided that the product LC remains constant.

Q_r also expresses the voltage magnification of a resonant circuit for it can be shown that if V is the applied voltage, then multiplying this by Q_r gives the voltage across the capacitor (V_c) or the inductor (V_L). Note that at resonance these are equal although of opposite sign. Therefore at resonance:

$$V_c = Q_r \times V \qquad V_L = Q_r \times V.$$

A useful graphical representation of the relevancy of Q in resonant circuits is given in Figure Q1. At (i) is a series circuit and at (ii) is a group of selectivity curves for it, expressed by the voltage developed across the capacitor as ω varies above and below 1000 rads/sec, $(f_r = 159$ Hz).

For $Q_r = 10$ the values used are $L = 1$ H, $C = 1$ μF, $R = 100$ Ω and we get a curve showing hardly any selectivity at all.

Reducing R to 50 Ω makes $Q_r = 20$, which shows some improvement. However, by increasing the L/C ratio 25 times, the result is $Q_r = 50$, giving a response which is truly selective and this is even with R restored to 100 Ω.

The Q-factor is the reciprocal of the *dissipation factor*, the latter gives us a measure of the degree to which a circuit *fails* to reach perfection.

(* Resonance, Inductance, Capacitance, Tuned Circuit, Resistance, Effective Resistance, Selectivity, Dissipation Factor, L-C Circuit, Radian)

QUADRATURE   Two similar waves are said to be in *quadrature* when they have a phase difference of 90° $(\pi/2$ radians). The waves must be at the same frequency otherwise the phase difference varies with time. In quadrature when one wave is at zero, the other is at either its positive or negative peak. In a pure reactance the current and voltage are always in quadrature.

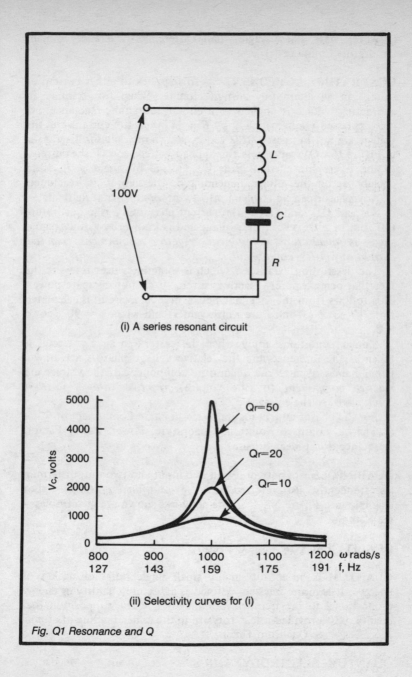

(i) A series resonant circuit

(ii) Selectivity curves for (i)

Fig. Q1 Resonance and Q

(* Wave, Phase, Phase Angle, Phase Difference, Reactance, Radian, Quadrature Component)

QUADRATURE COMPONENT   This applies to either current or voltage in an alternating current circuit.   When for example an alternating voltage is applied to a circuit containing reactance, i.e. it is expressed mathematically by $R + jX$, then the current and the voltage are not in phase. This can be shown on a phasor diagram as in Figure I6. OV represents the applied voltage and OI the current. In the figure the current leads the voltage by angle ϕ, it could equally lag on the voltage, depending on the sign of the reactance.

Any phasor can be resolved into two *components* at right angles, in this case OI_R and OI_X. The current phasor OI_X is in quadrature (90° out of phase) with the voltage and is known by various names such as *quadrature component, reactive component, reactive current* or *wattless component.*

The description "wattless" which is sometimes used refers to the fact that being a purely reactive current, it cannot dissipate power. This follows from the fact that power in an a.c. circuit is calculated from $VI \cos \phi$ (V and I are r.m.s. values) and when $\phi = 90°$, $\cos \phi = 0$.

Similar conditions apply when the current in an a.c. circuit is taken as the reference and the relative voltage phasors are drawn. Other names given to the quadrature component of the voltage are *reactive component* (of the voltage), *reactive voltage, wattless component* (of the voltage).

For the phasor OI_R in Figure I6 see In-Phase Component.
(* Phasor, Complex Notation, Quadrature, Power, Power Factor, Reactance, Root Mean Square)

QUADRIPOLE is a network with two input and two output terminals, frequently also referred to as a *4-terminal network.*   For examples see Figure N2 – all the networks shown are quadripoles – see Network.

QUALITY FACTOR – see Q-Factor.

QUANTUM is an infinitesimally small single burst or packet of energy. It is more precisely defined as a discrete quantity of energy proportional to the frequency of radiation. The supposition that quanta exist provided a leap forward in the understanding of atomic processes – see Quantum Theory.

QUANTUM ELECTRODYNAMICS – see Quantum Mechanics.

QUANTUM MECHANICS is a mathematical theory arising from the earlier quantum theory initiated by Max Planck. It got under way soon after 1925 by which time many scientists had become aware that Newton's laws on forces and motion were satisfactory when describing things on a large scale but failed when applied to things on an atomic scale. In quantum mechanics the idea that a particle can have a definite location and speed as we would normally expect, is not allowed. The theory also unifies the ideas of waves and particles (i.e. that waves can behave like particles and vice versa).

Quantum mechanics has been of great help in the study of energy levels in atoms and molecules and in electron behaviour generally. When combined with the basic laws of electricity, the theory is sometimes given the name *quantum electrodynamics.*
(* Atom, Electron, Quantum Theory, Energy, Energy Levels, Planck Constant, Photon, Phonon, Spin)

QUANTUM NUMBER – see de Broglie Waves.

QUANTUM THEORY   Before 1900 the theories in vogue could not satisfactorily explain the emission of light from a very hot metal. Generally too it had been found that at atomic level Newton's rules seemed to be misleading. Then Max Planck (a German scientist) evolved a theory which successfully predicted what was observed. He suggested that energy, particularly in the form of light, could be radiated or absorbed not at any energy level but only at one of the discrete values, 0, hf, $2hf$, $3hf$ . . . nhf where n is a positive integer, f the frequency of radiation and h, what is now known as Planck's constant (6.626×10^{-34} joule seconds). Each single burst (or "packet") of energy is known as a *quantum.* The energy (E) of a quantum is therefore related to the frequency of the radiation by the simple formula:

$$E = h \times f.$$

Planck's work, together with Einstein's, led to the early development of quantum theory at the beginning of the 20th Century.
See also Quantum Mechanics.
(* Energy, Energy Levels, Frequency, Spin, Planck Constant, Light)

QUARTZ CRYSTAL   Certain crystalline substances develop an electric charge when subjected to mechanical stress and conversely exhibit strain when a voltage is applied to certain surfaces. This is the piezoelectric effect and one of the most widely used crystals is that of quartz, an exceptionally hard substance. Quartz is a mineral

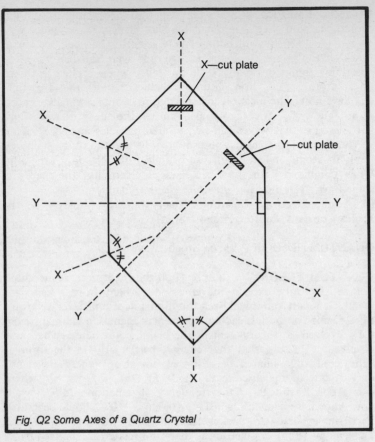

X

X—cut plate

Y

Y—cut plate

X

Y — — — — — — — — — — — — — — — — — Y

X

X

Y

X

Fig. Q2 Some Axes of a Quartz Crystal

form of silica (silicon dioxide) and in fact most sands are largely quartz crystals which have been "weathered". A crystal of quartz is basically a hexagonal body with a hexagonal pyramid at each end. A typical crystal may be 10 or so centimetres long and a few centimetres in diameter. From the crystal, thin plates are cut at various angles according to the characteristics required.

To describe the angles at which a plate is cut, reference is made to the *crystallographic axes*, some of which are shown on a cross section of the body of a natural crystal in Figure Q2. The *electric* axes are labelled X and are those which bisect an angle between a pair of adjacent faces. The *mechanical* axes are labelled Y and are perpendicular to any face. The Z axis is known as the *optical axis* and this runs between the two tips of the crystal. A plate cut so that its faces are perpendicular to an X-axis is known as an X-cut

360

crystal, similarly for Y-cut plates as shown. Many other types of cut are also used, an example is the AT-cut crystal (cut at 35° to the Z-axis), much used for its very low temperature coefficient. After cutting the plate undergoes grinding and polishing to achieve the resonances required. Opposite faces are then coated with a thin gold film for the electrical contacts.

(* Crystal, Piezoelectric Effect, Resonance >> Crystal Oscillator, Crystal Filter, Crystal Microphone)

QUIESCENT CURRENT is the current drawn by an active device such as a transistor or thermionic valve when no input signal is present.

See also Quiescent Point.

QUIESCENT POINT is a point on a characteristic or load line of an active device such as a transistor which indicates the mean values of the current and voltage in the output circuit when no signal is present.

(* Characteristic >> Load Line, Operating Point)

R

RADIAN A unit of angle, it is the angle at the centre of a circle which is subtended by an arc of that circle equal in length to the radius (see Fig.R1). Because the circumference of a circle is equal in length to 2π times the radius, there are 2π radians in a circle. The other unit of angle is the degree, there are 360 degrees in a circle, hence

$$1 \text{ radian} = 360°/2\pi = 57.3° .$$

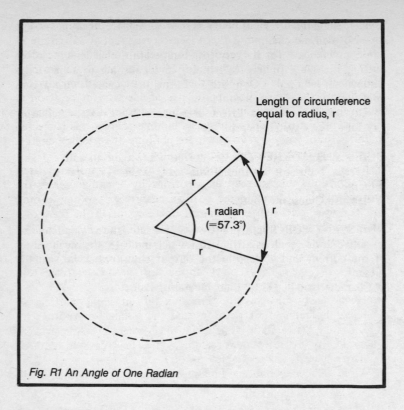

Length of circumference
equal to radius, r

r

1 radian
(=57.3°)

r

r

Fig. R1 An Angle of One Radian

RADIO is the transmission and reception of information through the medium of electromagnetic waves generally travelling via the atmosphere and/or space, but not over connecting wires (note the original term, *wireless*).

Electromagnetic frequencies used are from around 100 kHz up to 100 GHz. This definition must therefore include television but the term radio is used more in reference to the transmission of audio frequency signals rather than television signals.
(* Electromagnetic Wave, Electromagnetic Radiation, Electromagnetic Spectrum >> Radio Receiver)

RADIOACTIVITY arises because some atomic nuclei are unstable. This was first observed by Henri Becquerel (a French physicist) in 1896. His work was soon followed by experiments by Marie Curie (a Polish physicist), Lord Ernest Rutherford (a New Zealand physicist) and others. Radioactivity occurs when an atom contains too many or too few neutrons in which case the nucleus is unstable and

362

gradually obtains better stability by emitting either an *alpha particle* or a *beta particle.*

The alpha particle is equivalent to a helium nucleus, hence consists of 2 neutrons held tightly to 2 protons, therefore having a positive charge of $2e$ (where e is the fundamental electronic charge). On the other hand, a beta particle is an electron or positron (a positively charged electron). Following emission of either particle the nucleus may be left with excess binding energy, this is ejected in the form of *gamma rays* which are photons of very high energy. These changes and emissions occur as follows:

Nuclei with excess of neutrons − a neutron transforms itself into a proton, this reduces the neutrons by 1 and increases the protons by 1. To create the positive charge for the new proton and conserve the balance of charge, one electron in the form of a beta particle is emitted. The atomic number increases by 1.

Nuclei with a deficiency of neutrons − a proton becomes a neutron with the emission of a positron, again a beta particle. Alternatively the nucleus may capture one of the electrons from the innermost shell. In this case no particle is emitted.

Alpha decay involves the emission of an alpha particle so reducing the number of neutrons and the number of protons by 2. This increases the ratio of neutrons to protons.

Frequently a succession of alpha and beta decays is required before a nucleus becomes stable.

(* Atom, Nucleus, Binding Energy, Gamma Rays, Photon, Shell, Positron)

RANDOM is a general term which means the same in electronics as it does elsewhere. If, for example, a particle is said to move at random, this implies that its movement is haphazard, the *chance* of its going in one particular direction is the same as the chance that it will go in any other direction. The direction in which it moves has no relationship with the previous direction and its future moves cannot be predicted. An example of random motion might be from thousands of small fishes in a pool, swimming about aimlessly. Put some food in however and the randomness of the motion ceases.

An easily appreciated everyday example of the generation of random numbers comes from the roulette wheel. It is designed especially for this and on spinning, each of the numbers is as likely to come up as is any other number. If the wheel is properly balanced, prediction of the next number is impossible.

(* Probability)

RANDOM NOISE is electrical noise arising from any randomly occurring disturbance and also from the random movements of large numbers of particles, especially electrons — see Noise.

RATIONALISATION is a technique used in complex algebra for eliminating the imaginary component from the denominator of a fraction. It is based on the fact that in ordinary algebra $(a + b)(a - b) = a^2 - b^2$, hence with complex numbers:

$$(a + jb)(a - jb) = a^2 - j^2b^2 = a^2 + b^2 \quad (j^2 = -1)$$

Each of the two factors, $(a + jb)$ and $(a - jb)$ is said to be the *complex conjugate* of the other, meaning that the sign of the imaginary component is reversed. To rationalize, both numerator and denominator of a fraction are multiplied by the complex conjugate of the denominator. It is easier to understand the method through a simple example:

$$\frac{6 + j5}{4 - j3} \text{ becomes } \frac{6 + j5}{4 - j3} \times \frac{4 + j3}{4 + j3} = \frac{(6 + j5)(4 + j3)}{4^2 + 3^2} = \frac{9 + j38}{25}$$

$$= 0.36 + j1.52$$

(* Complex Notation)

RAYLEIGH–CARSON RECIPROCITY THEOREM In many ways the same antenna can be used both for transmitting and receiving — see Reciprocity Theorems, Antenna.

REACTANCE is the component of the impedance in an alternating current circuit due to capacitance and/or inductance. It is the means by which a.c. circuits can be analysed by Ohm's Law. To do this the resistance to an alternating current due to capacitance (X_C) is stated as $1/j\omega C$ ohms and that due to inductance (X_L) as $j\omega L$ ohms where in both cases ω is the angular frequency of the current and j is the complex operator. The j indicates that the reactance is in quadrature with the circuit resistance. Reactance can therefore also be defined as that part of the impedance which is not resistive. Capacitive reactance is given a negative sign, inductive reactance, positive, the total reactance, (X) of a circuit then being $j(X_L - X_C)$.

The way in which the two types of reactance vary with frequency is illustrated typically by Figure R2. It is seen that as frequency increases, inductive reactance increases linearly but capacitive reactance falls non-linearly and eventually approaches (but never quite

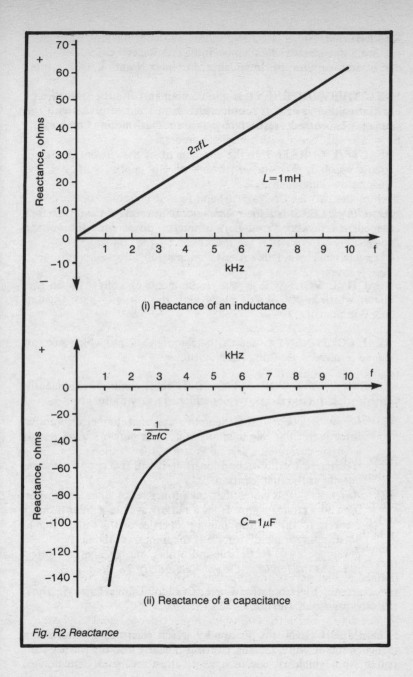

(i) Reactance of an inductance

(ii) Reactance of a capacitance

Fig. R2 Reactance

reaches) zero.

See also Capacitive Reactance, Inductive Reactance.

(* Alternating Current, Impedance, Complex Notation, Quadrature)

REACTIVE COMPONENT is the component of either the current or the voltage in an a.c. circuit which is 90° out of phase with the voltage or current respectively — see Quadrature Component.

REACTIVE CURRENT is the component of the current in an a.c. circuit which is 90° out of phase with the applied voltage — see Quadrature Component.

REACTIVE LOAD is a load which contains reactance and therefore the current flowing through it is out of phase with the voltage applied.

(* Reactance, Phase, Phase Angle >> Load)

REACTIVE VOLTAGE is the component of voltage in an a.c. circuit which is 90° out of phase with the current — see Quadrature Component.

REAL COMPONENT is one of the components into which a phasor can be resolved — see Complex Notation.

RECIPROCITY THEOREMS   Reciprocal conditions frequently arise in electronic systems, two of which are very useful are:

(1) *Linear networks* — the theorem states that if an electromotive force (e.m.f.) at one location in a linear network gives rise to a certain current at a second location, then if the same e.m.f. is transferred to this second location, it will give rise to the same current at the first location.

(2) *Antennas* — this states that the properties of an antenna when used to extract energy from a radio wave are similar in most respects to the corresponding properties of the same antenna when acting as a radiator. This theorem was originally developed by J. R. Carson and others and is sometimes referred to as the *Rayleigh-Carson Reciprocity Theorem.*

(* Network, Electromotive Force, Current, Ohm's Law, Antenna, Electromagnetic Radiation)

RECOMBINATION is a process by which electrons and holes in a semiconductor unite, i.e. the electron is taken into the valence shell of an atom which has one or more electron vacancies. The process is governed by the rule that the product of the densities of the electrons and the holes in the material is constant. Hence at a given temperature:

$$n_e n_h = n_i^2$$

where n_e is the number of electrons, n_h, the number of holes and n_i, the concentration of carriers (positive or negative) in the pure material.

Band-to-band recombination occurs when a free electron, i.e. one with energy in the conduction band, is captured by a hole in the valence band. The energy lost by the electron as it moves down to the lower energy level is emitted as a photon of radiation.

(* Atom, Electron, Hole, Energy Bands, Energy Levels, Valency, Photon)

RECTIFICATION means taking an alternating current and making a direct current out of it. Graphically the process is as illustrated in Figure R3(i). The a.c. input is usually at a frequency of 50 – 60 Hz but can be as high as 400 Hz. Apart from mechanical methods (see later), a.c. to d.c. conversion rests on the use of a rectifier, i.e. a device which passes current only in its forward direction. The semiconductor diode is ideal for this purpose. Mercury arc and mercury vapour rectifiers are also used, especially for heavy loads.

With static rectifiers there are two different types, the relatively inefficient but cheap *half-wave rectifier* which simply ignores one half of each a.c. input cycle and the *full-wave rectifier* which is a more expensive way of doing the job but is more efficient.

A half-wave circuit is shown in (ii) of the figure. The diode conducts during the positive half-cycle but blocks during the negative half-cycle of the applied alternating voltage. If the output current is examined by Fourier analysis it is found to consist of a d.c. component (the circuit would be useless if it did not) plus a component at the supply frequency plus even harmonics. Neither the supply frequency component nor the harmonics add to the rectified current, hence the circuit is relatively inefficient at around 40%. If a smooth d.c. supply is required then the frequency components must be removed, a relatively difficult task in this case when compared with the circuits which follow.

There are two quite different full-wave arrangements but which lead to the same output as shown in (iii) and (iv) of the figure. In (iii) a centre-tapped secondary winding of the transformer provides two equal voltages in antiphase, hence when D_1 is conducting, D_2 is reversed biassed and vice versa. The result is rectification of the full wave as shown. The bridge circuit in (iv) avoids using a

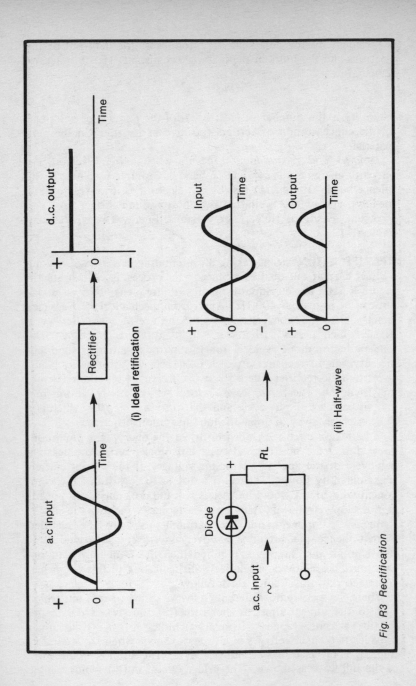

a.c input

+
0
−

Time

d.c. output

+
0
−

Time

Rectifier

(i) Ideal retification

Input

+
0
−

Time

Output

+
0

Time

Diode

RL

+

a.c. input ∿

(ii) Half-wave

Fig. R3 Rectification

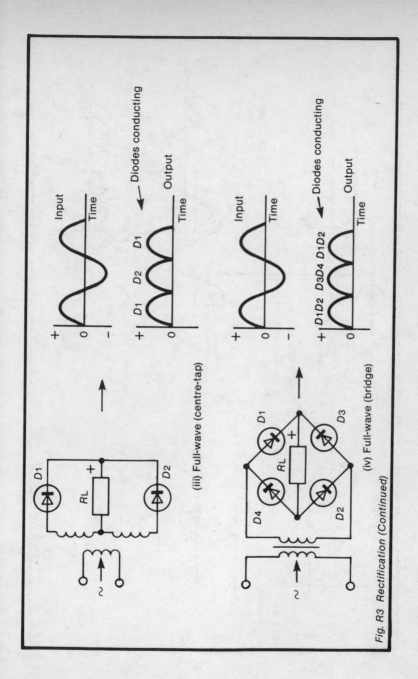

Input

Time

→ Diodes conducting

Output

D_1 D_1

D_2

D_1

Time

(iii) Full-wave (centre-tap)

D_1

R_L

D_2

+

Input

Time

→ Diodes conducting

Output

D_1D_2 D_3D_4 D_1D_2

Time

(iv) Full-wave (bridge)

D_1

D_3

R_L

+

D_4

D_2

Fig. R3 Rectification (Continued)

369

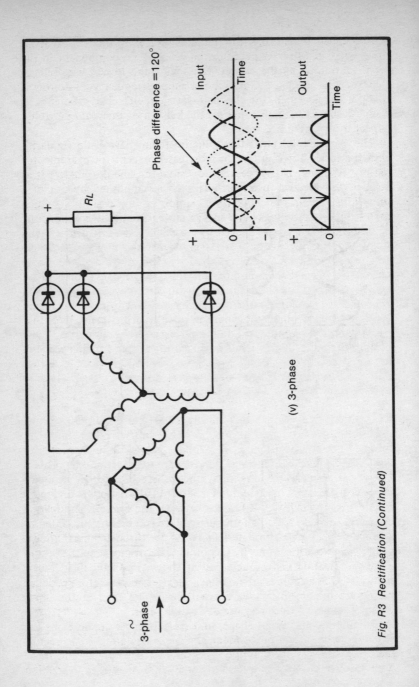

Input

Phase difference = 120°

Time

Output

Time

+

0

–

+

0

+

RL

(v) 3-phase

3-phase

Fig. R3 Rectification (Continued)

centre-tapped transformer but requires two extra diodes. Analysis shows that in full-wave rectification there is no component in the rectified output at the supply frequency, the lowest harmonic is therefore the second, i.e. double the supply frequency. Filtering is therefore easier than for the half-wave circuit. The efficiency is theoretically 81%, double that for the half-wave circuit as one would expect from Figure R3.

The rectified outputs shown in the figure have little similarity with the ideal shown in (i). In most cases, except for example, for battery charging, it is necessary to "smooth" the output to get as near to the ideal as possible. This is accomplished by use of a *smoothing circuit* or *ripple filter*, simply a low pass filter which passes the d.c. but blocks or bypasses all the frequency components.

Rectification is also achieved by mechanical means such as by an a.c. motor driving a d.c. generator. Generally, however, a single armature is used. The a.c. supply drives the motor and the d.c. is picked off from a commutator on the same shaft. Three phase rectifier systems are used when high power conversion is required as for railway traction. A simple 3-phase circuit is shown in Figure R3(v). As each phase goes more positive than the other two, that particular diode conducts. Filtering is easier because the "raw" output from the diodes is already smoother than for single phase. (* Rectifier, Diode, Fourier Analysis, Filter >> Ripple Filter, Polyphase System, Voltage Doubler, Peak Inverse Voltage, Mercury Arc Rectifier, Mercury Vapour Rectifier)

RECTIFIER is a device which ideally allows current to pass in one direction only through it. In practice it has a *forward* direction with low but not zero resistance. If a voltage is applied in the opposite direction then current flow is almost completely blocked. This is known as the *reverse* direction, the resistance is high but not infinitely so. A typical rectifier characteristic is shown in Figure P10(iv) from which the difference between the forward and reverse currents is evident. If an alternating voltage is therefore presented to a single device, only alternate half-cycles get through, this is known as half-wave rectification. By combining two or more rectifiers, full-wave rectification can be achieved as shown in Figure R3. Static rectifiers such as diodes are non-linear devices and therefore produce harmonics in the output wave even when none exist in the input wave. These are reduced by use of a ripple filter.

Rectifiers come in all shapes and sizes, in most applications the semiconductor diode predominates. Tiny ones are used to rectify radio signals, very large supply d.c. for battery charging and those with forward currents in excess of some 1000 A are used in traction systems. Other types generally in use for heavy loads are mercury arc, mercury vapour, rectifiers and mechanical a.c./d.c. converters. (* Rectification, P-N Junction, Diode, Filter >> Ripple Filter, Selenium Rectifier, Metal Rectifier, Peak Inverse Voltage, Mercury Arc Rectifier, Mercury Vapour Rectifier)

REFLECTION arises on a transmission line whenever it is terminated in an impedance other than its characteristic impedance. This follows from the Maximum Power Transfer Theorem. Put rather non-technically, if the power flowing down a line cannot be completely absorbed by the termination, then that which is left over has to go somewhere and the only course open to it is to flow back along the line towards the sending end. We call this *reflection*. It can be explained in more detail by considering the line current to be made up of two components, I_1, the current which would flow into a matched termination and I_2, the current flowing back due to a fictitious generator accounting for the difference between the characteristic impedance (Z_0) and the actual terminating impedance (Z_R). By Ohm's Law and other network theorems it can be shown that:

$$\frac{I_2}{I_1} = \frac{Z_0 - Z_R}{Z_0 + Z_R}$$

which gives the ratio of the *reflected* current to the *incident* current in terms of the characteristic and actual impedances. The reflected current can be considered as that portion of the current which is returned due to incorrect matching:

$$\frac{Z_0 - Z_R}{Z_0 + Z_R}$$

is called the *reflection coefficient* (symbol r or ρ).

Maximum reflection arises when the distant end of the line is on open-circuit or short-circuit. In the first case (open circuit, $Z_R = \infty$), the voltage is maximum but the current is zero hence no power can be delivered to the termination (one does not really exist). When the termination is a short-circuit, the current is maximum but the voltage is zero, again no power is delivered. In both cases the reflection coefficient is equal to 1, i.e. $I_2 = I_1$, showing that all the current is reflected. When $Z_R = Z_0$, the reflection coefficient is zero so there is no reflected current. Hence the reflection coefficient has a range $0 - 1$.

(* Impedance, Characteristic Impedance, Transmission Line,

Maximum Power Transfer Theorem, Network, Reflection Loss, Standing Wave >> Matching)

REFLECTION COEFFICIENT   This is the complex ratio of the reflected signal current to the incident signal current at the termination of a transmission line with a terminating impedance not equal to the characteristic impedance − see Reflection.

REFLECTION LOSS   When a generator is connected to a load to which it is not matched, then at any given frequency the reflection loss is the ratio of the power delivered to that which would be delivered if the generator and load were correctly matched. It can be shown that if Z_G is the generator impedance and Z_L that of the load, then the reflection loss expressed in decibels is:

$$10 \log_{10} \frac{(Z_G + Z_L)^2}{4 Z_G Z_L}$$

(* Generator, Reflection, Decibel >> Load, Matching)

REJECTOR CIRCUIT is another name for a parallel resonant circuit which at resonance presents a high impedance. It can be used in series within a system to reject signals at an unwanted frequency − see Resonant Circuit.

RELATIVE PERMEABILITY − see Permeability.

RELATIVE PERMITTIVITY − see Permittivity.

RELATIVISTIC EFFECT (RELATIVITY)   This was first explained by Albert Einstein (the Swiss-German theoretical physicist) in the early 1900's. Then it was considered a revolutionary concept by the scientific world but today scientists working with high particle velocities cannot ignore it. Einstein's *Special Theory of Relativity* is indeed complicated hence we note only those conclusions which are of importance to us. These are:

(i)   nothing travels faster than c, the velocity of light in a vacuum;
(ii) the mass (m) of an object increases as its velocity (v) increases according to:

$$m = \frac{m_0}{\sqrt{1 - (v/c)^2}}$$

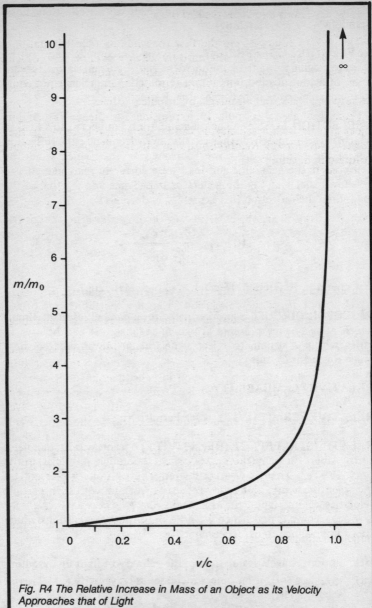

Fig. R4 The Relative Increase in Mass of an Object as its Velocity Approaches that of Light

where m_0 is known as the *rest mass*.

The second follows from the first for when an object is stationary, $v = 0$, then $m = m_0$; alternatively when $v = c$, $m \rightarrow \infty$, which surely cannot happen. The complete story is shown by the curve in Figure R4. Evidently the relativistic effect is only significant at the very high velocities attainable by atomic particles.

From the above formula an expression for the energy of an object moving with a velocity, v, can be derived. It is known as the *Einstein Mass-Energy Relationship*, one which is simple in form but profound in meaning:

the energy of an object, $E = mc^2$.

Since $E = 0$ for an object at rest $(= m_0c^2)$, then the energy of motion becomes

$$E = (m - m_0)c^2 .$$

Einstein also predicted that the type of energy (kinetic or potential) does not affect the conclusion. Hence when the energy of an object changes by an amount ΔE, its mass changes by Δm according to $\Delta E = (\Delta m)c^2$, for any kind of energy.

The statement that mass can be converted into energy and vice versa was certainly difficult for people to accept at the time but the advent of the atomic bomb soon dispelled any lingering doubts.

An electron gun is a device which provides a very high velocity beam of electrons, for example as used in a cathode-ray tube. We can use the electron gun as an example to calculate the velocity (v) of the electrons in the beam when the accelerating potential is 20 000 V. Ignoring the relativistic effect and assuming that the electrons start from rest, then the kinetic energy (E_K) gained by each electron is $1.602 \times 10^{-19} \times 20\ 000 = 3.204 \times 10^{-15}$ joules and since the kinetic energy is given by $\frac{1}{2}mv^2$ then v becomes 8.39×10^7 metres per second.

However, going through the same process but now adding in the relativistic effect, we get:

$$\Delta m = \frac{\Delta E_K}{c^2} = \frac{3.204 \times 10^{-15}}{(3 \times 10^8)^2} = 3.56 \times 10^{-32} \text{ kg} .$$

Also $m = m_0 + \Delta m = (9.109 \times 10^{-31}) + (3.56 \times 10^{-32}) = 9.465 \times 10^{-31}$ kg and this substituted in the main formula rearranged

as $v^2 = c^2 [1 - (m_0/m)^2]$, shows that a more accurate answer is $v = 8.15 \times 10^7$ m/s, a noticeable reduction – but it needed 20 000 V!
(* Energy, Kinetic Energy, Potential Energy, Mass >> Electron Gun, Cathode-Ray Tube)

RELAXATION TIME (1) is the mean time between collisions between charge carriers of the same type when moving along a conductor under the influence of an electric field. It is given the symbol τ – see Drift Velocity.

(2) it is the time for the electric polarization at a point in a dielectric to fall to $1/e$ of its original value – see Electric Polarization.

RELUCTANCE This indicates the opposition to the flux in a magnetic circuit. It is analogous to resistance in an electrical circuit and in fact is sometimes known as the *magnetic resistance*. Like resistance, it is directly proportional to the length of the path (l) and inversely proportional to its area of cross-section (a). The symbol used is R or R_m and the unit, amperes per weber (or since the unit of inductance, the henry is webers per ampere then reluctance is also given by the unit henry^{-1}). From the magnetic circuit point of view reluctance is the ratio of the magnetomotive force (F) to the magnetic flux (Φ), i.e.:

$$R_m = \frac{F}{\Phi} \qquad \text{Also } R_m = \frac{l}{\mu a}$$

where μ is the permeability of the material in henrys per metre, l and a are as given above.

For a composite magnetic path, individual series reluctances are additive as are resistances in the electrical circuit, hence the total reluctance:

$$R_m = \frac{l_1}{\mu_1 a_1} + \frac{l_2}{\mu_2 a_2} + \frac{l_3}{\mu_3 a_3} + \dots$$

Examples of devices employing composite magnetic paths are given by electromagnetic relays and record/replay heads, in these the main magnetic path is interrupted by at least one air-gap – see Figure M1 which shows the basic features of a record/replay head.
(* Magnetism, Magnetomotive Force, Magnetic Flux, Permeability >> Electromagnet, Permeability Tuning, Magnetic Recording)

REMANENCE is a term used to describe the magnetisation remaining when a ferromagnetic material is first magnetically saturated, then the applied magnetic field strength is reduced to zero. It varies greatly depending on the magnetic material, being high for magnetically *hard* materials and sufficiently low to be almost negligible in magnetically *soft* materials.

See also Magnetic Hysteresis.

(* Magnetism, Ferromagnetism, Magnetisation)

RESIDUAL INDUCTION is a term used to describe the magnetic flux density remaining when a ferromagnetic material is first magnetically saturated, then the applied magnetic field strength is reduced to zero. It varies greatly depending on the magnetic material, being high for magnetically *hard* materials and sufficiently low to be almost negligible in magnetically *soft* materials.

See also Magnetic Hysteresis.

(* Magnetism, Ferromagnetism, Magnetic Flux Density)

RESIDUAL MAGNETISM is synonymous with *remanence*. When a ferromagnetic material is magnetised and the magnetising force is subsequently removed some magnetisation remains as shown in Figure M3 (point b). Remanence varies over a wide range, in soft iron it is small whereas in magnetically hard materials such as steel or certain iron alloys, it is very high — see Magnetic Hysteresis.

RESISTANCE is the ability of a material of given dimensions to resist current flow and in doing so generate heat, i.e. convert electrical energy into heat energy. The symbol used is R and the unit, the ohm (Ω). The resistance of any object is given by the ratio of the potential difference applied to the current flowing between the points of application (see Ohm's Law). It can also be calculated for a material of uniform cross-section (e.g. wire or bar) provided that the dimensions and the resistivity are known:

$$R = \rho \times l/a \text{ ohms}$$

where ρ is the resistivity in ohm-metres, l is the length in metres and a is the area of cross-section in square metres.

Resistance is the reciprocal of conductance hence a conductance of 0.1 siemens (S) is equivalent to a resistance of 10 Ω. It is also the real component of impedance.

The simplest forms of connection of two or more resistances are the *series* and the *parallel*. An example of the series is shown in Figure R5(i) where, given individual resistances $R_1, R_2, R_3 \ldots$, the

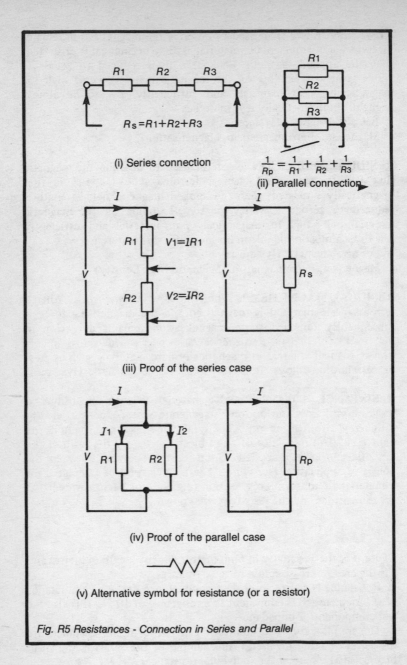

(i) Series connection

$R_s = R_1 + R_2 + R_3$

(ii) Parallel connection

$$\frac{1}{R_p} = \frac{1}{R_1} + \frac{1}{R_2} + \frac{1}{R_3}$$

$V_1 = IR_1$

$V_2 = IR_2$

(iii) Proof of the series case

(iv) Proof of the parallel case

(v) Alternative symbol for resistance (or a resistor)

Fig. R5 Resistances - Connection in Series and Parallel

series network has an overall resistance of $R_s = R_1 + R_2 + R_3 + \ldots$

To understand this we need Ohm's Law. Consider two resistances only, R_1 and R_2 and let a voltage, V, be applied to them with a current, I, flowing as in Figure R5(iii). The potential difference developed across R_1 is therefore IR_1 and that across R_2 is IR_2. If the two resistances are to be replaced by a single resistance, R_s, then for the same current, I to flow, since $V_1 + V_2 = V$, then

$$V = IR_1 + IR_2 = IR_s ,$$

so that:

$$IR_s = IR_1 + IR_2 \qquad \therefore R_s = R_1 + R_2 .$$

A parallel connection is shown in (ii) of the figure. For this the reciprocal of the overall network resistance is equal to the sum of the reciprocals of the individual resistances, i.e.

$$1/R_p = 1/R_1 + 1/R_2 + 1/R_3 + \ldots$$

For three resistances only therefore,

$$R_p = \frac{R_2 R_3 + R_1 R_3 + R_1 R_2}{R_1 R_2 R_3} .$$

This can be proved using the same technique as for the series case, see (iv) of the figure. The main current I splits up into I_1 and I_2 in the parallel network. Then $I_1 = V/R_1$ also $I_2 = V/R_2$ hence

$$I = V/R_1 + V/R_2 .$$

For the current to be the same in the two networks:

$$\frac{V}{R_p} = \frac{V}{R_1} + \frac{V}{R_2} \qquad \text{i.e.} \quad \frac{1}{R_p} = \frac{1}{R_1} + \frac{1}{R_2} .$$

See also Temperature Coefficient of Resistance.
(* Electromotive Force, Potential Difference, Resistivity, Conductance, Impedance, Complex Notation, Ohm's Law)

RESISTIVITY is the opposite of conductivity, i.e. it is an expression of how greatly a material opposes the flow of current through it. Resistivity is in fact the reciprocal of conductivity, hence the lower the resistivity of a given material, the better an electrical conductor it is.

The resistance, R of a conductor is proportional to its length, l and inversely proportional to its area of cross-section, a, i.e. $R \propto l/a$. By introducing a constant for a particular material known as its *resistivity*, a practical formula is obtained from which the value of R can be calculated provided that l and a are known. The symbol used for resistivity is the Greek lower case rho (ρ) hence:

$$R = \rho l/a .$$

If $l = 1$ metre and $a = 1$ square metre, then $R = \rho$ which leads to a definition of resistivity as "the resistance between opposite faces of a metre cube of the material" (see Fig.R6). Put in other words, it is

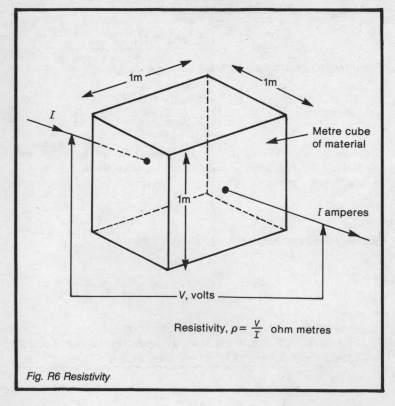

Fig. R6 Resistivity

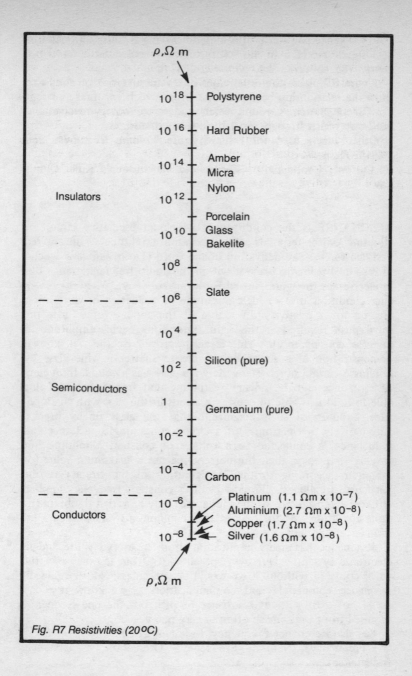

Fig. R7 Resistivities (20ºC)

"the resistance per metre of a material having a cross-sectional area of 1 square metre". In the S.I. system, ρ is expressed in *ohms per metre cube*, abbreviated to *ohm-metre* (Ω m).

Figure R7 places the resistivities of several materials on a scale to show the relationship between *conductors* which encourage current flow, *semiconductors* around which modern technology revolves and *insulators* which strongly resist the passage of current.

Other terms used for resistivity are *Volume Resistivity* and *Specific Resistance.*

(* Current, Conductivity, Resistance, Matthiessen's Rule, Ohm's Law)

RESONANCE is the condition in which an oscillating circuit or vibrating object responds with maximum amplitude to an applied periodic force. The derivation of the word (Latin, *resonare* – echo or resound) seems to place it within the audio frequency range but in electronics the word is used for any frequency. When the resonance condition arises, a high amplitude of oscillation or vibration is created for a relatively low value of the applied force (note the small push required at the right times for a swing amplitude to increase considerably). This is again proved by the well known demonstration of a singer being able to shatter a wine glass by holding a certain note. Here the wine glass has a *natural* frequency of resonance and the singer, by finding that frequency and being able to hold it is able to cause vibrations in the glass with an amplitude build-up of such magnitude that the glass finally breaks. Alternatively in electronics, if a circuit containing capacitance and inductance is connected to a voltage of constant amplitude but varying frequency, then the current reaches a maximum value (or minimum according to the configuration of the circuit) at one particular frequency. Equally, with a constant frequency applied either the capacitance or the inductance may be varied to obtain the same condition. At the maximum (or minimum) values of current, resonance is present.

Resonance has many applications both in everyday life and in electronic systems. Our own speech arises from resonance in the vocal cords so without it we would be speechless! Music relies on resonance completely and communication as we know it today could not exist without resonance to pick out the one frequency required from a mishmash often of very many.

See also Resonance Frequency, Resonant Circuit.

(* Frequency, Natural Frequency, Oscillation, Capacitance, Inductance)

RESONANCE FREQUENCY   This term follows on from the terms Resonance and Resonant Circuit. It refers to the frequency at which resonance occurs in a particular electronic circuit. This we give the symbol f_r. We consider the *series resonant circuit* first because apart from it being the simplest, through it the basic principles of resonance are most easily understood, see Figure R8(i).

At the resonance frequency the total reactance in the circuit is zero, hence $X_C = X_L$ where X_C is the capacitive reactance ($= -j/\omega C$ where $\omega = 2\pi f$) and X_L is the inductive reactance ($= j\omega L$). When $j/\omega C = j\omega L$, having a 180° phase difference, the two cancel, hence:

$$j/\omega C = j\omega L \quad \therefore \ \frac{1}{2\pi f_r C} = 2\pi f_r L$$

from which

$$f_r = \frac{1}{2\pi \sqrt{LC}} \ .$$

With no reactance in the circuit at the frequency of resonance, the impedance, Z is equal to the total resistance, R. The fact that the reactances cancel does not mean that there is no reactive voltage, on the contrary, because as shown in (ii), at f_r the current is maximum, then both V_C and V_L are at their highest — but even so they cancel. There is in fact a *resonant rise* in voltage across both L and C which can be much greater than the applied voltage. At frequencies below f_r the capacitive reactance predominates so the impedance has a negative angle, conversely at frequencies above f_r the inductive reactance is greater so giving the impedance a positive angle.

With the *parallel resonant circuit* we usually cheat a little by assuming that all the resistance is in the inductive arm and this is normally admissible. This circuit is shown in (iii) of the figure. It is more complicated than for the series circuit but briefly, considering the two paths in parallel:

$$\frac{1}{Z} = \frac{1}{R + j\omega L} + j\omega C$$

which by rationalizing and equating the j terms to zero for resonance gives:

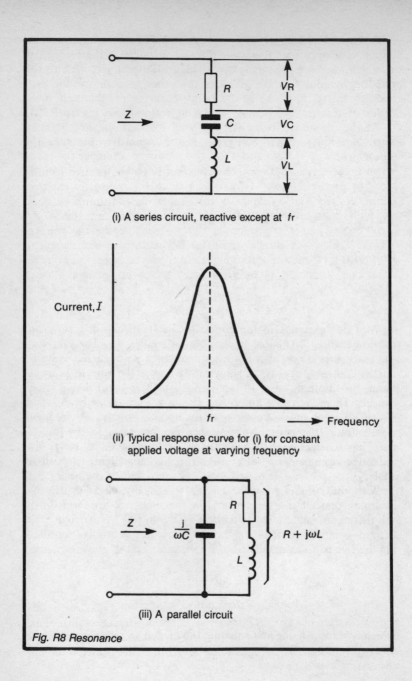

(i) A series circuit, reactive except at f_r

(ii) Typical response curve for (i) for constant
applied voltage at varying frequency

(iii) A parallel circuit

Fig. R8 Resonance

$$f_r = \frac{1}{2\pi} \sqrt{\frac{1}{LC} - \frac{R^2}{L^2}}$$

and

$$Z_r = L/CR$$

where Z_r is the impedance at resonance, also known as the *dynamic impedance*.

Note the term R^2/L^2 which has crept in on the change from a series to parallel circuit. It is a fact that this term usually changes f_r only slightly hence frequently the simpler series formula suffices for both cases. From the formula for the circuit impedance, Z_r becomes very large at resonance if R is small, hence the voltage developed across a parallel circuit at resonance can be very high. (* Complex Notation, Rationalization, Capacitance, Capacitive Reactance, Inductance, Inductive Reactance, Impedance, Phase, Phase Angle)

RESONANT CIRCUIT is an electronic passive circuit in which both capacitance and inductance are present. In such a circuit a frequency of resonance can be found at which for a given applied voltage the current reaches a maximum or minimum value depending on the circuit configuration. In a pure capacitance the current leads the voltage across it by 90° (negative reactance) whereas in a pure inductance the current lags on the voltage by 90° (positive reactance). Any combination of resistance with reactance has an impedance of value greater than that for the resistance alone, hence if the reactance can in some way be reduced to zero, the circuit will have a minimum impedance equal to the resistance. Put in symbols for a capacitive circuit:

$$Z = R - jX$$

where Z is the impedance, R the resistance and X the reactance. Because

$$Z = \sqrt{R^2 + X^2}$$

then it is clear that because R cannot be reduced in a passive circuit, Z is always greater than R. However, if the positive reactance of an inductance can be added to the circuit so that the capacitive reactance is just cancelled, then $Z = R$ and this is the principle of the resonant circuit.

Capacitive and inductive reactances do not change in the same way with frequency, that for capacitance falls with frequency in a non-linear way, on the other hand that for inductance rises linearly (see Fig.R2). Nevertheless, for any combination of the two there is one frequency at which their reactances are equal and being of opposite sign, together they cancel. There are two main types of resonant circuit:

Series Resonant Circuit (see Fig.R8(i) – in this the capacitor and inductor are in series. Inevitably there is resistance in both, especially in the inductor but this can also be considered to be in series. If required a separate resistor may also be connected. At the frequency of resonance the circuit current is at its highest. This circuit is also known as an *acceptor circuit* because it presents a *low* impedance at resonance.

Parallel Resonant Circuit (see Fig.R8(iii) – this has the capacitor and inductor in parallel. At the frequency of resonance the circuit current is minimum but the voltage developed across the circuit is maximum. Because the circuit presents a high impedance at resonance it is also known as a *rejector circuit*.

(* Complex Notation, Capacitance, Inductance, Reactance, Impedance, Passive, Phase, Phase Angle, Quadrature)

RETENTIVITY – see Remanence.

RETURN CURRENT is the reflected current which arises at the sending or receiving end of a transmission line when the line is not matched to the generator or to the load. A return current also arises at any impedance discontinuity along the line. This current combines with the transmitted wave and is responsible for the creation of *standing waves* (see Fig.S8).

See also Reflection.

(* Transmission Line, Reflection Loss, Standing Wave >> Load, Matching)

REVERSE DIRECTION applies to electronic devices and is the direction in which the device has a higher resistance compared with the opposite direction. A voltage applied so that the device operates in the reverse direction is known as a reverse bias and the current it produces is the reverse current. These terms are especially used with diodes [see Fig.P10(ii) and (iv)].

See also Forward Direction.

(* Diode, Resistance)

386

REVERSE SATURATION CURRENT   Under reverse bias conditions in a p-n junction, a strong electric field exists across the depletion layer (the region around the junction containing few charge carriers).   Thermally generated carriers entering the depletion layer are swept across the junction by the electric field and these constitute the *reverse saturation current* [see Fig.P10(iv)]. The term *leakage current* is sometimes used — see P-N Junction.

R.F. RESISTANCE — see Effective Resistance.

RICHARDSON-DUSHMAN   EQUATION is   concerned   with thermionic emission and is the fundamental equation linking the emitted current density with temperature for emissive materials provided that certain constants and the work function are known — see Thermionic Emission.

RISE TIME of a pulse.   It is a measure of the steepness of the leading edge — see Pulse and/or Figure P15(ii).

ROOT MEAN SQUARE   This is that value of voltage or current applicable to a wave which dissipates the same power in a resistive circuit as it would under d.c. conditions.   It is also known as the *effective value*.   To calculate the value, firstly instantaneous values (e.g. of current) are taken at regular intervals over one complete cycle and since power is equal to current squared times resistance, each value is *squared* and multiplied by the chosen value of resistence.   The average or *mean* of these individual powers is then calculated which produces the *mean squared* value. To find the equivalent effective value therefore, the square root of this mean is required.   This is known as the *root mean square* (r.m.s.) value which is usually given the label E or I (no subscript).   Such calculations result for a sine wave in a value $E = E_{max}/\sqrt{2} = 0.707$ E_{max}, equally $I = 0.707\ I_{max}$ where E_{max} and I_{max} are the maximum values of the wave.   On the other hand, for a square wave the maximum and r.m.s. values are equal.
(* Voltage, Current, Power, Sine Wave, Square Wave)

S

SCHERING BRIDGE is a particular a.c. bridge network used for the measurement of capacitance and dissipation factor. The circuit is shown in Figure S1. C_x and R_x represent the capacitor being

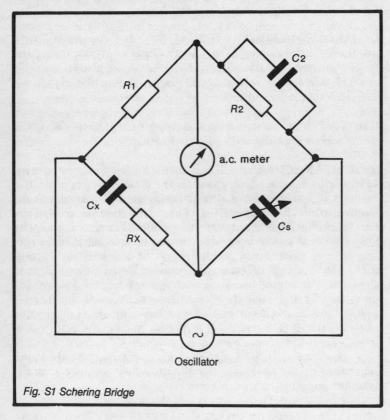

Fig. S1 Schering Bridge

measured, C_s is a standard (calibrated) capacitor). The bridge balances (i.e. there is no deflection on the meter) when:

$$C_x = C_s \times \frac{R_2}{R_1} \qquad R_x = R_1 \times \frac{C_2}{C_s}$$

from which:

$$\text{dissipation factor} = \omega C_x R_x$$

where $\omega = 2\pi \times$ the bridge frequency.
(* Bridge, Capacitance, Dissipation Factor)

SCHOTTKY BARRIER   Through the Schottky effect an external electric field increases electron emission from a material in a vacuum by reducing the surface potential barrier, hence effectively reducing also the work function. The same effect arises when certain metals are in contact with semiconductors but not necessarily in a vacuum. As an example, consider a metal such as aluminium and a heavily doped n-type silicon semiconductor. When not in contact the n-type silicon has more electrons available for conduction with a higher Fermi level than for the aluminium. When the two materials are brought into contact therefore, conduction band electrons flow across the junction from the silicon into the aluminium (until the Fermi levels in the two materials become equal). This produces a junction barrier potential V_b equal to the initial Fermi level difference (or to the difference between the work functions of the two materials). Clearly the silicon side of the barrier becomes positive and the aluminium, negative.

If the silicon is biased positively with regard to the aluminium, electrons in the conduction band of the aluminium are accelerated towards the junction but they must now overcome the barrier potential V_b to reach the silicon, the number which can do this depends upon the potential applied but is obviously small. On the other hand, if the silicon is biased negatively, the barrier potential is reduced and a large current flows. This is rectification and the potential barrier between the two materials is known as a *Schottky barrier*. The process has some similarities with the p-n junction illustrated in Figure P10(ii) and (iii) when the metal is substituted for the p-region.
(* Schottky Effect, Semiconductor, Doping, Electric Field, Emission, Energy, Energy Levels, Energy Bands, Fermi Level, Work Function, Space Charge)

SCHOTTKY DIODE (SCHOTTKY BARRIER DIODE) is a diode incorporating the rectifying action of a Schottky barrier formed from the junction between a metal and a semiconductor. This type of diode is very suitable for integration, for example, using aluminium as the metal and n-type silicon as the semiconductor. How simple an integration arrangement can be is shown in Figure S2. A forward bias applied to the diode (positive to the metal) lowers the barrier height and so allows majority carriers with sufficient energy

389

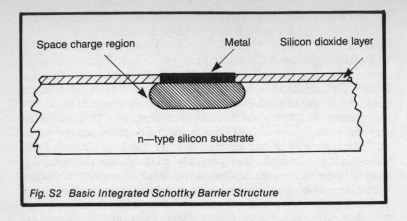

Fig. S2 *Basic Integrated Schottky Barrier Structure*

Within the figure:
- Space charge region
- Metal
- Silicon dioxide layer
- n—type silicon substrate

(greater than the barrier potential) to cross, hence current flows. Reverse bias increases the barrier height with only a minute reverse saturation current flowing.

Schottky diodes have the significant advantage over p-n junction diodes in that current flow is by majority carriers and minority carrier diffusion is small. Storage time delays are therefore smaller resulting in switching speeds being greater.   The diode is also favoured for microwave mixing and detection for the same reason. (* Diode, Schottky Barrier, Semiconductor, Charge Carrier, Majority Carrier, Minority Carrier, Energy, Reverse Saturation Current, P-N Junction >> Integrated Circuit)

SCHOTTKY EFFECT   Thermionic emission is an electron current leaving the surface of a material by virtue of the thermal energy each electron possesses. To do this the energy must exceed the work function of the material, i.e. be sufficient for the electron to cross over the surface potential barrier. In a vacuum, thermionic electron emission can be increased if an electric field is applied to the material. The effect of the field is to lower the surface potential barrier, thereby lowering the energy needed to release electrons and effectively also reducing the work function. More electrons therefore escape from the surface of the material. This is known as the *Schottky effect.*

In a thermionic valve the effect can be seen as a slight increase in the current obtained from a cathode above the normal saturation value when the anode voltage is raised further. The increased electric field normal to the surface of the cathode lowers the work function hence more electrons cross over the barrier. The current from the cathode therefore continues to rise slowly with anode voltage.

(* Thermionic Emission, Cathode, Energy, Work Function, Space Charge, Potential Barrier, Electric Field, Thermionic Valve)

SCINTILLATION is the flash of light produced in certain materials by ionizing particles, the energies of which determine the frequency of the light emitted. A typical material used in a *scintillation counter* consists of specially prepared sodium iodide crystals, one of the luminescent materials known as phosphors. This particular material gives a flash of light of maximum frequency around 7.3×10^{14} Hz which is in the violet range (see Fig.L5). Several other materials are also used, they generally emit light in the same frequency range but have different *decay times*, ranging from some 2 microseconds to a few nanoseconds. Such materials are known as *scintillators*.
(*· Light, Ionization, Luminescence, Phosphor, Visible Spectrum >> Scintillation Counter)

SCREEN GRID − see Thermionic Valve.

SECOND   Time until recently was defined on an astronomical basis, i.e. on the revolution of the earth. The second was therefore 1/86 400 of the mean solar day. It is now defined scientifically as being the duration of a certain number of periods (over nine thousand million) of the radiation of a certain type of caesium atom.

The second is the S.I. unit of time, symbol s.
(* S.I.)

SECONDARY CELL   This is a device which produces electricity from a chemical reaction. Generally this type of cell consists of two dissimilar plates immersed in an electrolyte. It is capable of delivering a certain quantity of electricity and when exhausted the cell can be "recharged" by passing a current through it in the opposite direction to that of the discharge current. To do this a "charging" voltage is applied to the cell terminals, + to + and − to −. The charging voltage must exceed that of the cell to a degree that the required charging current is obtained. As the cell becomes charged the chemical action which resulted in the discharge current is reversed.

Quantity of charge is usually reckoned in *ampere-hours*, e.g. a cell of 20 ampere-hours capacity can deliver 20 amperes for one hour, 10 amperes for 2 hours, etc. Such a cell when discharged would require 20 ampere-hours charge (plus a little extra to provide for losses) to restore it to the fully charged condition.
(* Cell, Electrolyte >> Lead-acid Cell, Nickel-cadmium Cell, Nickel-iron Cell, Silver-zinc (Silver Oxide) Cell)

SECONDARY ELECTRON   When high velocity particles strike the surface of certain materials, some electrons in the material receive sufficient energy for escape from the surface, these are known as secondary electrons — see Secondary Emission.

SECONDARY EMISSION occurs when high velocity and therefore high energy particles (usually electrons) strike the surface of a metal, semiconductor or insulator, causing it to emit electrons. The bombarding electrons are known as *primary electrons*, those emitted are *secondary electrons.*

When a high velocity primary electron collides with another electron at the surface of a material the second electron receives energy and if it is excited above the energy level required for escape across the potential barrier of the space charge, it then becomes a free secondary electron. The total secondary emission current is not composed entirely of "pure" secondaries because also included are some primary electrons which have been reflected on collision. There are basically two kinds of collision, (i) *elastic* in which the total momentum of the two electrons remains the same but is redistributed and (ii) *inelastic* in which some energy is dissipated on collision yet the primary retains sufficient for escape with the secondaries. Unless the primary electrons have very high energies, the secondary electrons leave with relatively low energies of some $10 - 50$ eV.

The *secondary emission ratio* or *secondary yield* is defined as the number of secondary electrons per primary incident electron, equally as the ratio of secondary to primary electron current. It is denoted by the Greek letter, δ. As primary energy increases from a low value, the emission ratio, δ also increases simply because of the increasing energies imparted to electrons at the surface of the material. However, there is an eventual reduction in the ratio at high primary energies because of their increased penetration into the surface of the material with the result that secondaries must traverse a longer path to freedom with greater risk of being deflected on the way. This effect begins to cause a fall in δ at a primary energy level which depends on the particular material. δ_{max} is unlikely to be greater than 2 for the elements but can be much higher with suitable metal alloys. Two alloys for example, with high values of δ at low primary energies are copper-beryllium and oxidised silver-magnesium, the latter having $\delta_{max} = 10 - 12$ at around 600 eV. There are other materials capable of even higher values of δ.

Secondary emission is the basis on which *electron multipliers* function. These are devices used for amplifying very weak electron currents and in which copper-beryllium is used extensively.

(* Emission, Energy, Collision, Energy Levels, Potential Barrier, Space Charge, Kinetic Energy, Electron-Volt >> Electron Multiplier)

SECONDARY EMISSION RATIO — see Secondary Emission.

SECONDARY YIELD — see Secondary Emission.

SEEBECK EFFECT   When two dissimilar metals are joined at both ends to form a thermocouple as in Figure T4(i) and the two junctions are maintained at different temperatures, an electromotive force is developed around the circuit. The effect is named after its discoverer — see Thermoelectric Effect.

SELECTIVITY is a feature of resonant circuits and radio receivers and is a measure of the ability to respond to one particular frequency (or band of frequencies) while not responding to others. For the radio receiver, it is therefore the ability to discriminate against incoming radio transmissions other than the one required. Selectivity cannot be defined simply, so it is usually expressed in the form of curves (see below).

Both the sensitivity and selectivity of a resonant circuit are related to its Q factor and curves showing the selectivity of a series resonant circuit are given in Figure Q1. It is more instructive, however, if in such curves the sensitivity feature is removed so that the principle of selectivity can be better seen. This is done in Figure S3 which shows two response/frequency curves for resonant circuits of different values of Q but adjusted to have the same maxima. It is therefore assumed that the input to the $Q = 75$ circuit is raised accordingly. The curves show clearly that, as an example, at 20 kHz off resonance the response of the $Q = 75$ circuit is well over twice that of the $Q = 125$ circuit although both have the same response at resonance. Accordingly the $Q = 125$ circuit has the greater selectivity for its response to frequencies off resonance is lower.

(* Q Factor, Resonance, Resonant Circuit >> Radio Receiver)

SELENIUM is one of the elements, atomic number 34. Its symbol is Se. Selenium is obtainable in a non-crystalline form from which, if heated, the silvery grey metallic form is produced. All forms of selenium are semiconductors. If metallic selenium is heated to about $210°C$ for some time, it then possesses an electrical resistance which varies on exposure to light, the resistance decreasing as the intensity of illumination increases. It is therefore used in various

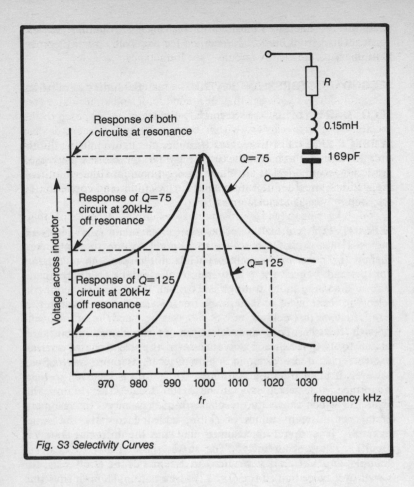

Fig. S3 Selectivity Curves

types of photoconductive photocells. In addition it can also be used as a photovoltaic element, hence the *selenium cell.*

Selenium is also used for the production of rectifier elements although generally semiconductor diodes have taken over.
(* Element, Semiconductor, Selenium Cell, Photoconductivity, Photovoltaic Effect >> Selenium Rectifier)

SELENIUM CELL   A cell which generates an electromotive force when light falls on it – see Photovoltaic Cell.

SELF-INDUCTANCE is that property of an inductor by which an electromotive force (e.m.f.) is generated in it when the current and therefore the associated magnetic flux change. The term is used to distinguish it from *mutual inductance* for which the e.m.f. is generated in a separate nearby circuit — see Inductance.

SEMICONDUCTOR   Basically this is a material having a resistivity (or conductivity) between that of a conductor and an insulator (see Fig.R7). The material is used in its "solid state" (as opposed to the motion of charge carriers within a vacuum) and as such, devices such as diodes, transistors, integrated circuits, light emitting diodes and photodiodes are manufactured. By far the most widely used semiconductor materials are silicon and germanium although others, e.g. gallium arsenide, cadmium sulphide, selenium and copper oxide are used in special circumstances.

We take silicon and germanium as examples because of their wide use in semiconductor technology. Both of these are elements with 4 electrons in the outer (valence) shells. The atoms are linked together by *covalent bonds*, each of which contains a shared pair of electrons. A few of the valence electrons are free at room temperature and able to move through the crystal, the higher the temperature, the more electrons there are free. Vacancies, or *holes* left in the lattice as an electron moves out can be filled by an adjacent valence electron. The holes move in an opposite direction to that of the electrons and hence can be considered as positive charge carriers. The materials are called semiconductors because only a few electrons are available in the conduction state.

Intrinsic (or pure) semiconductors are as described above and have a negative temperature coefficient of resistance. It so happens that this is usually an undesirable feature because the release of thermally generated charge carriers may limit the operating temperature of the device in which the material is used.

The minimum energy required to free a valence electron is, for silicon, 1.1 electron-volts (eV) and for germanium, 0.7 eV. These are the energy gaps between the valence and conduction energy bands, indicating that higher temperatures are required for the same concentration of charge carriers in silicon compared with germanium. Semiconductors generally have energy band gaps less than about 2 eV.

Extrinsic (or doped) semiconductors are those to which an "impurity" has been added. This increases the material conductivity greatly. If an impurity atom which has 5 valence electrons is added to the crystal, 4 of the electrons can be accommodated within the lattice structure, leaving one thrown spare which is then available as an additional charge carrier. The impurity atoms are known as *donors* and they create an *n-type* semiconductor.

Conversely a *p-type* semiconductor is formed when impurity atoms having only 3 valence electrons are added, in this case the lattice is incomplete and vacancies for electrons (called "holes") arise. Again, however, conductivity is increased. The numbers of impurity atoms introduced is minute, e.g. one impurity atom per some 10^8 semiconductor atoms. Electrons in n-type semiconductor materials and holes in p-type are known as *majority carriers*, the remaining carriers (holes in n-type, electrons in p-type) are very much smaller in number and are known as *minority carriers*.
(* Covalent Bond, Valency, Charge Carrier, Electron-Volt, Hole, Energy Band, Intrinsic Semiconductor, Doping, Transistor, Silicon, Germanium, Gallium Arsenide, Temperature Coefficient of Resistance >> Integrated Circuit)

SERIES RESONANT CIRCUIT   A circuit consisting of inductance, capacitance and resistance, all in series. The circuit is resonant when the net reactance is zero — see Resonance Frequency.

SHELL   Electrons surround their atom nucleus travelling at extremely high speeds in orbits which for illustration we regard as circular although in fact they may be anything but circular. Because of its motion there is a centrifugal force tending to move an electron outwards from the centre. This is balanced by the attractive force between electron and nucleus, bearing in mind that other electrons may be orbiting in between. The electron orbits fall into distinct concentric layers or *shells*. These are labelled alphabetically and also numbered, starting with K (= 1) for the one nearest the nucleus as shown in Figure S4 for the germanium atom as an example. The maximum number of electrons which can occupy a shell is $2n^2$ where n is the shell number but shells are not necessarily completely filled. The highest shell number is 7 (Q) which is only required by atoms with atomic numbers 87 − 103. Electrons within a shell may not follow each other in the same orbit, the shells are sub-divided into *sub-shells* labelled s, p, d, or f, as required (see Fig.S4).

These ideas are greatly simplified. For a start electrons do not travel in a smooth curve, they have a wave motion imposed on them. There are also other restrictions on the number in an orbit (see Quantum Theory).
(* Atom, Electron, Charge, Orbit, Germanium)

SHOT NOISE arises from the random variations affecting certain charge carriers — see Noise.

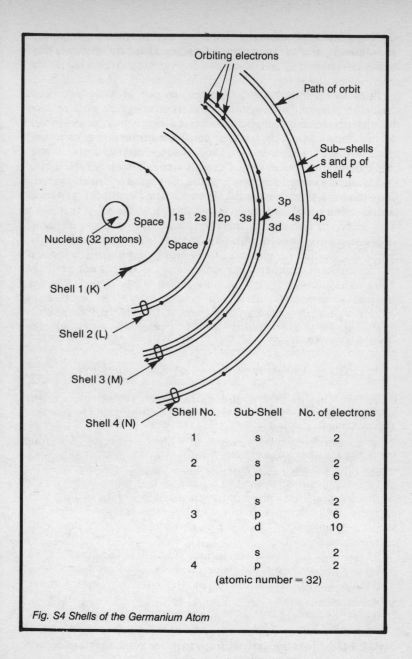

Fig. S4 Shells of the Germanium Atom

Shell No.	Sub-Shell	No. of electrons
1	s	2
2	s	2
	p	6
	s	2
3	p	6
	d	10
	s	2
4	p	2

(atomic number = 32)

S.I. (Systéme International d'Unités) is as its French name implies, an internationally agreed system of units. These are for mechanics, heat, illumination and electrotechnics, our interest is mainly in the later.

Previous to international agreement on the S.I. system in 1960, countries had their own systems of units although the metric which has the advantage of simplicity in using a single multiple only (10), predominated. On this was first based the centimetre-gram-second system (c.g.s.) and later in 1904, Giorgi suggested the metre-kilogram-second system (m.k.s.). This was followed in 1950 by the metre-kilogram-second-ampere (m.k.s.a.) system which greatly simplified electromagnetics calculations. The present S.I. system is an extension of the m.k.s.a. One advantage of the S.I. is that it is a fully *coherent* (joining together) or *rational* system (i.e. expressible as a ratio of whole numbers). A system of units is said to be coherent if the product or quotient of any two unit quantities is the unit of the resultant quantity. Put more simply, S.I. does not need the extra complications (such as 4π) which some earlier systems, because of their irrational definitions of base units, required for circular or spherical shapes. The factor π, however, still crops up in the permeability and permittivity of free space. As an example, in S.I. the unit of energy:

$$1 \text{ joule} = 1 \text{ newton metre} = 1 \text{ kilogram metre}^2/\text{second}^2$$

Here the joule is defined directly in terms of other units in the system. All other S.I. units are defined in this way, i.e. no other factors need to be introduced.

A coherent unit system must start with the selection of a group of independent base units which must then be defined unambiguously. The S.I. has 7 such units:

Quantity	Unit Name	Unit Symbol
length	metre	m
mass	kilogram	kg
time	second	s
current	ampere	A
temperature	kelvin	K
luminous intensity	candela	cd
amount of substance	mole	mol

All other units are derived from the base ones, they are defined under their names elsewhere in the book.

Metric system prefixes to the unit names are used to denote a multiple or sub-multiple of each unit:

Factor	Prefix	Symbol
10^{12}	tera	T
10^9	giga	G
10^6	mega	M
10^3	kilo	k
10^2	hecto	h
10	deca	da
10^{-1}	deci	d
10^{-2}	centi	c
10^{-3}	milli	m
10^{-6}	micro	μ
10^{-9}	nano	n
10^{-12}	pico	p
10^{-15}	femto	f
10^{-18}	atto	a

(* Derived Units, Arbitrary Unit)

SIDEBAND is a group of frequencies within a modulated wave. *Lower sideband* frequencies are below that of the carrier, *upper sideband* frequencies are above.

See Carrier Wave and Amplitude Modulation.

SIDE FREQUENCY is a single frequency which is a product of the modulation process. A *lower side frequency* is below that of the carrier, an *upper side frequency* is above.

See Carrier Wave and Amplitude Modulation.

SIEMENS is the S.I. unit of electrical conductance, admittance and susceptance (after Werner von Siemens, a German electrical engineer). It is given the symbol, S. As an example, the conductance, G of a circuit is given by $G = I/V$ where I and V are current and voltage. Because from Ohm's Law the resistance, $R = V/I$, then conductance is the reciprocal of resistance. Accordingly, a circuit possesses a conductance of one siemens (1 S) if it has a resistance of one ohm. Before S.I. the unit of conductance was the *mho* and one old fashioned mho is equal to one modern siemens. (* Conductance, Admittance, Susceptance, Ohm's Law, Current, Voltage)

SIGNAL   In electronics this is an electrical quantity (such as voltage or current) which varies with time and is used for the transmission of information.

SILICON (symbol, Si) is a grey, crystalline, non-metallic element. Except for oxygen it is the most abundant element in the earth's crust, hence is not particularly expensive. It is usually found as silica (silicon dioxide, SiO_2) in quartz or sand. Pure silicon is obtained from silica by the use of powerful reducing agents in a furnace to remove the oxygen. Once made, silicon has a great affinity for oxygen so returning to the form of silicon dioxide which conveniently for us in the manufacture of semiconducting devices, is stable and has good insulating properties. It is therefore the most widely used material in planar technology.

The atomic number of silicon is 14. It is tetravalent, i.e. it has 4 electrons in the valence shell (2 in s subshell, 2 in p). The energy band gap of silicon is 1.1 electron-volts (eV).
(* Element, Atom, Shell, Energy Bands, Semiconductor, Electron-Volt, Doping >> Planar Process)

SILICON CELL   A cell which generates an electromotive force when light falls on it — see Photovoltaic Cell.

SILICON DIOXIDE — see Silicon.

SILVER is one of the *noble* metals (gold, silver, platinum). It is an element, symbol Ag, atomic number 47, with one electron only in its outer (5th) shell. Silver is the best conductor of electricity we have, it has a resistivity of 1.62 Ωm × 10^{-8}, slightly better than copper at 1.72 Ωm × 10^{-8} (both at 20°C).
(* Element, Shell, Resistivity)

SINE WAVE   This is a waveform conforming to $i = I_{max} \sin \phi$ or $i = I_{max} \cos \phi$ (e and E_{max} can be substituted for i and I_{max}), where ϕ is the angle through which the wave has moved from a given starting point. A cosine curve is identical in shape to that of a sine wave but has a value of 1 at $\phi = 0$ whereas the sine has a value of 0. An example which also shows how a sine wave is generated by a rotating phasor, is shown in Figure S5. The x-axis can be labelled in one of several different ways as shown.

The periodic time (T) is that for one cycle, hence $T = 1/f$.
The magnitude of a sine wave can be expressed in several different ways, each having a simple relationship with the others. The *peak* value is the maximum value which the wave reaches and only

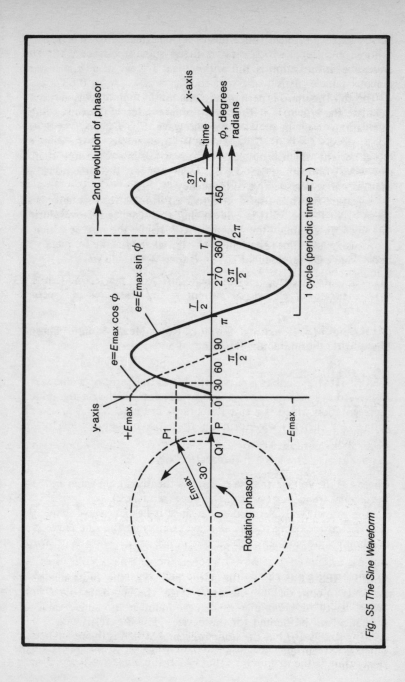

Fig. S5 *The Sine Waveform*

occurs twice per cycle (once positive, once negative). It is usually denoted by E_{max} or I_{max} (V is often substituted for E). The *average* or *mean* value is the arithmetical average of all the instantaneous values. This works out to $E_{av} = 2E_{max}/\pi$ or $0.637E_{max}$.

The third method is perhaps the one most commonly used, i.e. to calculate the *effective or root mean square* value of the wave. Such calculations result in values for a sine wave, $E = E_{max}/\sqrt{2} = 0.707$ E_{max}, equally $I = 0.707I_{max}$. Hence if, for example, i is the value of direct current which produces a certain power in a resistance, then a sine wave of maximum value $\sqrt{2} \times i$ will dissipate the same power in that resistance, irrespective of frequency.

A feature which is useful in deriving formulae for reactance is as follows. In Figure S5 it is evident that the distance P moves during one cycle is 2π times the length of OP, hence the *rate* at which P moves is $2\pi \times f$ times the length of OP, where f is the frequency in hertz. Since OP represents E_{max} or E then, for a sine wave:

(i)   the rate of change of voltage $= 2\pi fE$ volts per second (r.m.s.);
(ii) the rate of change of current $= 2\pi fI$ amperes per second (r.m.s.).

(* Waveform, Alternating Current, Root Mean Square, Phasor, Phase Angle, Form Factor, Reactance, Power)

SINUSOIDAL describes a curve which has the form of a sine wave. It therefore describes any voltage or current which has a graphical representation which is a sine function as in Figure S5. A sinusoidal voltage (or current) waveform can therefore be represented by the expression:

$$v = V_{max} \sin \omega t$$

where v is the voltage at time t, V_{max} is the maximum value and ω is the angular frequency ($= 2\pi \times$ the wave frequency).

A *cosine* curve is also sinusoidal since it has sine wave shape, the only difference being that if at some given time the sine curve is at maximum, the cosine is at zero and vice versa – see Sine Wave.

SLOPE RESISTANCE is the term used for the resistance at a particular point on the current/voltage characteristic of a non-linear device or component. Being non-linear, no single value of resistance can be quoted for the device. The d.c. resistance at any point is simply V/I but the *slope resistance* which is the resistance to small signal currents is given by $\delta V/\delta I$ where δ means "a small change in".

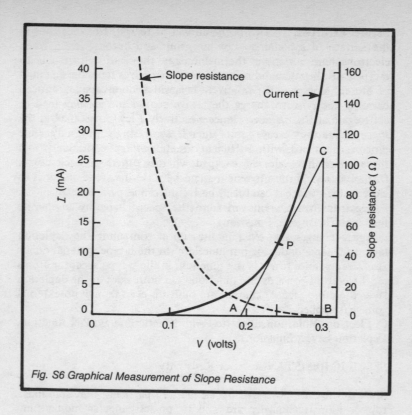

Fig. S6 Graphical Measurement of Slope Resistance

If the equation to the curve is known, the slope resistance can be calculated. Alternatively, it can be determined approximately by drawing the tangent to the curve at the required point, say at point P on a transistor input characteristic as shown in Figure S6. The tangent is AC and from the triangle ABC the slope resistance is given by AB/BC, in this example, 0.108 V/26.5 mA, giving a slope resistance of 4.08 ohms (the d.c. resistance at this point is about 20 Ω). Note that the triangle ABC can be of any size because we are interested in the ratio of the two sides at right angles and the ratio does not change with size of the triangle.

Clearly the steeper the slope of the curve, the lower is the slope resistance and vice versa as shown in the figure. As an example, the collector slope resistance of a bipolar junction transistor can be judged to be high over most of the collector voltage range because the characteristic curves are almost flat.

(* Resistance, Ohm's Law, Characteristic, Non-Linearity, Transistor)

SPACE CHARGE   This is the answer as to why free electrons at the surface of a metal do not jump out and become lost. When electrons have sufficient thermal energy they are in fact able to escape into the surrounding space but themselves repel the emission of more. Moreover the relatively few which do escape are enticed back by the positive charge they leave behind and so they tend to congregate at the surface. Hence effectively a few do escape but the *space charge* they create limits the release of others. It is a dynamic process, electrons with sufficient kinetic energy continually join those which have already escaped whereas others go back home. Overall an equilibrium is reached and because the space charge is so close to the surface it can really be considered as part of it.

Electrons can be removed from the space charge by an electric field (see Thermionic Emission).

Space charges also exist in the region containing the depletion layer of a semiconductor p-n junction. In the n-type material donor atoms repel holes towards the junction, in the p-type acceptor atoms repel electrons towards the junction. On both sides of the depletion layer therefore (space) charges are built up even though no external voltage is applied.

(* Electron, Hole, Ion, Electric Field, Kinetic Energy, P-N Junction, Depletion Layer, Emission)

SPECIFIC RESISTANCE – see Resistivity.

SPIN is a feature possessed by elementary particles, they spin like a top or more technically are said to possess angular momentum. Taking the electron as an example, quantum theory is able to show that in certain respects it behaves like a spinning charged sphere (although experiments seem to indicate that they are more like points with no measurable size rather than spheres). A spinning electron behaves like a tiny bar magnet and has its own magnetic moment as illustrated in Figure M5.

The magnitude of the angular momentum (or spin speed) of both electrons and protons is the same for every one and it is given a *spin quantum number* depending on the spin direction. This number indicates how an electron aligns itself in an externally generated magnetic field.

(* Particle, Momentum, Electron, Charge, Magnetism, Magnetic Field, Magnetic Moment, Quantum Theory)

SQUARE WAVE   For this type of wave the graph of amplitude versus time is a succession of squares as shown in Figure S7. The wave is a *pulse train* which alternates between two fixed amplitudes

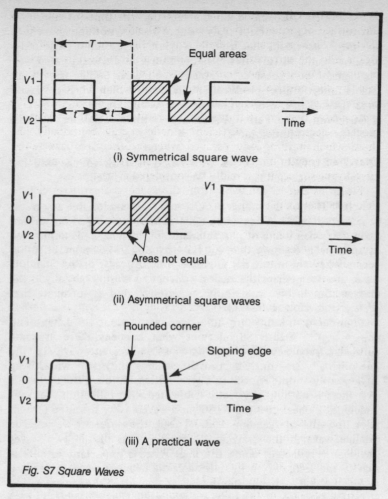

Fig. S7 Square Waves

v_1 and v_2 with the same time interval (t) between each transition. Relative to the time axis, although still square, a wave may be classified as *symmetrical* or *asymmetrical* as demonstrated in (i) and (ii) of the figure. The period of the waveform is the time interval T as shown in (i), hence the wave frequency, $f = 1/T$.

Fourier analysis shows that a square waveform actually consists of a fundamental sine wave of frequency f plus an infinite series of odd harmonics progressively decreasing in peak value. Unfortunately no channel can transmit an infinite frequency band so square waves usually end up with rounded corners — this is illustrated in

Figure F6(ii). Also based on the fact that the times of transition between v_1 and v_2 cannot truly be zero because nothing happens in no time, it is evident that a perfect square wave cannot exist in the practical world so (iii) of the figure shows in an exaggerated way what might be expected. Actually a modern oscillator (e.g. an astable multivibrator) produces square waves which when displayed on an oscilloscope, although not perfect, would appear so.
(* Waveform, Pulse, Period, Frequency, Harmonic, Fourier Analysis, Oscillation >> Multivibrator)

STANDARD CELL   A cell with a known stable voltage used as a voltage reference standard — see Weston Standard Cell.

STANDING WAVE   This occurs on a transmission line as a result of reflection which arises when a line is mismatched with its termination, i.e. when a line of characteristic impedance, Z_0 is terminated by an impedance other than Z_0 (say, by Z_R). Maximum reflection occurs when the mismatch is greatest, i.e. $Z_R = 0$ or ∞. Standing waves are not perhaps the easiest concept to grasp, especially as the mathematics involve hyperbolic functions, so it is fortunate that sketches can show us instead.

Consider a transmission line open-circuited at its distant end ($Z_R = \infty$). Figure S8 pictures what happens there at some particular frequency. In both drawings an *incident* wave (i.e. the one originally transmitted from the sending end) is shown arriving at the termination. We call it a termination although in fact in this case there is nothing physically connected. On reflection the wave undergoes a phase change of 180° and travels away from the termination towards the sending end. This is the *reflected* wave. The full-line wave in the drawings shows the sum of the two waves (incident + reflected) along the line. What is important to note is that in the second drawing, although the incident wave arrives at a different phase angle, the standing wave remains in the same position as can be seen from the points marked *node* (Latin, *nodus*, a knot) where the voltage is zero. In fact it does not matter how we draw the incident wave, it and the reflected wave together always result in a standing wave for which points along the line of maximum and zero voltage arise. This is an interesting feature of a mismatched transmission line, i.e. irrespective of the power sent down the line, there are points half a wavelength apart where no voltage (or current) can be measured even though both incident and reflected waves are passing. At the antinodes the standing wave swings between maximum positive and maximum negative as can be seen from the figure. Hence the description standing or *stationary* wave.

406

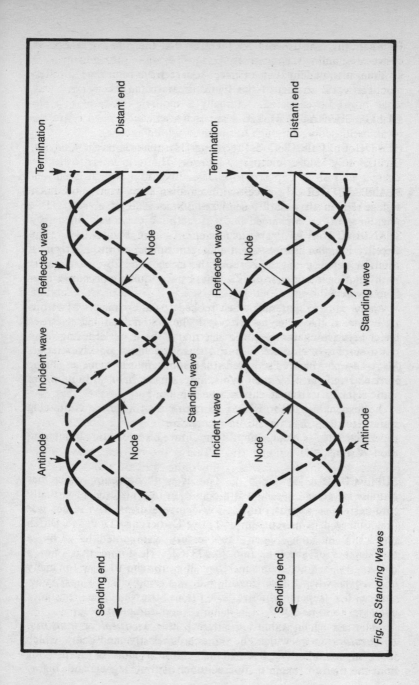

Fig. S8 Standing Waves

When the line is correctly terminated, there is no reflection, hence no standing waves are set up.
(* Transmission Line, Impedance, Characteristic Impedance, Reflection, Phase, Phase Angle, Node >> Stub, Matching)

STATIC CHARACTERISTIC – see Characteristic.

STATIC ELECTRICITY is of interest because in earliest days it was the only kind of electricity known. The term refers to electric charges at rest as opposed to charges in motion which is current electricity. The early Greeks noticed that when a piece of amber was rubbed with a cloth, it picked up small light objects. This phenomenon, i.e. a charged body attracting a previously uncharged one, arises from *electrostatic induction* – see Figure E10. The Greek for amber is *elektron*, hence our subject name, *electronics*. Friction between the amber and the cloth builds up a charge on both, that on the amber does not leak away quickly because amber is an insulator.

Many pairs of materials when rubbed together transfer electrons from one to the other by friction. The material gaining electrons has a negative charge of static electricity, the material losing them has a surplus of positive ions and therefore has a positive charge. Many people have discovered that some motor vehicles, being isolated from earth by their tyres, have a nasty habit of building up static electricity from all the friction going on.

A charged capacitor is also an example of a device containing static electricity, both positive and negative.
(* Electricity, Charge, Capacitor, Ion, Electrostatic Induction, Positive, Negative)

SUPERCONDUCTIVITY   This is a phenomenon which has promise of great reward, it is a condition in a material of virtually zero resistance – but only at low temperatures. The effect was first observed in mercury in 1911 by Kamerlingh Onnes (a Dutch physicist), but only when the mercury was cooled to within a few degrees of absolute zero ($-273°C$). He found that once a current was set up in the mercury, it continued to flow for many hours, even when the originating p.d. was removed. We now know that under superconductive conditions the material resistance decreases to some 10^{-15} of its value at room temperature.

Materials which exhibit the effect have a *critical* or *transition temperature* above which the material is resistive and below which it is superconductive. Continual research aims at identifying materials which exhibit superconductivity at higher and higher temperatures. The work goes on as much by experimental trial as by scientific reasoning for the mechanism is a complex one. Onnes' original experiment required liquid helium for the cooling but development has already reached the stage where temperatures higher than 100 K ($-173°$C) are feasible, cooling is by liquid nitrogen, much less expensive and easier to handle compared with helium.

Some explanations of superconductivity have already been put forward but we can only get a general idea. Normally thermal vibrations of atoms and ions within the crystal lattice hinder the conduction electrons as they pass. However, when at low temperatures the thermal motions within the lattice are reduced sufficiently, it is possible for there to be a change over in that an electron itself can disturb the lattice. Such disturbance can be transmitted to a second nearby electron and it appears that in some materials this can result in an effective attractive force between the two electrons which is greater than the normal electrostatic repulsion. When this happens the paired electrons continue together at the lowest energy state available for them and because there are no lower energy states available, they cannot dissipate energy in their travels. This implies no loss.

(* Conductivity, Atom, Ion, Lattice, Charge, Energy Levels >> Cryotron)

SUPERHETERODYNE RECEPTION is a system of radio reception in which the incoming radio signal is changed to a lower, more manageable frequency but still carrying the same modulation. The term is a peculiar mixture from Latin and Greek, originally "supersonic heterodyne". "Heterodyne" can be interpreted as the production of a lower frequency from a combination of two higher ones and "supersonic" indicates that the new frequency is above the audio frequency (sonic) range. The word is often shortened to "superhet".

Compared with straightforward amplification of the radio signal, superheterodyne reception has so many advantages, especially in its achievement of high gain and high selectivity without instability, that it is used in practically all radio receivers. A block diagram of the superheterodyne section of a radio receiver is given in Figure S9(i). It works on the principle that it is possible to take a modulated wave and change the *carrier* frequency without affecting the modulation, i.e. to shift the modulation onto a new carrier. By doing this with a new carrier of a lower frequency, more amplification can be applied before instability sets in. The new carrier is called the *intermediate frequency* (i.f. — symbol f_{if}) and by arranging that the incoming signal frequency is always changed to the same

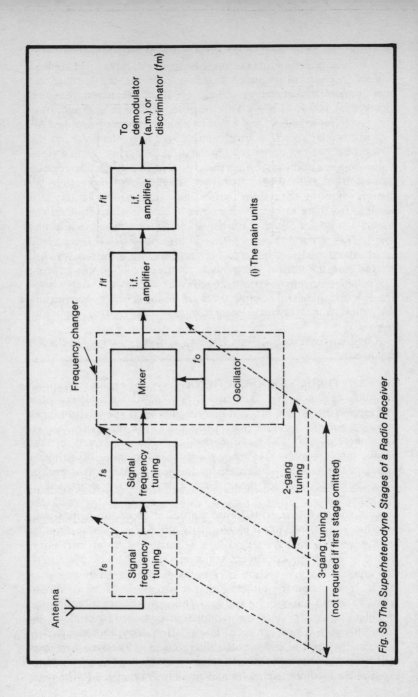

Fig. S9 *The Superheterodyne Stages of a Radio Receiver*

(i) The main units

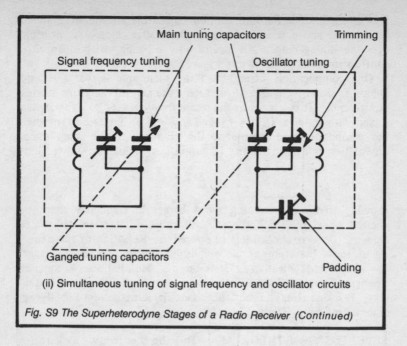

Fig. S9 The Superheterodyne Stages of a Radio Receiver (Continued)

i.f., the i.f. amplifiers once set up need no retuning for the reception of different transmissions. Generally in domestic receivers $f_{if} =$ 450 − 470 kHz. The i.f. amplifiers employ double-tuned coupled circuits adjusted for the bandwidth required by the particular type of transmission (e.g. amplitude or frequency modulation).

The technique involves frequency changing from signal to i.f. as outlined in Figure S9(i). The oscillator and mixer together form a *frequency changer* in which the signal frequency, (f_s) and oscillator frequency (f_o) are applied together to a non-linear device. Sum and difference frequencies $(f_o + f_s)$ and $(f_o - f_s)$ are generated and because it can be shown that f_o must be higher than f_s, the second is filtered off as the i.f. Hence:

$$f_{if} = (f_o - f_s).$$

The i.f. is then amplified to a level suitable for demodulation.

The signal frequency circuits and the oscillator are tuned by a variable capacitor having two or three separate sections on one shaft or by varicap diodes so that all circuits are tuned together (see Fig. S9). This is not as straightforward as it may seem because the capacitance changes for signal and oscillator circuits are different.

411

Special small *trimming* and *padding* capacitors are therefore added so that the above relationship is maintained as closely as possible over the tuning range. An idea of how a 2-gang variable capacitor controls the tuning is shown in Figure S9(ii).

One complication arising from the technique is that a second incoming signal is capable of producing the i.f. and therefore causing interference. It is known as the *image frequency*, (f_{im}). This, when mixed with f_o, gives ($f_{im} + f_o$) and ($f_{im} - f_o$). Trouble arises when the second of these is equal to the i.f. for then the image signal modulation is carried by the i.f. amplifiers. It can be shown that:

$$f_{im} = f_s + 2f_{if}$$

showing that any incoming signal higher in frequency than the wanted signal by twice the i.f. will cause what is termed *image channel* (or *second channel*) *interference*. Rejection of the *image-signal* must therefore be accomplished before the mixing stage. (* Amplifier, Selectivity, Heterodyne, Modulation, Frequency Changer, Coupled Circuits, Resonance >> Radio Receiver, Instability, Tracking, Image Frequency, Double Superheterodyne Reception, Permeability Tuning)

SUPERPOSITION THEOREM   This the theroem we look to for help in the analysis of complicated networks which contain more than one generator. The theorem states that in such a network the current at any point is the vector sum of the individual currents which would flow if each generator were considered in turn with the remaining generators replaced by their internal impedances.

Solving moderately simple networks, say with two generators only, can be accomplished just as easily using Kirchhoff's Laws. However, as the complexity of the network increases, the Kirchhoff method involves more and more simultaneous equations together. These are somewhat difficult to handle hence the Superposition Theorem takes over.
(* Network, Generator, Impedance, Phasor, Kirchhoff's Laws, Complex Notation)

SUPPRESSOR GRID – see Thermionic Valve.

SUSCEPTANCE is the imaginary component of the admittance (Y) of an alternating current circuit and which is 90° out of phase with the conductance (G). It arises from inductance or capacitance in the circuit and is the reciprocal of reactance. The symbol used is B and the unit, the siemens. Admittance is given by:

$$Y = G + jB$$

where all quantities are in siemens.

When inductance only is present, the susceptance is given by $1/\omega L$ and for capacitance only, $-\omega C$ (where ω is the angular frequency). The relationship between susceptance and the components of impedance is:

$$B = \frac{-X}{R^2 + X^2} \text{ siemens,}$$

when R and X are in ohms.
(* Inductance, Capacitance, Reactance, Complex Notation, Admittance, Conductance, Quadrature, Siemens)

SUSCEPTIBILITY, ELECTRIC expresses the response of a dielectric when subjected to an electric field. It is the ratio of dielectric polarization to the electric field strength. The symbol used is χ or χ_e (Greek, lower case chi) and it is given by $\chi_e = P/\epsilon_0 E$ where P is the dielectric polarization in coulombs per square metre, E is the electric field strength in volts per metre and ϵ_0 is the permittivity of free space in farads per metre. Putting these units together shows that χ_e is dimensionless (a number only).

Electric susceptibility is also related to the permittivity ϵ_r of a material by:

$$\chi_e = \epsilon_r - 1$$

again showing χ_e to be dimensionless as is ϵ_r.
(* Dielectric, Electric Polarization, Electric Field, Electric Field Strength, Permittivity)

SUSCEPTIBILITY, MAGNETIC expresses the response of a material when subjected to a magnetic field. It is the ratio of magnetisation to magnetic field strength. The symbol used is χ or χ_m (Greek, lower case chi) and it is therefore given by $\chi = M/H$ where M is the magnetisation in amperes per metre and H is the magnetic field strength, also in amperes per metre. χ is therefore dimensionless (a number only).

Magnetic susceptibility is also related to the relative permeability, μ_r of a material by:

$$\chi = \mu_r - 1$$

again showing χ to be dimensionless as is μ_r.
(* Magnetisation, Magnetic Field, Magnetic Field Strength)

413

SYSTÈME INTERNATIONAL D'UNITÉS − the internationally agreed system of units − see S.I.

T

TEMPERATURE COEFFICIENT OF RESISTANCE

Most materials exhibit a change in resistance with temperature. Generally conductors show an increase in resistance as temperature rises (they are said to have a *positive temperature coefficient of resistance*), semiconductors and insulators show a resistance decrease (negative coefficient). In conductors added energy from heat increases the vibration of the atoms so causing a greater scattering of conduction electrons on their way through. Such interference results in a decrease in electron mobility, therefore a rise in resistance, albeit generally very small unless very high temperature changes are involved, for example in a tungsten filament lamp operating at over 2000°C.

In semiconductors few electrons are available as current carriers and in insulators even less. Resistances are high but extra energy provided by heat to the electrons increases their mobility, so resulting in a decrease in resistance.

In practice we are mostly concerned with the resistance changes of conductors and taking copper as an example, Figure T1 shows the results of measurements on a copper conductor over the range 0 to 100°C. The graph happens to be a straight line over this range but this cannot be taken for granted in all cases. Indeed, for copper the graph curves slightly over about 150°C and the formulae then require extra terms if great accuracy is required. The symbol used for the temperature coefficient of resistance is the Greek lower case alpha (α) and a subscript is employed to indicate the initial temperature. From Figure T1, the temperature coefficient of resistance,

$$\alpha_0 = \frac{\text{slope of graph}}{R_0} = \frac{R_2 - R_0}{(\theta_2 - \theta_0) \times R_0}$$

Similarly:

414

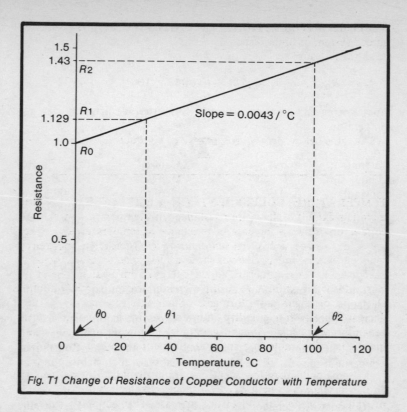

Fig. T1 Change of Resistance of Copper Conductor with Temperature

$$\alpha_1 = \frac{\text{slope of graph}}{R_1} = \frac{R_2 - R_1}{(\theta_2 - \theta_1) \times R_1}$$

Hence, for this particular sample of copper:

$$\alpha_0 = 0.0043 \text{ per } °C, \quad \alpha_1 = \frac{0.0043}{1.129} = 0.00381 \text{ per } °C$$

Using α_0, α_1, etc., the resistance at any other temperature (within the linear range) can be calculated, as for example:

$R_1 = R_0(1 + \alpha_0 \theta)$ where θ is the temperature rise

$\therefore \quad R_1 = 1[1 + (0.0043 \times 30)] = 1.129$ ohms as shown on Figure T1.

415

$$R_2 = R_1(1 + \alpha_1\theta) = 1.129[1 + (0.00381 \times 70)] = 1.43\ \Omega$$

(as shown). Equally:

$$R_2 = R_0(1 + \alpha_0\theta) = 1[1 + (0.0043 \times 100)] = 1.43\ \Omega$$

thus arriving at the same answer but from a different starting temperature.

The table below gives α_0 for a range of conductors:

Material	α_0	Material	α_0
Aluminium	0.004	Manganin	0–0.0002
Constantan	0.0002	Mercury	0.0009
Carbon (graphite)	−0.0005	Nichrome	0.0002
Copper	0.0043	Nickel	0.005
Gold	0.0035	Silver	0.004
Iron	0.006	Tin	0.004
Lead	0.0035	Tungsten	0.0045

To avoid so many noughts, α is often quoted in parts per million per degree Celsius (ppm/°C).

Of particular interest for precision laboratory equipment are the resistive materials Manganin (an alloy of copper, manganese and nickel), Nichrome (nickel, iron and chromium) and Constantan (copper and nickel), all developed specially for high stability in that the resistance is almost constant over a wide range of temperature (i.e. α is very low).

(* Conductor, Semiconductor, Insulator, Resistance, Current, Energy, Mobility >> Resistance Thermometer)

TESLA   The S.I. unit of magnetic flux density. It is defined as one weber of magnetic flux per square metre of circuit area. The symbol used is T [after Nikola Tesla, an American (but Yugoslav born) electrical engineer].

The earth's magnetic field is some $3 - 4 \times 10^{-5}$ T whereas a good permanent magnet has a flux density around 1.0 T.

(* S.I., Magnetic Field, Magnetic Flux Density, Weber)

TETRODE is any electronic device containing 4 electrodes but on its own the term usually describes a certain type of thermionic valve. It is equivalent to a triode (cathode, control grid and anode) with an additional *screen grid* inserted between the control grid and the anode. The screen grid is held at a positive potential relative to the cathode and effectively reduces the grid-anode capacitance − see Thermionic Valve.

THERMAL AGITATION NOISE is a general term used to describe the special noise generated by electron movement arising from heat — see Thermal Noise.

THERMAL NOISE arises from the random nature of the electron movements within a conductor. "Free" electrons move at high speeds in all directions, linking up with positive ions and breaking away from them in a purely random manner. At each end of a conductor the net charge is a function of the number of electrons and positive ions near the end and their distances from it. Because this is a random process then at any instant it is unlikely that there will be exactly the same charge at both ends. Hence there is a minute charge or potential difference across the two ends of the conductor and this is when nothing else is connected to it. This potential difference varies extremely rapidly and Figure N4 gives an idea of how it would appear on an oscilloscope over a very short period of time. Also when a current flows, although the number of electrons passing a given point is *on average* constant, there are momentary changes. These effects appear as thermal noise. The description "thermal" arises because the actual noise voltage measurable depends on the absolute temperature and the higher the temperature, the greater is the noise voltage. This is because the number of free electrons and their velocities increase owing to the added heat which provides them with more energy. Because the changes within the conductor occur at random, the thermal noise frequency extends over the whole spectrum. Boltzmann has given us the relationship between particle energy and temperature which leads to the general formula for thermal noise voltage:

$$V_n = \sqrt{4kTRB} \text{ volts r.m.s.}$$

where V_n is the noise voltage, k is Boltzmann's constant (1.38×10^{-23} joules per degree Kelvin), R is the conductor resistance, T is the temperature in kelvins and B is the bandwidth in Hz. For an amplified system or channel, B is usually taken as that between the upper and lower frequencies at which the response has fallen by 3 dB. Simplified for a standard room temperature of 290 K, the formula becomes:

$$V_{n(room)} = 1.265 \times 10^{-4} \sqrt{RB} \ \mu V .$$

If the noise voltage feeds power into a matched load, the voltage across the load resistance is $V_n/2$ and the power into the load is

$$\frac{(V_n/2)^2}{R} = \frac{V_n{}^2}{4R}$$

from which the noise power delivered into a matched load = kTB watts, but note that in addition to this the load also generates its own quota of noise.

Thermal noise is also known as *Johnson* noise.

(* Random, Electron, Ion, Charge, Potential Difference, Absolute Temperature, Boltzmann's Constant, Noise, Bandwidth, Kelvin, Decibel, White Noise, Noise Temperature >> Matching, Pink Noise)

THERMIONIC EMISSION   This is the emission of electrons from the surface of a material due to the effects of heat.   At room temperatures, the few electrons which have sufficient energy to escape from, say, a wire are prevented from moving away altogether by the space charge of which they are a part. If, however, the wire is heated, more electrons gain the energy needed for escape and accordingly the space charge increases, it is of course, negative. Without help, electrons cannot escape from the vicinity of the heated wire and even if they could, there would be collisions with gas molecules of the surrounding air.   The latter hindrance is removed by mounting the wire (now called a *cathode*) in an evacuated glass envelope. Also the restraining effect of the space charge is countered by surrounding the wire with a metal cylinder charged positively (the *anode*).   The electric field the anode creates produces an attractive force on the electrons within the space charge and provided that they can be replaced and have somewhere to go, there is a flow of electrons through the vacuum from cathode to anode. This constitutes a *diode valve* as shown in Figure T2 – a device through which current can flow in one direction only.

Thermionic emission is an essential feature of the cathode-ray tube as used in television sets.   Electrons are emitted from the cathode and are accelerated by positive potentials towards the screen on which they come to a halt and give up their kinetic energies to produce light.

Provided that the emitted electrons are removed as rapidly as they are released, the Richardson-Dushman Equation can be used to calculate the emission current density:

$$J = AT^2 \exp -(\phi/kT) \text{ amperes per metre squared (A/m}^2).$$

A is a constant for the particular material and is usually of such value that the result is given in amperes per square centimetre, ϕ is

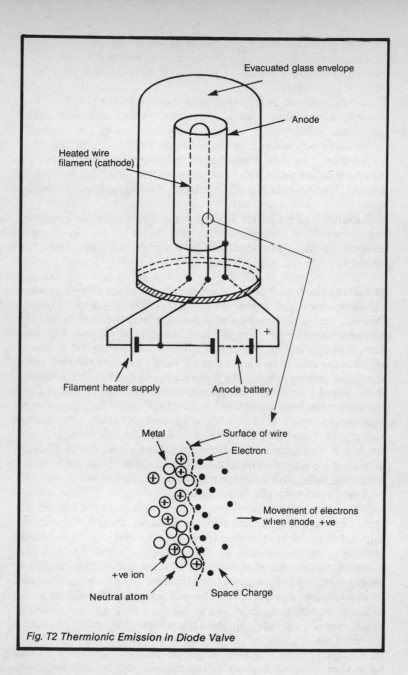

Fig. T2 Thermionic Emission in Diode Valve

the work function of the material, T is the temperature in degrees Kelvin and k is Boltzmann's Constant. Note that ϕ and k are in different units, the value used for k should therefore be 8.61×10^{-5} eV per degree Kelvin.

Taking tantalum as an example (a metal much favoured for this purpose), for which $A \simeq 40$ and $\phi \simeq 4.1$ eV, then J at 2400 K works out to 0.56 A/cm^2. This infers that over one square centimetre of surface area of tantalum at 2400 K the electrons have sufficient energy that up to 0.56 A can be continuously emitted. However, at room temperature (293 K), J is so small (9×10^{-65} A/cm^2) that not even one electron has much chance of being emitted. From the above, this is to be expected.

(* Emission, Space Charge, Energy, Kinetic Energy, Work Function, Electric Field, Boltzmann's Constant, Schottky Effect, Primary Electron, Anode, Cathode, Diode >> Cathode-Ray Tube, Television Receiver)

THERMIONIC VALVE is a component consisting of two or more electrodes contained within an evacuated glass or metal envelope. Operation relies on thermionic emission, hence its name. Before the transistor came along, thermionic valves reigned supreme for rectification, amplification and even switching. Arrival of the transistor which is capable of doing the same jobs but at lower voltages, more efficiently and with relatively minute size, has more or less eclipsed them except for high power applications (e.g. the magnetron, klystron, travelling-wave tube). Nevertheless it is instructive to examine the method of operation because not only is it a prime example of thermionic emission in action (see this term) but also because it highlights some of the basic laws governing the restlessness of the electron. Happily with thermionic valves we are only concerned with electron flow, the complication of *holes* does not arise as it does with semiconductors.

There are many different types of thermionic valve but all are built around a heated cathode which is the source of electrons. The cathode is either a wire coated with emissive material (directly heated) as shown in Figure T2 or a coated metal cylinder enclosing a heating wire (indirectly heated). Electrons gaining sufficient energy from the heat would normally leave the cathode surface and form a space charge but an anode, positively charged relative to the cathode, attracts them away and an electron current flows across the space between cathode and anode, a perfect illustration of current flowing from negative to positive. The electrons enjoy an unimpeded passage between the two electrodes because most air molecules have been pumped out. Current flow is in one direction only

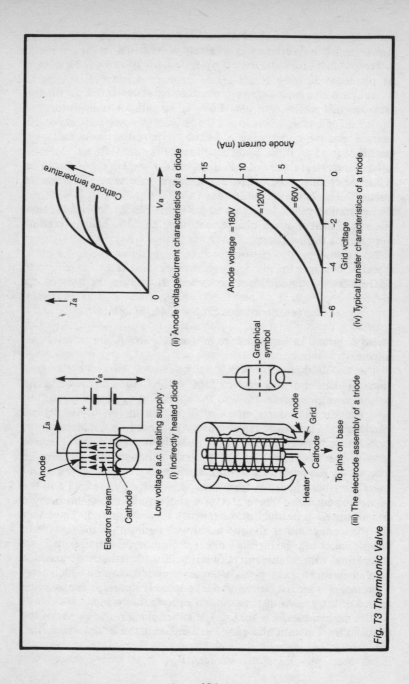

(ii) Anode voltage/current characteristics of a diode

Cathode temperature

I_a

V_a

0

Anode current (mA)

15

10

5

0

Anode voltage =180V

=120V

=60V

-6   -4   -2

Grid voltage

(iv) Typical transfer characteristics of a triode

Graphical symbol

Anode

Grid

Cathode

Heater

To pins on base

(iii) The electrode assembly of a triode

Anode

Electron stream

Cathode

V_a

I_a

+

Low voltage a.c. heating supply

(i) Indirectly heated diode

Fig. T3 Thermionic Valve

(cathode to anode) hence this simple arrangement acts as a rectifying diode. The operation in a circuit is sketched in Figure T3(i).

Clearly the anode current (I_a) varies with (i) the anode voltage (V_a) because higher voltages create stronger positive electric fields at the space charge and therefore reduce its effect and with (ii) the heat supplied to the cathode. For a given cathode temperature, as V_a is increased, I_a increases until a point is reached where all emitted electrons are being collected. Thereafter even for large increases in V_a, little additional anode current flows. If the cathode temperature is increased, V_a has a similar effect but at a higher level of anode current and again a *saturation voltage* is reached. This is illustrated in (ii) of the figure. When I_a is less than the saturation value, it is said to be *space charge limited* because there is sufficient space charge remaining to deter some electrons from leaving the cathode.

A measure of the performance of a thermionic valve which is useful in design is the *anode a.c. resistance*, also known as *electrode a.c. resistance* or *anode slope resistance*. It is given the symbol, r_a:

$$\text{anode a.c. resistance, } r_a = \delta V_a / \delta I_a \text{ ohms}$$

where δ means "a small change in" and V_a and I_a are in volts and amperes.

The *triode* thermionic valve has one more electrode than the diode in the form of a grid or mesh of fine wires surrounding the cathode and closer to it than to the anode. A typical construction (not including the outer envelope) is shown in (iii) of the figure. The electrode is known as the *control grid* because if maintained at a negative potential relative to the cathode, it exercises considerable control over the effect of the positive anode field on the space charge. As the negative potential on the grid is increased, fewer and fewer electrons are drawn from the space charge by the anode so the anode current falls. The effect of a grid is most easily shown by a set of *transfer* or *mutual* characteristics as shown in (iv). The effect the grid voltage has on the anode current is not unlike that exercised by the base voltage on the collector current of a transistor. An alternating voltage applied between grid and cathode of a triode valve therefore results in an alternating anode current which is of such magnitude that an anode load resistor develops a magnified replica of the grid voltage, i.e. amplification takes place.

The *mutual conductance* (g_m) of a thermionic valve expresses the relationship between the anode current and the grid voltage, i.e.:

$$g_m = \delta I_a / \delta V_g$$

where δV_g is the grid voltage, (V_a is kept constant) while the *amplification factor* (μ) shows how the anode voltage reacts to grid voltage changes:

$$\mu = \delta V_a/\delta V_g \quad (I_a \text{ is kept constant}).$$

Hence:

$$\mu = g_m \times r_a$$

for

$$\frac{\delta I_a}{\delta V_g} \times \frac{\delta V_a}{\delta I_a} = \frac{\delta V_a}{\delta V_g} .$$

From μ, g_m and r_a much about the behaviour in practical circuits can be determined.

Triode valves suffer from a major disadvantage at high frequencies. This arises from the capacitance between anode and grid which effectively links input and output circuits and therefore causes feedback which may result in instability. To reduce the capacitance, other electrodes are introduced, e.g. in the *tetrode* (4 electrode) valve a positive *screen grid* is employed. This reduces the grid-anode capacitance but brings in another problem of secondary emission which has to be reduced by yet another electrode mounted adjacent to the anode and known as a *suppressor grid*. This one is connected to the cathode and serves to repel secondary electrons back to the anode. This is the *pentode* valve (5 electrodes). There are several other more complicated types.

As mentioned above, thermionic valves still have a part to play for special purposes, especially when very large powers are involved, e.g. with anode voltages up to 20 000 or more and anode dissipations of some 100 kW.

(* Emission, Thermionic Emission, Anode, Cathode, Charge, Electric Field, Space Charge, Diode, Transistor, Capacitance, Feedback, Secondary Emission, Characteristic >> Indirectly Heated Cathode, Instability, Magnetron, Klystron, Travelling-Wave Tube)

THERMODYNAMIC TEMPERATURE The Celsius (or Centigrade) scale of temperature was devised in 1742 by Anders Celsius (a Swedish astronomer) and this is the scale most commonly used in everyday life. $0°C$ is the temperature of melting ice and $100°C$ that of boiling water, both at one atmosphere of pressure. The scale can be extended above and below these two points.

For scientific work a partly theoretical scale was later devised by Lord Kelvin (a Scottish physicist and mathematician). 0 degrees on his scale corresponds to *absolute zero* ($-273.16°C$) and the size of the Kelvin degree is the same as the Celsius. This is the basis of the *thermodynamic temperature* scale, the symbol used is T and the unit is the kelvin (K). The kelvin is defined as the fraction 1/273.16 of the thermodynamic temperature of the *triple point* of water. Triple point refers to the one temperature at which a solid, its liquid and its vapour can coexist in equilibrium. For water therefore the triple point is that temperature maintained by a mixture of pure ice, water and water vapour in a sealed vacuum flask and it has a value of 273.16 kelvin. For boiling water the thermodynamic temperature is therefore 373.16 kelvin.

Just to confuse us, it is admitted that there is a slight difference between the thermodynamic and practical scales. "Scale" temperature (degrees Celsius) is the thermodynamic temperature minus 273.15, hence $0°C$ corresponds to 273.15 K and the triple point of water is therefore $0.01°C$. This probably is of little concern to the practical engineer who usually rounds down to 273 anyway.

(* Kelvin, Absolute Zero)

THERMOELECTRIC EFFECT   This is mainly concerned with what happens when two metals come into contact. It is a fact that the distribution of heat energy among its electrons depends on the metal itself. At the junction between two different metals, electrons are more likely to move one way than the other depending on the contact potential across the junction. A certain amount of energy in the form of heat is therefore also transported. This is known as the *Peltier Effect* and the *Peltier coefficient* may be defined as the quantity of heat absorbed at the junction when unit charge flows across it (after Jean Charles Athanase Peltier, a French physicist). Equally it is the quantity of heat released if the current flows against the contact potential, i.e. $\alpha_P = W/Q$ volts where α_P is the Peltier coefficient, W is the energy in joules and Q, the charge in coulombs. One joule per coulomb can also be expressed as one volt which is equal to P/I where P is the power in watts and I, the current in amperes. Accordingly the formula for the coefficient can be extended as:

$$\alpha_P = W/Q = P/I \text{ volts}$$

which is of the order of 3 mV at room temperature for most metals but there is a wide variation. Higher values are obtained when semiconductors are involved.

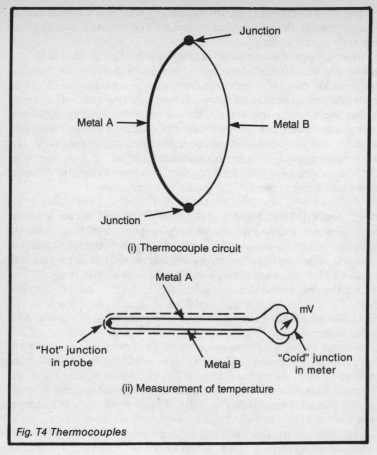

Metal A

Junction

Metal B

Junction

(i) Thermocouple circuit

Metal A

mV

"Hot" junction
in probe

Metal B

"Cold" junction
in meter

(ii) Measurement of temperature

Fig. T4 Thermocouples

A *thermocouple* is a circuit comprising two dissimilar wires with two junctions as shown in Figure T4(i). If the junctions are both at the same temperature, the amount of heat absorbed at one junction is equal to that released at the other. Thomas Johann Seebeck (a German physicist) however discovered that a tiny loop current could be detected if the two junctions were maintained at different temperatures. This is known as the *Seebeck Effect* and it is ascribed to the fact that electron energies are different at the two junctions so creating different Peltier coefficients, hence a voltage difference between the two junctions.

The *Seebeck coefficient* (α_s) is expressed by the open-circuit voltage produced by unit temperature difference, i.e. $\alpha_s = dV/dT$ volts per degree Celsius and it is sometimes referred to as the *thermoelectric power* (i.e. when $dT = 1\ ^{\circ}C$). α_s for metals ranges from some 10 $\mu V/^{\circ}C$ upwards to 1 mV/$^{\circ}C$ for certain semiconductors.

The theories above are sufficient for a general understanding of thermoelectric effects, however in the Seebeck effect no account has been taken of the electromotive force generated along each wire owing to the difference in temperature at its two ends. This brings in another correction known as the *Thomson* (or *Kelvin*) *coefficient* [after Lord Kelvin (William Thomson)] which must be taken into account in the design of temperature measuring devices if the temperature gradient along the conductor is high.

(* Thermocouple, Contact Potential, Work Function, Charge, Coulomb, Energy, Joule, Electromotive Force, Power)

THÉVENIN'S THEOREM is used in the analysis of complicated networks containing one or more generators. It is a powerful theorem which enables such networks to be greatly simplified. The theorem states that: Any two-terminal network can be replaced by a single generator having an electromotive force (e.m.f.) equal to the open-circuit output voltage of the network in series with an impedance equal to the input impedance of the network when all generators have been replaced by their own internal impedances.

We can perhaps put this more simply by looking at the network as a voltage generator. The generator e.m.f. (E) is equal to the voltage at the output terminals with no load connected and the generator impedance is given by E/I where I is the current through a short-circuit across the terminals. E and I can be calculated or measured.

To help clarify the theorem, let us take a simple resistive network as an example. This is certainly not the complex type of network for which the theorem is intended but it does allow us to make Ohm's Law calculations in order to demonstrate the use. The theorem applies equally to a.c. networks as it does to d.c. Figure T5 at (i) shows a 60 V generator with 5 Ω internal resistance feeding the output terminals 1 and 2 via a T network. We need to replace this network by nothing more than a single generator with a known internal resistance.

Clearly the open-circuit voltage at terminals 1 and 2 is by Ohm's Law, 30 V [see (iii) of the figure]. The resistance looking back into terminals 1 and 2 is from (iv) 5 + 5 = 10 Ω.

From Thévenin's theorem therefore the equivalent network as shown in (ii) of the figure, has $E = 30$ V, with $R = 10\ \Omega$ and we can connect any resistance across terminals 1 and 2 and obtain the

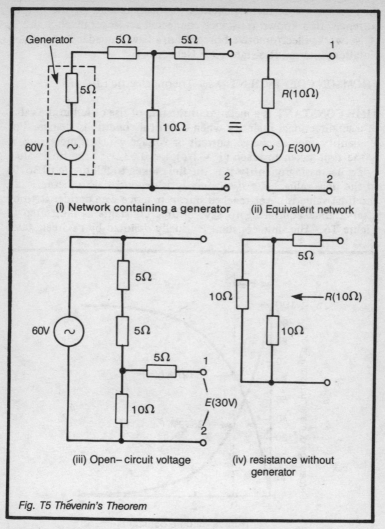

(i) Network containing a generator   (ii) Equivalent network

(iii) Open–circuit voltage   (iv) resistance without generator

Fig. T5 Thévenin's Theorem

same current through it as with the circuit in (i).

This could also have been calculated from the short-circuit current which in fact works out to 3 A. Then the equivalent network generator internal resistance, $R = 30/3 = 10\ \Omega$ as already calculated.

In this illustration we have worked in terms of resistance. If, however, the generator internal impedance is complex, i.e. in the form $R + jX$, this introduces another unknown quantity. Solution

427

then requires a further calculation or measurement of the output current with a known resistance connected across terminals 1 and 2. (* Network, Electromotive Force, Ohm's Law, Impedance, Complex Notation, Internal Resistance >> Generator)

THOMSON COEFFICIENT – see Thermoelectric Effect.

TIME CONSTANT is a measure of the rate of rise or fall in the value of a unidirectional quantity when electrical conditions change. For a quantity such as charge, current or voltage which is increasing, it is the time taken to reach $(1 - 1/e)$, i.e. 0.6321 of the final value. For a decreasing quantity it is the time taken to fall to $1/e$ (0.3679) of the final value. The rise or decay is exponential so theoretically the final value is never reached but in practice we consider it to be after a time equivalent to say, 5 time constants as illustrated in Figure T6. The time constant is usually denoted by τ (Greek, tau).

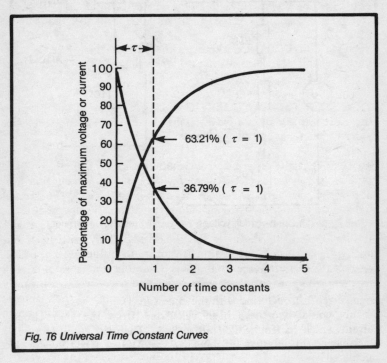

Fig. T6 Universal Time Constant Curves

Time constants are most frequently associated with capacitive and inductive circuits. Take a capacitor as an example. If a d.c. supply is suddenly connected to a discharged capacitor C in series

428

with a resistance R, the initial charging current is high, only limited by the value of the resistance. However, as the capacitor charges the voltage across it increases so reducing the charging current. Ultimately when the supply and capacitor voltages are equal, the charging current has fallen to zero. This process is pictured by the rising curve of Figure T6. For a capacitive circuit the time constant τ is given by $C \times R$ seconds where C is in farads and R is the total resistance in ohms. Hence for a capacitor of 2 μF in series with a resistor of 1 MΩ, i.e. $CR = 2$ seconds, then from Figure T6 the capacitor will be charged to 63.21% of the applied voltage in 2 seconds (one time constant) and would not be considered to be fully charged until 10 seconds have elapsed (5 time constants). The same reasoning applies on discharge. For an inductor in series with a resistor the time constant is given by L/R seconds where L is the inductance in henries. The meaning of the word *universal* in the itle of Figure T6 is now evident for these curves give useful information regarding any circuit with a time constant.

(* Charge, Current, Voltage, Resistance, Capacitance, Inductance)

TRANSCONDUCTANCE expresses the current change at the output of an active device relative to the voltage change at the input – see Mutual Conductance.

TRANSFER CHARACTERISTIC shows the relationship between the electrical conditions on different electrodes of an active device – see Characteristic.

TRANSFORMER is an electromagnetic device which at any given frequency transforms electrical energy at one voltage to another (not necessarily different) voltage. It does this through the mutual inductance between two or more magnetically coupled coils, symbolized in Figure T7(i). Here an alternating current in coil 1 sets up a changing magnetic flux linking not only with itself but also with any other coil within its sphere of influence, e.g. coil 2. An electromotive force (e.m.f.) is therefore induced in coil 2 whenever the current changes in coil 1 and this e.m.f. is obviously at the same frequency. To reduce the reluctance of the magnetic circuit a magnetic core is often employed, the symbol is also shown in (i). Typical transformer constructions are shown in (ii). The winding connected to the supply is known as the *primary*, the other one which delivers energy to the load is called the *secondary*. There can be more than one secondary.

Consider first an "ideal" transformer, i.e. one with no power losses and in which all the flux produced by the primary winding

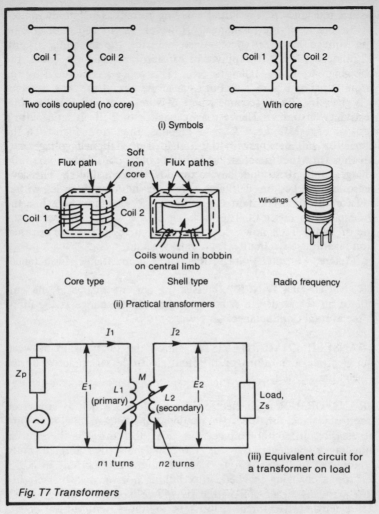

Fig. T7 Transformers

links with the secondary, see Figure T7(iii).

The e.m.f. (e) induced in a coil of n turns is given by $n(\mathrm{d}\Phi/\mathrm{d}t)$ where $(\mathrm{d}\Phi/\mathrm{d}t)$ is the rate of change of flux, hence

$$\frac{\mathrm{d}\Phi}{\mathrm{d}t} = \frac{e}{n}$$

The same flux cuts both coils so if the primary voltage is E_1 and the secondary, E_2:

$$\frac{d\Phi}{dt} = \frac{E_1}{n_1} = \frac{E_2}{n_2}$$

or

$$\frac{E_1}{E_2} = \frac{n_1}{n_2} = n$$

where n is the *turns ratio* of the transformer. The *voltage per turn* in both windings is therefore the same.

This transformer is loss free, so the power supplied to the primary is equal to that induced into the secondary, from which it can be shown that because power factors cancel out, $E_1 I_1 = E_2 I_2$ hence, putting it all together:

$$\frac{E_1}{E_2} = \frac{I_2}{I_1} = \frac{n_1}{n_2} = n .$$

If $E_2 > E_1$ the transformer has a *step-up voltage ratio*. If $E_2 < E_1$ the transformer has a *step-down voltage ratio*.

Summing up:

(i)   the voltage per turn is the same in both windings;
(ii) the volt-ampere product is the same in both windings;
(iii) since $I_1 n_1 = I_2 n_2$, the ampere-turn balance is maintained between the two windings.

In the ideal transformer, the mutual inductance (M) between the two windings is given by:

$$M = \sqrt{L_1 L_2}$$

where L_1 and L_2 are the separate winding inductances.

In a practical transformer, however, coupling is never fully complete so we introduce a *coupling factor* which is given the symbol, k. If all the flux generated by L_1 cuts L_2 then $k = 1$, if not, k is less than 1. The mutual inductance in the practical transformer is therefore:

$$M = k\sqrt{L_1 L_2} \text{ henries}$$

(when L_1 and L_2 are in henries).

Transformers are also used in communication circuits for impedance matching. If Z_p and Z_s are the impedances connected to a transformer as shown in Figure T7(iii) then $Z_s/Z_p = n^2$, i.e. the impedance ratio is equal to the square of the turns ratio.

Apart from the *copper loss* which is simply the I^2R losses in the windings, iron cores bring with them two other losses:

(i) *eddy current* loss — eddy currents are induced in the iron, the latter has resistance therefore power losses arise;

(ii) *hysteresis loss* — energy is consumed every time the magnetic state of the iron is reversed.

From the above it is evident that an iron core, while useful for increasing the magnetic flux, has certain disadvantages and clearly these increase with frequency. At radio frequencies the laminated iron core creates more difficulties than it solves so cores with higher electrical resistance are used mainly to reduce eddy currents (e.g. dust cores, ceramics). Alternatively, the core may be dispensed with altogether as shown for the radio frequency transformer in Figure T7(ii). Whatever technique is used, the basic theory of the transformer remains unchanged.

In electronics transformers have many uses, the most obvious perhaps being the supply of low alternating voltages from the electricity mains. This type of transformer uses a laminated core and also isolates the equipment it supplies from the mains, i.e. there is no direct connection to either mains live or neutral (all power flows via a magnetic field). If isolation between primary and secondary circuits is not required, a single tapped winding can be used, this is known as an *autotransformer*.

See also Coupled Circuits.

(* Inductance, Mutual Inductance, Magnetic Flux, Electromotive Force, Reluctance, Electromagnetic Induction, Power, Power Factor, Coupled Circuits, Eddy Current, Hysteresis Loss Magnetic, Core >> Matching, Autotransformer, Current Transformer, Core-Type Transformer, Shell-Type Transformer, Isolating Transformer, Lamination)

TRANSIENT is an electrical condition which is of short duration or fleeting. It is a voltage or current surge or oscillation which persists for a short time following a sudden disturbance of the steady-state condition. Thus impulse noise, lightning and switching surges may be classed as transients.

The *transient response* of an amplifier is measured as the change in output for a specified impulse input.

(* Amplifier, Oscillation, Impulse)

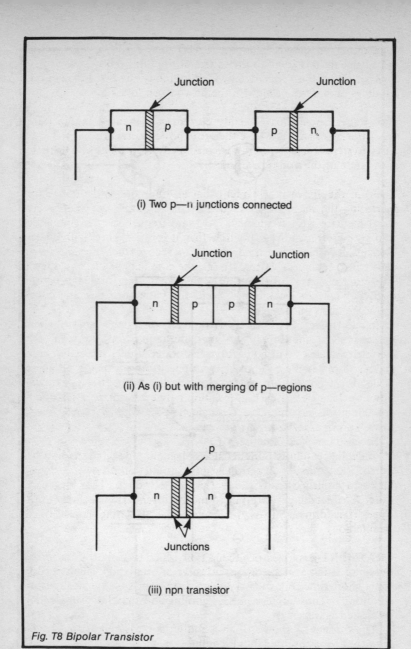

(i) Two p—n junctions connected

(ii) As (i) but with merging of p—regions

(iii) npn transistor

Fig. T8 Bipolar Transistor

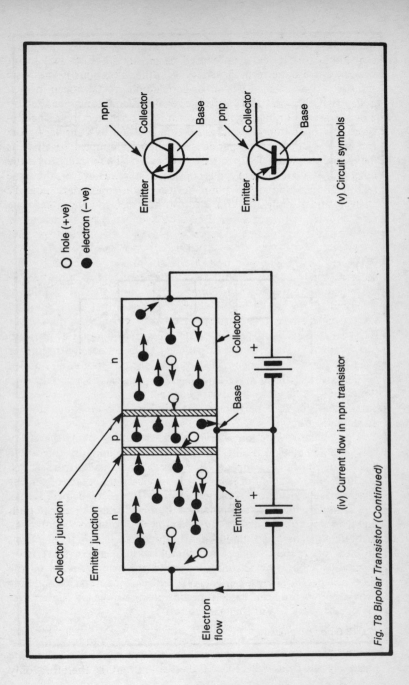

Fig. T8 Bipolar Transistor (Continued)

(iv) Current flow in npn transistor

(v) Circuit symbols

○ hole (+ve)
● electron (−ve)

TRANSISTOR   Generally refers to a *bipolar* transistor, this is a semiconductor device mainly used as an amplifier or switch but which can also perform a variety of other functions. The basic transistor consists of a silicon or germanium crystal doped in such a way that there are three separate regions, two p-type separated by a single n-type or alternatively, two n-type separated by a single p-type. Its operation is perhaps best understood by considering the transistor first as two separate p-n junctions coupled together as developed in Figure T8(i) to (iii). The n-p-n silicon transistor is the most widely used so this type is considered here. However, the same reasoning also applies to p-n-p devices with appropriate polarity changes and reading hole for electron and electron for hole. The term bipolar transistor is used because it depends for its action on the flow of two different types of charge carrier (electrons and holes).

Figure T8(iv) shows an n-p-n transistor biased for action by two batteries (in practical circuits one battery only is required). The three regions are known as *emitter, base* and *collector* as shown. The emitter region is heavily doped so that there is a plentiful supply of electrons. The base p-region is very thin (less than about 0.05 mm) and lightly doped. The emitter junction is forward biased and therefore of low resistivity. A good supply of emitter electrons, therefore, encouraged by the negative potential applied to the emitter, flows towards and easily crosses the junction into the base. This is normal forward-bias p-n junction action. Recombination within the narrow p-region is low because there are not many holes around.

The collector junction is reverse-biased and has a higher battery voltage connected to it. In a reverse-biased p-n junction the potential barrier normally impedes the flow of majority carriers across the junction but aids the flow of minority carriers. Electrons in the p-type base are minority carriers and are therefore helped across. The relatively high positive potential on the collector therefore pulls the electrons straight across the collector junction into the n-region. Although the base is thin and lightly doped so that most electrons shoot across it to the collector, recombination means that a relatively small number of electrons are lost to the main current and the same number of holes are filled. To replace the latter, a small hole current flows into the base from the positive pole of the emitter battery (0.5% or less of the main current).

Put very simply, the emitter "emits" a copious supply of electrons into the base, a few get lost on the way and form the base current. Most however shoot across the thin base into the welcoming positively charged collector. Collector current is therefore only slightly less than the emitter current. This leads to the basic transistor equation:

$$I_e = I_b + I_c$$

where the subscripts e, b and c refer to emitter, base and collector respectively.

Of major importance is the fact that the main flow of current through the device can be controlled by the biasing of the emitter-base junction:

(i) for amplification, a small change in the emitter-base current or voltage controls a relatively large change in the collector current;

(ii) for switching, small emitter-base potential changes can turn the collector current almost completely on or off.

Figure T8(v) shows the graphical symbols for the two types of bipolar transistor. Note that the arrow points in the direction of *hole* current flow. This may seem an odd way of indicating current direction especially when holes are really only electron vacancies. However, the hole is a useful concept in semiconductor theory and it does avoid a clash with the existing diode symbol which has always considered current flow as from positive to negative.

See also Field Effect Transistor, Unijunction Transistor.
(* Semiconductor, Doping, Charge Carrier, Electron, Hole, Potential Barrier, P-N Junction, N-type Semiconductor, P-type Semiconductor >> Hybrid Parameters, Switching Transistor, Common-Emitter, Common-Base, Common-Collector Connections)

TRANSMISSION LINE   This is a pair of wires (or exceptionally it could be one wire and earth) over which either power or communication signals are transmitted. Power transmission lines can be seen overhead on pylons and they transmit power from the power stations to substations for eventual distribution to consumers. Not seen are the power lines buried underground which serve the same purpose.

In communication, transmission lines are connected between two remote points and serve to carry audio or radio frequency waves. The 2-wire lines connecting telephones to the local telephone exchanges are examples of audio transmission lines. Lines connecting a radio transmitter to the antenna are also transmission lines which frequently are carried overhead on poles. Overhead wires have a constant spacing (some 20 − 30 cm) and are supported by insulators. Underground cables enclose the pairs of wires in a waterproof sheath, the wires themselves are insulated with dry paper or plastic. Coaxial cables are transmission lines specially constructed for carrying high frequencies.

Transmission line theory is wide ranging because unlike the network comprising a group of passive components, a signal takes time to travel from one end to the other and the transmission time depends on the nature of the line. All lines have what are known as *primary coefficients*, these are:

(i) R, the loop (there and back) *resistance* in ohms;

(ii) G, the *shunt conductance* (also known as the *leakance*) which is the loss due to the conductance of the insulating material between the wires. Being a conductance it is measured in siemens;

(iii) C, the *capacitance* between the wires in farads;

(iv) L, the *inductance* of the 2-wire loop in henries.

Usually the values are quoted per metre of line length. Except for C, the coefficients are appreciably frequency sensitive. Even C exhibits some variation. What matter most in line transmission theory are:

(1) *Characteristic Impedance* (Z_0) – every line has a characteristic impedance of its own. For maximum efficiency overall the line should be terminated at both ends in its characteristic impedance, this avoids reflections along the line which are generally undesirable and result in less power being delivered at the distant end.

(2) *Propagation Coefficient* (γ) – this is complex and therefore has two parts, α, the *attenuation coefficient* and β, the *phase-change coefficient*. From α the attenuation of the line can be determined while from β we get the wavelength at any given frequency. Knowing the wavelength, the velocity of the wave, v is obtained. As an instructive example, v for a typical 0.9 mm diameter paper insulated underground copper pair at 1600 Hz is approximately 9.5×10^7 metres per second which is considerably slower than the 3×10^8 one normally expects of an electromagnetic wave.

(3) The *Distortionless Condition* – the fact that the primary coefficients vary with frequency means that the characteristic impedance and the propagation coefficient also vary. Accordingly, the wave velocity varies which results in undesirable changes in the waveform. It was originally suggested by Oliver Heaviside (the English physicist) that if $LG = RC$, then the distortionless condition is achieved. Then Z_0, α, β and v are all independent of frequency, a

437

condition which is desirable but achieved with difficulty. On practical lines LG is much smaller than RC so LG is increased by the addition of inductance either along the line or in lumps. This is known as *loading*. The fully distortionless condition is not practicable but some loading is worthwhile. Loading is mainly used in telephone systems to provide a flat frequency response over the audio range. Above this, however, there is a sharp cut-off. The use of loading is decreasing owing to the replacement of audio circuits by digital, the last thing a digital circuit needs is a narrow frequency band.

(* Network, Waveform, Coaxial Cable, Resistance, Conductance, Capacitance, Inductance, Characteristic Impedance, Complex Notation, Propagation Coefficient, Travelling Wave, Standing Wave >> Matching, Strip Transmission Line, Stub)

TRAVELLING WAVE is an electromagnetic wave which is confined to a transmission line. If we first consider a lossless, correctly terminated line with a sinusoidal voltage input, then energy is transmitted along the line from the sending end and at any point on the line it will be found that the magnitude of voltage measured across the line (or current measured in the line) vary sinusoidally. This is demonstrated on a basis of time in Figure T9. Let the wave frequency be 100 kHz and suppose that its velocity is that of light, c (not true for cables but this does not affect the explanation), then:

$$\text{wavelength}, \lambda = c/f = (3 \times 10^8)/10^5 = 3000 \text{ metres}$$

and the period (time taken per cycle) is equal to:

$$1/f = 10 \, \mu s .$$

With these figures, Figure T9 can be labelled. Assume $V = 1$ volt. The arrow at the head of the wave shows how far the wavefront has progressed down the line at the stated times. After $10 \, \mu s$ the process repeats.

A practical line is, of course, not lossless hence the voltage and current decrease as the wave travels down the line. If the wave meets an impedance discontinuity there is a partial reflection and energy travels back towards the sending end. On the line, therefore, there are two waves, the forward and the reflected and these add together to result in *standing waves*.

(* Transmission Line, Energy, Sinusoidal, Frequency, Wavelength, Impedance, Reflection, Standing Wave)

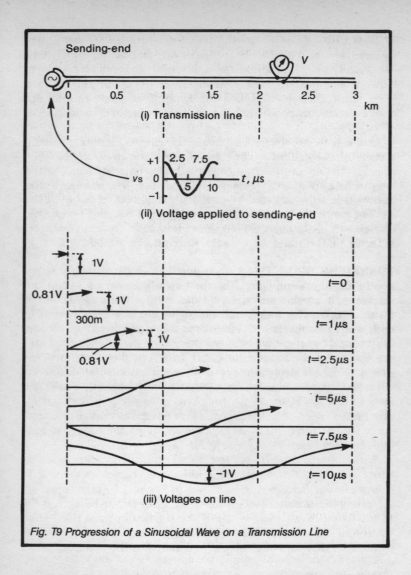

Fig. T9 *Progression of a Sinusoidal Wave on a Transmission Line*

TRIODE is any electronic device containing three electrodes but on its own usually describes a certain type of thermionic valve, i.e. one comprising a cathode, control grid and anode — see Thermionic Valve.

TRIPLE POINT — see Thermodynamic Temperature.

TUNED CIRCUIT is a resonant circuit in which the resonance frequency can be varied. The adjustment can be made (i) only occasionally, e.g. to adjust the output of an oscillator to that required and readjust later if necessary or (ii) continually as in a radio receiver where twiddling the knobs is in fact adjusting the resonance frequencies of circuits so that the desired radio station is "tuned in".

In the radio receiver signal frequency circuits, tuning is usually accomplished by adjusting the value of a resonant circuit capacitance using a variable air-dielectric capacitor. On the other hand, in the intermediate frequency amplification section the resonance frequency is initially adjusted by screwing a dust core in or out of the winding which forms part of the resonant circuit coupling two stages. (* Resonance, Resonance Frequency, Resonant Circuit, Capacitor, Inductor, L-C Circuit >> Radio Receiver, Permeability Tuning)

TUNNEL DIODE This is a p-n junction with sufficiently heavy doping for the Fermi levels of the two regions to be within the valence and conduction energy bands respectively as shown in Figure T10(i). This means that the higher electron energies exist in both energy bands at the same time, accordingly charge carriers can "tunnel" energy-wise between the top of the valence band and the bottom of the conduction band. In effect, therefore, they can tunnel across the depletion layer even when no potential difference is applied. Put in other words, electrons which normally would not have sufficient kinetic energy for overcoming the potential barrier, now have no need of it, the energies they possess as valence electrons are sufficient for them to leave home and jump the barrier as conduction electrons.

With forward bias (p positive to n), tunnelling takes place as above and while this is happening, the diode characteristic exhibits a negative resistance region as shown in Figure T10(iii). However, increasing the forward bias further inhibits tunnelling because as (ii) of the figure shows, the bottom of the conduction band rises above the top of the valence band. The current/voltage characteristic then approaches that of a normal p-n junction with the same degree of doping.

Negative resistance, i.e. when current increases as voltage falls, has many uses. The tunnel diode is used in amplifiers, oscillators and for switching.

The graphical symbol is shown in (iv) of the figure. (* Semiconductor, Diode, Doping, P-N Junction, Energy, Energy Band, Fermi Level, Depletion Layer, Potential Difference, Tunnel Effect, Negative Resistance)

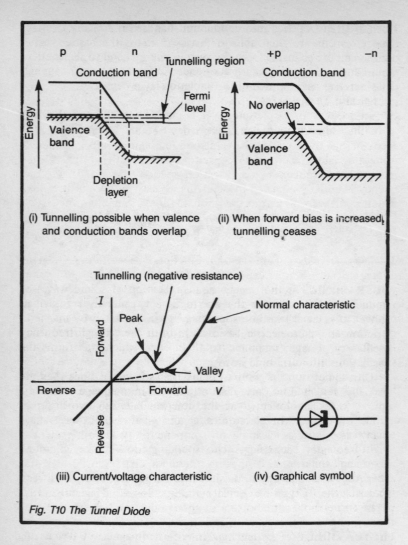

p   n   Tunnelling region   +p   −n

Conduction band   Conduction band

Energy

Fermi level

Valence band

Tunnelling region

Depletion layer

No overlap

Valence band

Energy

(i) Tunnelling possible when valence and conduction bands overlap

(ii) When forward bias is increased, tunnelling ceases

Tunnelling (negative resistance)

I

Normal characteristic

Peak

Forward

Valley

Reverse   Forward V

Reverse

(iii) Current/voltage characteristic

(iv) Graphical symbol

Fig. T10 The Tunnel Diode

TUNNEL EFFECT Normally in a p-n junction, the potential barrier prevents electrons from crossing the depletion layer unless they have received sufficient additional energy to do so. The tunnel effect, however, allows electrons to traverse the barrier even though they do not have the kinetic energy required. The effect arises with high doping levels and reverse bias or alternatively with even heavier doping and a small forward bias [see Fig.T10(i)]. Under these conditions the depletion layer is narrow and the energy levels are such that the valence and conduction bands can actually overlap. The electrons are then able to "tunnel" across the barrier region since they are changing from the valence energy band to the conduction band with no further input of energy. The likelihood of tunnelling increases as the width of the depletion layer decreases.

See also Tunnel Diode.

(* Semiconductor, Depletion Layer, Doping, Energy, Kinetic Energy, P-N Junction, Energy Levels, Energy Bands)

U

ULTRASONICS is the science and application of sound waves of frequencies too high for the ear to detect, generally regarded as above 20 kHz. Ultrasonic sound waves are generated by magnetostriction and piezoelectric devices. In both cases a high frequency oscillatory voltage is applied to the device which transforms the oscillations into ultrasonic waves.

Ultrasonic sound is used to detect flaws in metal since they are partially reflected at any discontinuity. In medicine ultrasonic sound waves are reflected at the junction between two different kinds of tissue. In electronics generally ultrasonic waves have many uses such as cleaning of components by vibrating them at high frequency, degassing, echo sounding, underwater communication and sonar.

(* Audio Frequency, Magnetostriction, Piezoelectric Effect, Piezoelectric Crystal, Oscillator >> Sonar, Magnetostrictive Transducer)

ULTRAVIOLET is the label given to electromagnetic waves having frequencies above those of the visible spectrum and extending to the region of X-rays (see Fig.E5).

(* Frequency, Light, Visible Spectrum, Electromagnetic Radiation, Electromagnetic Spectrum)

UNIJUNCTION TRANSISTOR   This is a special type of transistor usually with an n-type channel and in construction not unlike that of the field-effect transistor. It is, however, based on different operating principles with the result that part of its characteristic exhibits negative resistance. A lightly doped n-type channel runs between two base contacts as shown in Figure U1(i). A single p-n

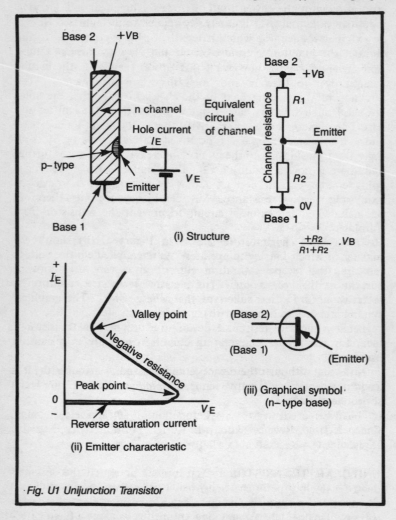

(i) Structure

$$\frac{+R_2}{R_1+R_2}.V_B$$

(ii) Emitter characteristic

(iii) Graphical symbol
(n–type base)

Fig. U1 Unijunction Transistor

junction is formed in the bar, off-centre and using heavily doped p-type material. To this a third connection is made, known as the emitter.

Consider that relative to base 1, a positive potential, V_B is applied to base 2. The equivalent circuit in the figure indicates that the channel potential near the emitter region is less than V_B and in fact is given by $V_B \times R_2/(R_1 + R_2)$ as shown. This ratio is usually designated by η which is known as the *intrinsic stand-off ratio*, i.e. it is a function of the device itself. Hence for practical values of V_B a positive potential ηV_B is internally applied to the emitter. Now if an external voltage V_E which is less than ηV_B is connected to the emitter, the junction is reverse-biased and the usual reverse saturation current flows. If however V_E is greater than ηV_B, the biasing changes over to forward and holes flow into the channel. The direction of the electric field in the channel is such that the holes are accelerated towards base 1 and being between the emitter and base 1 they increase the conductivity there. R_2 therefore decreases and so the emitter becomes less positive (relative to base 1). Accordingly the forward bias on the junction increases, I_E increases further and there is now a condition of falling emitter voltage creating a rising emitter current because R_2 is decreasing, i.e. the device is exhibiting negative resistance. Sufficient resistance must therefore be included in the external circuit to prevent the transistor from burning out.

The typical characteristic shown in Figure U1(ii) shows the manner in which the device operates. As the applied emitter voltage increases the reverse saturation current gives way to a forward current at the *peak point*. The negative resistance condition is effective until V_E has fallen to the *valley point*. The graphical symbol is shown in Figure U1(iii).

Being a negative resistance device, the unijunction transistor is ideal for use in pulse generating circuits, especially in relaxation oscillators.

Note that although the device is here classed as a transistor, it is also known by the alternative name, *double-base diode*, Figure U1(i) shows clearly why.

(* Field-Effect Transistor, P-N Junction, Electric Field, Doping, Channel, Hole, Reverse Saturation Current, Conductivity, Negative Resistance >> Relaxation Oscillator)

UNIPOLAR TRANSISTOR is a transistor in which the action is due to a single type of charge carrier. Field-effect transistors (f.e.t.) are of this type and for example in an n-channel f.e.t. the charge carriers (majority carriers) are electrons — see Field-Effect Transistor.

V

VALENCE BAND is that part of an energy-level diagram for a solid material which contains the range of energy levels possessed by valence electrons, i.e. those electrons in the outermost shells of atoms and which therefore are not free — see Figure E12.
(* Atom, Shell, Energy, Energy Bands, Energy Diagram, Energy Levels, Valency)

VALENCE ELECTRONS are electrons which are orbiting in the outermost shells of atoms and which are shared by other atoms when bonding takes place to form molecules — see Bond.

VALENCY   This term has its origins in chemistry but by understanding it, more experience can be gained with one of the techniques of *bonding* which atoms employ to form molecules (see Bond).   The valency of an element is its combining (or replacing) power as compared with hydrogen as the standard.   It is measured for a particular element by the number of hydrogen (or equivalent) atoms which unite with one atom of that element.   A few examples will help to unravel this statement.

Chlorine (Cl) is said to be *univalent* because one atom of chlorine combines with one of hydrogen to make a molecule of hydrochloric acid, (HCl).   The p sub-shell of Shell 3 (M) of chlorine (see Fig.S4) has 5 electrons in it.   For completion it needs 6 so it takes the only one from hydrogen, the two ions therefore combine to form the molecule.

Oxygen (O) is *bivalent* because one atom of oxygen combines with two of hydrogen (= water, H_2O).   The p sub-shell of Shell 2 (L) of oxygen has 4 electrons, 2 are required for completion.

Nitrogen (N) it *trivalent*.   Its p sub-shell of Shell 2 (L) has only 3 electrons, hence 3 more are required for completion to form the ammonia molecule NH_3.

Valencies up to 8 are possible but although hydrogen is the standard, it need not be involved.   As an example, since oxygen is bivalent, the number of atoms of oxygen which combine with two atoms of an element is a measure of the valency of that element.

See also Electrovalent Bonding and Covalent Bonding in Bond.
(* Atom, Electron, Ion, Molecule, Shell)

VECTOR   This is defined as a quantity having both magnitude and direction.   It is represented on paper by a line having a length representing the magnitude of the quantity and drawn at an angle to some known reference line to indicate the direction. In electronics when vectors are used to indicate the magnitude and phase of an electrical waveform, they are then known as *phasors*, see Figure P4.

(* Phasor, Phase Angle)

VELOCITY MODULATION is a process which periodically changes the velocity of the electrons in an electron stream when a radio frequency component is introduced, i.e. the velocities of the electrons are modulated. Velocity modulation is found in practice in microwave oscillators and amplifiers such as klystrons and travelling-wave tubes. The following explanation, although lacking in some detail, serves to illustrate the basic process.

Consider the evacuated tube of Figure V1(i). We can imagine it as a thermionic valve containing two closely spaced grids. Relative to the earth or chassis line, the cathode is maintained at a negative potential, V_K. The anode is connected to chassis via R and is therefore positive with respect to the cathode. The first grid is at chassis potential but the second carries the modulating frequency. It is clear that the velocity of the electrons in the stream from cathode to anode is a function of both the direct voltage applied and the a.c. signal. Let v_0 be the velocity of an electron on leaving the cathode. When energy exchanges between the electron beam and the electric field due to the incoming signal are considered, it can be shown that the instantaneous velocity as the electron travels along the tube is approximately:

$$v = v_0 \left[1 + \frac{V_m \sin \omega t}{2V_K} \right]$$

where $V_m \sin \omega t$ represents the signal.

This shows that the velocity is modulated sinusoidally. Looking at this more closely:

(i)   when the input signal is zero, $v = v_0$ – there is no change in velocity;

(ii) when the input signal is positive, there is an increase in velocity up to a maximum of $v_0 [1 + (V_m/2V_K)]$;

(iii) when the input signal is negative, there is a decrease in velocity up to a maximum of $v_0 [1 - (V_m/2V_K)]$.

This is best illustrated by an *Applegate Diagram* as shown in (ii) of the figure. In this the distance from the modulating grids (the

446

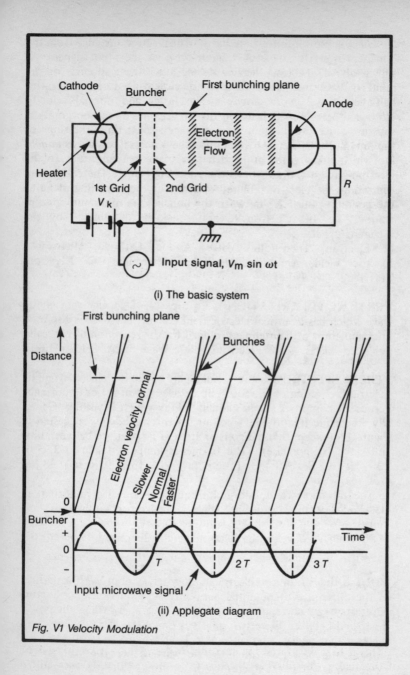

(i) The basic system

(ii) Applegate diagram

Fig. V1 Velocity Modulation

447

buncher) is plotted on a time basis. The electron distance from the buncher is plotted at each quarter-cycle of the input signal. As shown above, electrons leaving during a positive half-cycle of the input signal travel faster than v_0, those leaving during a negative half-cycle travel more slowly. The faster and normal velocity electrons therefore catch up on the slower ones at certain points as shown. Since the diagram plots distance against time, the slope of the line indicates electron velocity. The process is known as *bunching* which takes place at a particular plane perpendicular to the electron stream and known as the *bunching plane*. These high concentrations of electrons therefore arrive at the bunching plane at the periodic times, *T*. Between the bunches are minimum concentrations, i.e. the electron stream is velocity modulated by the incoming signal.

(* Electron, Thermionic Valve, Anode, Cathode, Microwave, Electric Field, Amplifier, Oscillator, Sinusoidal >> Klystron, Travelling-Wave Tube)

VERTICAL POLARIZATION is a property of an electromagnetic wave which has a vertical electric field vector. The term is also used in conjunction with antennas arranged for the reception of vertically polarized waves — see Electromagnetic Wave and/or Figure E6(i).

VISIBLE SPECTRUM is a very small part of the full electromagnetic spectrum, covering only about one octave, yet of major importance because it comprises all the radiant energy which is visible. Generally we divide it into the 7 colours of the rainbow as suggested in Figure L5 (except that indigo is omitted as its position between blue and violet is imprecise). The frequency range is taken as 3.95×10^{14} Hz to 7.9×10^{14} Hz (one octave), i.e. from 0.76 to 0.38 μm (760 to 380 nm).

The ultraviolet and infra-red frequencies are also important in electronics because many photoelectric devices operate within these ranges.

(* Frequency, Wavelength, Electromagnetic Spectrum, Photoelectric Effect)

VOLT is the S.I. unit of electrical potential, symbol V. It is defined as the difference of potential between two points of a conducting wire carrying a constant current (I) of one ampere when the power dissipated between these two points is one watt. This follows from the fact that power is equal to V × I and when V = 1 volt and I = 1 ampere, the power is equal to one watt, hence the volt can be expressed as watts per ampere (W/A). In terms of the energy required to transport electric charge, the volt can also be expressed as joules per coulomb (J/C). Since one watt (W) of power dissipated for one second is equal to one joule of energy and one coulomb is the charge carried by one ampere for one second, then:

$$\frac{J}{C} = \frac{W s}{A s} = \frac{W}{A}$$

The volt is the unit of electromotive force (e.m.f.) and also of potential difference. It is related to current and resistance by Ohm's Law.

For calibration of voltage a Weston standard cell is used. This is a primary cell which has a steady e.m.f. of 1.018636 volts at 20°C. Accordingly a further definition of the volt can be that it is equal to 1/1.018636 of the e.m.f. of the standard cell.

(* Power, Energy, Joule, Charge, Coulomb, Electromotive Force, Potential Difference, Ohm's Law, Weston Standard Cell)

VOLTAGE   This is a general term used for expressing the magnitude of an electromotive force or potential difference between two points in a circuit. The symbol used is V with the unit, the volt.

(* Electromotive Force, Potential Difference)

VOLTAIC CELL   This was the first electric cell, invented by Alessandro Volta, an Italian physicist in 1800. The cell consists simply of a plate of zinc and one of copper immersed in an electrolyte of dilute sulphuric acid. The copper plate is the positive electrode, the zinc plate, negative. Cell e.m.f. is about 0.75 volts.

In use, positive hydrogen ions give up their charges on the copper plate but then tend to adhere to the plate as bubbles of hydrogen gas. These unfortunately increase the internal resistance of the cell by reducing the effective area of the plate (polarization), hence the cell potential difference falls excessively on load. The Leclanché cell was developed later and avoided this type of problem by use of a "depolarizer" to remove gas bubbles.

(* Cell, Primary Cell, Electromotive Force, Potential Difference, Ion, Electrolyte, Positive, Negative)

VOLT-AMPERE is the S.I. unit of apparent power in an alternating current circuit, designated by VA. It is defined as the product of the root mean square values of voltage and current.

See also In-Phase Component, Quadrature Component.

(* S.I., Alternating Current, Power, Root Mean Square, Voltage)

VOLUME RESISTIVITY – see Resistivity.

WATT is the S.I. unit of power with the symbol W and named after James Watt the Scottish engineer and inventor (but better known for his work on steam engines). One watt is defined as the rate of working or the power developed when one joule of energy is dissipated in one second. In an electric circuit this corresponds to the product of one volt and one ampere.
(* S.I., Power, Energy, Joule, Ohm's Law)

WATTLESS COMPONENT – see Quadrature Component.

WAVE   This is any periodic disturbance, not necessarily electrical because there are many other types, e.g. sound waves and water waves. Some waves require a medium for propagation, for example, sound waves travel through materials and air but not through space. Others such as radio waves propagate through space in addition to other media.

With most waves travelling through a medium, the particles of the medium oscillate as the wave passes, they do not advance with the wave itself. A radio wave differs from this because it can travel through space where practically no particles exist.

Each type of wave (e.g. electromagnetic, sound wave) travels at its own particular velocity which is often affected by the medium. The time required for a single cycle of the wave to pass a given point is known as the *period* (T).

Transverse waves can be demonstrated by considering a taut string. If plucked, the individual particles of the string vibrate in a manner which is perpendicular to the direction of travel (e.g. up and down, side to side, etc.). On the other hand, *longitudinal waves* are those for which the individual particles vibrate back and forth in the direction of travel as might be imagined when a wave of compression moves along a long coiled spring. Electromagnetic waves are transverse, the electric and magnetic vectors have directions which are at right angles to the direction of travel.

(* Waveform, Wavelength, Frequency, Period, Oscillation, Electromagnetic Wave)

WAVEFORM   This is shown by a graph of amplitude plotted against time for a periodically varying quantity. A "pure" waveform is sinusoidal in shape.
(* Frequency, Sine Wave, Sinusoidal)

WAVEFRONT usually refers to an electromagnetic wave and is the imaginary surface joining those points where all of the waves involved are in the same phase of oscillation. Very close to a radio transmitter for example, the wavefronts are circular but at a long distance they can be considered as a succession of planes.
(* Electromagnetic Radiation, Oscillation, Wave)

WAVEGUIDE   Instead of transmitting electromagnetic waves through space, the wave can be confined within a metal guide usually of rectangular or circular cross-section. This has the advantage of a stable transmission medium with privacy but offset by cost of the guide and higher attenuation than for the radio wave. A sketch of a section of a rectangular type is given in Figure W1(i). Typically the internal dimensions might be 2×1 cm for carrying a 12 GHz transmission which has a wavelength of 2.5 cm, the dielectric is most likely to be dry air. Waveguides are used as feeders to and from microwave antennas and also were used extensively for telephony and television transmission although for this they are now superseded by the optical fibre.

   Because it is an electromagnetic wave which is being propagated, transmission is entirely through the dielectric and not along the walls of the guide. The wave cannot propagate axially along the guide otherwise its electric field would be continually short-circuited. Various *modes* of propagation are used to avoid this and these all require the wave to progress along the guide in a zig-zag fashion through reflections from wall to opposite wall as shown in Figure W1(ii). The mode is identified in the specification of the type of wave. As an example, for a rectangular waveguide the mode is described by TE_{mn} which denotes that the electric field is transverse to the direction of propagation (Transverse Electric) with m maxima occurring across the width of the cross-section and n maxima along the height. The most commonly used mode is TE_{10}.

   For each mode there is a frequency below which propagation through the waveguide fails. Propagation can only take place when the *propagation coefficient* is imaginary, hence the waveguide acts as a high-pass filter.

451

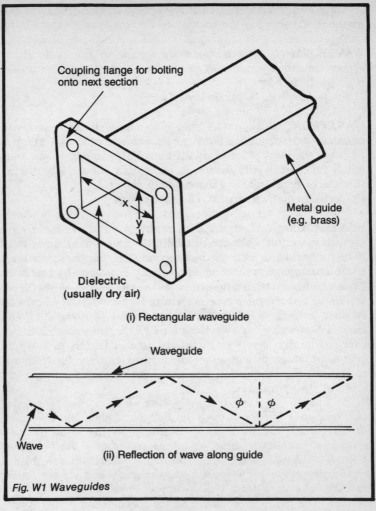

Fig. W1 Waveguides

Working from the formula for the propagation constant, it can be shown that for propagation to take place in a rectangular waveguide filled with dry air (for any other dielectric the relative permittivity and permeability must be taken into account), the frequency of cut-off:

$$f_{co} = \frac{c}{2\pi} \left[(m\pi/x)^2 + (n\pi/y)^2 \right]^{\frac{1}{2}}$$

where x and y are the internal waveguide dimensions as shown in Figure W1(i) and c is the velocity of electromagnetic waves in free space.

As an example, for the TE_{10} mode, $m = 1, n = 0$

$$\therefore \qquad f_{co} = \frac{c}{2\pi} \times \frac{m\pi}{x} = \frac{c}{2x}$$

and since

$$\lambda = \frac{c}{f} \qquad \lambda_{co} = 2x$$

a simple way of estimating the cut-off frequency, but only for this particular mode.

Various methods are used to launch the wave into, or collect it from the guide, for example by extending the centre conductor of a coaxial cable into the end of the guide or by probes or loops acting in fact as tiny antennas.

(* Electromagnetic Wave, Wavelength, Frequency, Microwave, Electric Field, Propagation Coefficient, Filter, Permittivity, Permeability, Antenna >> Coaxial Cable)

WAVELENGTH   A wave has a certain velocity (v) and the wavelength (λ) is the distance travelled (usually in metres) between two successive similar displacements (i.e. similar in amplitude and phase) along the direction of propagation. The frequency of vibration of the wave (f) and its wavelength are therefore related by:

$$\lambda = v/f \text{ metres,}$$

where v is in metres per second and f is in hertz.

The velocity varies with the type of wave, for example for radio waves it is approximately 3×10^8 m/s but for sound waves it is of the order of a mere 344 m/s.

(* Wave, Frequency, Phase)

WEBER   This is the S.I. unit of magnetic flux [after W. E. Weber, a German physicist (pronounced *vayber*)]. It is denoted by the symbol Φ and it is that flux which induces an electromotive force (e.m.f.) of one volt in a circuit of one turn when generated or removed in one second. In a magnetic circuit:

$$\text{total flux}, \Phi = \frac{\text{magnetomotive force } (F)}{\text{total reluctance } (S)} \text{ webers (Wb)}$$

where F is given in amperes or ampere-turns (A or At) and S in amperes per weber (A/Wb). Numerically, therefore, the induced e.m.f. in volts is equal to the rate at which the linked flux is changing in webers per second.
(* Magnetism, Magnetic Flux, Magnetomotive Force, Electromotive Force, Reluctance)

WESTON STANDARD CELL (also known as *cadmium cell*) is a primary cell used as a reference voltage standard in electrical measurements. It consists of a negative electrode of cadmium amalgam (cadmium dissolved in mercury) with a positive electrode of mercury covered by a layer of mercury sulphate as shown in Figure W2. The electrolyte is a solution of cadmium sulphate, kept saturated by cadmium sulphate crystals. The electrolyte is usually slightly acidifed by the addition of sulphuric acid.

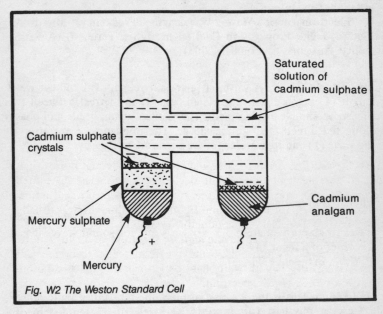

Fig. W2 The Weston Standard Cell

The cell has a highly stable e.m.f. of 1.018636 volts at 20°C. Such cells used for calibration must be kept at a constant temperature.

(* Cell, Electrolyte, Primary Cell, Potentiometer, Voltage, Positive, Negative)

WHEATSTONE BRIDGE   This is the best known of all bridges and was originally developed for measuring electrical resistance. It is named after Sir Charles Wheatstone, a British scientist who first put it into practical use although apparently it was first suggested by Samuel Hunter Christy, another British scientist.

A practical Wheatstone bridge circuit is shown in Figure W3. When used for the measurement of resistance, it is a *d.c. bridge* and is therefore powered by a battery or other d.c. supply. For accurate measurements the resistors themselves must be accurate and have high stability and a low temperature coefficient. They are usually wire-wound of, for example, nickel-chromium or nickel-copper wire. The bridge balances when:

$$R_1 R_v = R_2 R_x$$

i.e. when $R_1/R_x = R_2/R_v$ for then there is zero voltage across the voltmeter.

Similarly for balance, $R_1/R_2 = R_x/R_v$, hence if R_v is adjusted for zero deflection on the meter, then $R_x = R_v \times (R_1/R_2)$ and if $R_1 = R_2$ then $R_x = R_v$. Now if, say, R_v is variable over the range $1 - 1000 \ \Omega$ in $1 \ \Omega$ steps, and R_1 and R_2 are both switchable to 10, 100 or 1000 Ω so that the range of ratios R_1/R_2 is 0.01 to 100, then values of R_x from 0.01 to 100 000 Ω are measurable. R_1 and R_2 are known as the *ratio arms*.

(* Bridge, Network, Temperature Coefficient of Resistance, Kirchhoff's Laws, Impedance >> Hybrid Transformer)

WHITE NOISE is often used as a synonym for thermal noise. It is due to thermal agitation and it occurs at frequencies distributed uniformly over the whole of the frequency spectrum. Thermal noise has its uses for testing audio frequency equipment, it is usually generated by a special semiconductor diode but in this case its frequency range is restricted to the *audible* spectrum or slightly more. It is then called "white noise" and the term seems to be relevant since the analogy is with white light which has frequency components over the full *visible* spectrum.

Telephone trunk circuit noise is sometimes known as white noise although in this case it is a mixture of several different types of noise.

(* Noise, Thermal Noise >> Pink Noise, Telecommunication System)

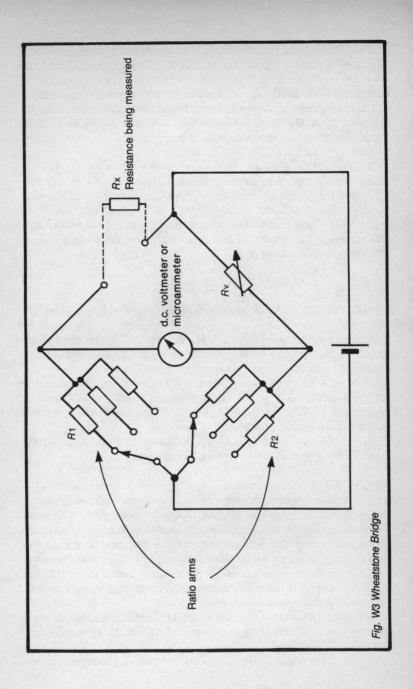

Fig. W3 Wheatstone Bridge

WIEN BRIDGE is an a.c. bridge circuit named after Wilhelm Wien (a German physicist). One arm of the bridge consists of a resistance (R) and capacitance (C) in series. The adjoining arm consists of resistance and capacitance in parallel. In its simplest form as shown in Figure W4(i), the bridge is used for measuring audio frequencies. Let the frequency to be measured be f Hz, then for balance, i.e. no current through the meter:

$$\frac{R_2}{(1/R) + j\omega C} = R_1 [R + (1/j\omega C)]$$

where $\omega = 2\pi \times f$. This can be simplified by making $R_2 = 2R_1$ and so:

$$\omega^2 = \frac{1}{C^2 R^2} \qquad \text{i.e. } f = \frac{1}{2\pi CR}$$

which indicates that the bridge balances at one frequency only. For measuring any one of a range of frequencies, both resistances R are made to vary simultaneously. In addition, by also changing the values of C simultaneously, the frequency range of the bridge can be increased.

The Wien bridge is also capable of measuring capacitance, see (ii) of Figure W4. Let the series capacitance–resistance network be R_s and C_s and the parallel, R_p and C_p. At balance it can be shown that:

$$\frac{C_p}{C_s} = \frac{R_2}{R_1} - \frac{R_s}{R_p} \qquad \text{also } C_p \times C_s = \frac{1}{\omega^2 R_p R_s}.$$

From these equations, knowing the values of the resistances and the frequency of the generator, C_p and C_s can be calculated.

Inductances can also be measured simularly although other bridge circuits are more likely to be used for this purpose (e.g. Maxwell). (* Bridge, Frequency, Resistance, Capacitance, Complex Notation)

WORK is the expenditure of energy, for example, work is done when a force moves a body. Work (W) is measured in *joules* (as is energy) and one joule (J) is the work done when the point at which a force (F) of one newton is applied is displaced through a distance (s) of one metre, i.e.

$$W = F \times s .$$

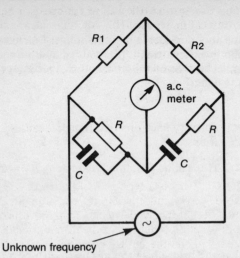

(i) Arranged for measuring frequency

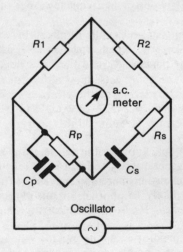

(ii) Arranged for measuring capacitance

Fig. W4 Wien Bridge

Note that a force does work only if a body is moved by it. If for instance we push against a brick wall which does not move, then no work is done, only a force is applied.

So far we have only considered movement in the direction of the force. If through some constraint the body moves in a direction which is not parallel to that of the force but is at an angle θ with it, then:

$$W = Fs \cos \theta .$$

Work is a scalar quantity because even though it causes a body to move, it has no direction itself.
(* Force, Newton, Energy)

WORK FUNCTION   This is a term most frequently used in consideration of photoelectric and thermionic emission of electrons. The two work functions for any particular material usually differ slightly. The work function is defined as the difference between the Fermi level in a material and the surface potential energy at absolute zero. In more practical terms it is the energy which must be supplied to an electron to enable it to cross over the surface barrier (the space charge) of a metal, i.e. to escape from the metal itself. The supply of energy may be from heat, light or through contact with a dissimilar metal (*contact work-function*). The symbol used is ϕ and the unit is the electron-volt.

Einstein, in trying to explain the effect light has on the emission of electrons from the surface of a metal was the first to suggest that if a photon of energy E acts upon an electron, then because an amount, ϕ is required to free the electron from the surface of a metal, the energy left over $(E - \phi)$ would act to increase the kinetic energy of the electron. He summed this up by:

maximum k.e. of an emitted electron $= hf - \phi$

where h is the Planck constant and f is the light frequency.

Still on the subject of photoelectric work functions, it may be illustrative to consider a method of determining the value for a particular material used as a photocathode in a photocell. This is by measuring the negative anode voltage required for zero anode current over a range of frequencies. At this voltage the escaping electron velocity is reduced to zero by the opposing electric field of the anode potential V_a, accordingly the electron falls back into the surface. Hence, working in electron-volts:

$$V_a = hf/e - \phi$$

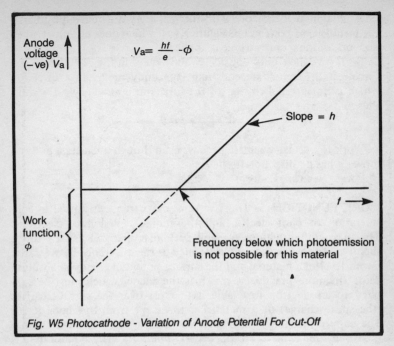

$$V_a = \frac{hf}{e} - \phi$$

Slope = h

Anode voltage (–ve) V_a

Work function, ϕ

Frequency below which photoemission is not possible for this material

$f \longrightarrow$

Fig. W5 Photocathode - Variation of Anode Potential For Cut-Off

where e is the electron charge.

By illuminating the cathode with light over a range of frequencies and measuring V_a, a graph of V_a against f should be a straight line of slope h as shown in Figure W5. Projecting the line (as shown dotted) to meet the V_a axis gives the value of the work function.

See Photoelectric Effect, Thermionic Emission.

(* Emission, Energy, Kinetic Energy, Joule, Electron-Volt, Fermi Level, Space Charge, Planck Constant, Light, Photocathode, Schottky Effect, Absolute Zero)

X-RAYS (X-RAY TUBE)   X-rays are a penetrating electro-magnetic radiation at frequencies above those of ultraviolet radiation up to gamma rays as shown in Figure E5, i.e. of a wavelength of the order of 10^{-10} metres. They are generated in an evacuated tube as sketched in Figure X1.

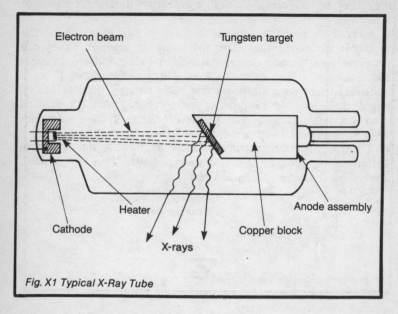

Electron beam

Tungsten target

Heater

Cathode

Anode assembly

X-rays

Copper block

Fig. X1 Typical X-Ray Tube

A heavy duty heater is surrounded by a cup-shaped cathode which is negatively charged with respect to an anode so that the electron beam focuses onto the target. The target which is usually of tungsten is part of the anode assembly constructed on a block of copper as shown. Copper has high thermal conductivity for the removal of heat and the whole anode is water cooled.

With a high potential difference existing between cathode and anode (as high as 10^6 volts), electrons which are emitted from the cathode by thermionic emission are accelerated towards the anode which they strike with considerable energy. The rapid deceleration of the electrons when they strike causes them to give up their energies with the consequent emission of x-radiation, much of the energy however produces heat which must be removed.

From Planck's constant (h) we can estimate the x-ray photon energy. For a wavelength of 10^{-10} metres, the frequency f is 3×10^{18} Hz, hence the photon energy:

$$E = h \times f = (6.626 \times 10^{-34}) \times (3 \times 10^{18}) = 2 \times 10^{-15} \text{ joules}$$

or just over 12 keV. Little wonder therefore that x-rays themselves are capable of releasing high energy electrons. This also indicates the energy levels required by the electron beam in an x-ray tube for they must be accelerated through a potential difference in excess of this.

X-rays have properties similar to those of light except that being of higher frequency they have much greater energies. They can therefore pass through denser materials and they undergo different absorptions according to the material density. Thus in medicine, a material such as bone absorbs x-rays more strongly than does flesh, hence it is possible to produce x-ray photographs for medical diagnosis. The same applies to the detection of flaws in metals. High intensities of x-rays are used to destroy diseased human tissue. (* Electron, Electromagnetic Radiation, Photon, Charge, Potential Difference, Cathode, Anode, Energy, Joule, Planck Constant, Thermionic Emission, Electron-Volt)

ZENER BREAKDOWN   This is named after C. M. Zener (an American physicist) who was one of the first to study the *avalanche effect* in semiconductor diodes. This type of breakdown arises in p-n junctions which are manufactured from semiconductor materials with heavy doping. Under reverse bias conditions the depletion layer becomes very narrow. Accordingly even when the reverse bias voltage is small, the electric field strength throughout the depletion layer is high. This provides sufficient energy for electrons in the atom valence shells (the peripheral orbits) to be liberated and hence electron-hole pairs are created. The process is further aided by the fact that because of the heavy doping, the valence and conduction bands may overlap hence an electron, once freed can "tunnel" its way across the barrier region because it needs no extra energy to cross.

This effect happens when the reverse bias reaches a certain *Zener breakdown voltage*, at which point the reverse current increases sharply and the voltage across the device remains practically constant.

Zener breakdown is possible at lower reverse voltages than are required for avalanche breakdown, hence p-n junctions can be manufactured so that zener breakdown is predominant. The process is reversible since no material change takes place.

(* Semiconductor, Diode, Avalanche, Doping, P-N Junction, Depletion Layer, Electric Field, Electric Field Strength, Energy, Energy Bands, Valency, Shell, Electron-Hole Pair, Tunnel Effect)

ZENER DIODE   This is a p-n junction with sufficiently heavy doping on both sides of the junction for zener breakdown to occur. Diodes are manufactured over a range of breakdown voltages and are used as voltage regulators (*voltage regulator diodes*), voltage references and surge suppressors. Some diodes which operate on the avalanche principle are also known as zener diodes. Although strictly speaking this is incorrect, the name "zener" seems to be well established for most diodes operating on the breakdown principle.

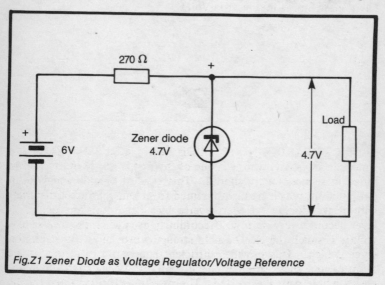

Fig.Z1 Zener Diode as Voltage Regulator/Voltage Reference

A typical zener regulator circuit is given in Figure Z1, this also shows the graphical symbol. The supply voltage must be in excess of the zener value and for example in the circuit shown, the zener breakdown effect within the diode draws sufficient current through the 270 ohm resistor to drop the diode voltage to 4.7 V. The diode maintains 4.7 V across the load irrespective of supply voltage or load changes.

(* Semiconductor, Doping, P-N Junction, Zener Breakdown >> Voltage Stabilization)

Index

468

Notes